The Story of Surgery

HARVEY GRAHAM

The Story of Surgery

WITH A FOREWORD BY OLIVER ST. JOHN GOGARTY

Halcyon House

GARDEN CITY, NEW YORK

1943
HALCYON HOUSE

For
ISABEL

THE AUTHOR'S REMARKS *about homeopathy
are his own and in no way a reflection of
the publisher's opinion of the subject*

Foreword

By Oliver St. John Gogarty

THIS is the best book on surgery I have ever read. I agree with every word of it except the reasons given for the removal of the Amazon's right breast. This was done, not to determine "all the strength and fullness to the right arm," but to save the breast from the bowstring, as anyone who has shot in a bow will realise. It was done in an age before brassieres were invented. It is one of the few operations of ancient surgery that was directly utilitarian and inspired by common sense. Let me remark that it is not the author who recounts the purport of the operation, but one of the Hippocratic writers.

This book is not a text-book. That is one of the reasons it is so good. In these days a text-book can at best be only provisional: it is soon out of date. Not alone is this a surgery, so far as the formulæ of surgery can be enunciated, but it is a history of surgery from the dawn of Man to the present day, and an instructive forecast of the future. From the first chapters, which tell of the taboos, incantations, superstitions, magic and mysteries by which fairy Fiction drest Truth severe, to the last, which prognosticate a time when with surgery as we now know it we may gradually dispense, it is intensely interesting and instructive. If it can interest the medical man so much, it should interest the layman more, for it introduces him behind the scenes and recounts procedures at which even the veteran surgeon might stand aghast. The amount of research and knowledge that went to the gathering of so many historical facts and biographical details is colossal. The biographical accounts of the great benefactors of mankind, who groped their way through the gloom that encircled them and overcame difficulties unimaginable by us now, alone would make a volume of outstanding interest. But the whole world-wide history of surgery is here in detail. And I can no more imagine a better way of treating it than I can imagine a livelier or wittier, and yet learned style of writing than that with which the author is endowed. He ends or emphasises many a paragraph or chapter as succinctly by his wit as the best Elizabethan dramatists ended their acts by epigrammatic rhymes.

Having read this engaging volume, one thing impresses the reader. The fact that surgery began in mystery and magic. These were its handicaps, but they appear also to be conditions inseparable from its advance. "Surgery," says the author, "was born of a queer muddle of demonology, tribal ritual, and social necessity, but in the earliest civilisations it developed rapidly into a lusty infant art." This sentence is enough to make one ponder on the concomitants of all progress in science. Magic? Why, even gold was at first sought for its magical properties: for the untarnishability, unlimited malleability, scarcity and immortality which it possessed. And not for its commercial uses. Even to-day it is prescribed mysteriously and somewhat equivocally to cure conditions which lead to its wastage, as in the gold cure for alcoholism. We shall never be wholly free from magic in medicine, and we never should be, for the human body is not a test-tube, but a mystic living thing. And where there is life there is mystery.

The limitations of the space at my disposal forbid philosophising on the significance of the fact that scientific Truth can be reached only by devious ways. The answers to our speculations must emerge like the prophecies of the priestess of Apollo through a mephitic vapour, or like a particle of an atom be recognisable only by the mist its passage makes. One must "have Chaos within him to give birth to a dancing star"; this the author recognises, though I am sure he would not go so far as Sir James Jeans, and assert that the universe was born of chaotic gas. When we come to realise that all invention and creative inspiration take place first in the subliminal—that is, in the irrational depths of the mind—we will become reconciled to the fact that mystery and magic are natural corollories of scientific progress. Conversely, "organised common sense," as Huxley defined Science, has been found wanting. It requires the irrational adjuncts of the imagination. Life is all magical: so is Love: so is Death. The male spider, one of the world's greatest lovers, who is capable of that high splendour of devotion which means the losing of one's self in another—thereby giving his spouse a Hollywood appetite for the next—performs unconsciously a passion play that is meaningless to us. The long prodromal death drama of the rabbit and the weasel makes them actors in some transcendental charade, for all we know. And with Science the rule is that complicated means must precede simple results. The author gives examples of this indirectness of method in discovery He shows how inventors have alighted on their discoveries by the way on a road to something often far removed from their original quest.

FOREWORD

"Professor Wilhelm Conrad Roentgen of Wurzburg was working in his darkened laboratory on November 8, 1895, experimenting with the so-called cathode rays, which Hertz and Lenard had described, when he noticed that a small piece of paper covered with barium platinocyanide shone brightly while the electric discharge was taking place in the Crookes tube. *He had no idea of the nature of this phenomenon.*" Yet that was the beginning of the *X* ray. The letter *X* stands witness to this day that the nature of the ray was unknown. Thus was discovered one of the greatest adjuvants to surgery, and one of the greatest boons to suffering humanity. It is unnecessary to recapitulate how that, out of a brewery or rather out of the study of yeast, Pasteur came upon another world to conquer—that of the myriad-thronged microcosm of the microbe.

What impresses the reader as much as Man's emergence from the taboos that beset surgery are the wonderful and inexplicable anticipations of the alchemists and astrologers of the ancient and mediæval world, magical and mysterious though they were. One marvels yet at the associations of ideas, probably the most fantastic, that lit on mercury as a cure for syphilis, an agent so valuable that with all our advance we cannot dispense with it wholly. The mouse was a partner inseparable from any well-equipped laboratory. It is even of greater interest now: it can foretell the future nine months ahead and sometimes earn the antipathy that ladies have evinced to it from the earliest times. The use of beetles, flies and reptiles is not so foolish. There is a Spanish beetle still in the Pharmacopœia Britannica; the powdered organs of animals are in daily increasing demand. A whole new therapy has been founded on them; and even the loathesome toad, the witches' familiar, is the latest help, and a potent cure for those suffering from certain organic deficiencies: anæmia, asthenia, depression, glandular defectiveness. Two c.cm. of a solution of the venom (*i.e.,* the perspiration that emanates from the body of the toad) have, according to Dr. Robert Cornilleau, a stimulating and tonic effect on the heart, kidneys, respiratory and nervous systems. But would these expedients have had any avail without a specific and uncommon language? Sir Thomas Elyot (*circa* 1550) is quoted as saying:

"The Greeks wrote in Greek" (the physicians did, but it was in the Doric dialect, the same dialect that was also used for menus), "the Romans in Latin" (wrong again, Sir Thomas: no Roman physician who did not know Greek had a practice), "and the great Arabians in Arabic, their owne proper and maternal tongues. Paynims and Jews though they were, they had more charity than Christian physicians, for they wrote in a language which could be understood." Well, such is the mystery inherent in all healing, that I make bold to say that there would be very little efficacy in toad's sweat if it were exhibited to a patient at the present day under its name in our proper and maternal tongue. Toad technique will work no cures, but *Bufotherapy!* Why, you are at leap-frog already, and fit for another round! No; plain language, even in these "enlightened" times, can make no headway against popular education and a little learning about endocrines, hormones, vitamins and all the mumbo-jumbo that has taken the place of a decent incantation which was probably as well written and as euphonious as one of our Caroline collects. Today even Health has become an "anxiety complex." Marvellous were the creative stress and foresight of our ancestral alchemists.

Records such as these are but a small part of this volume, which has very many more ways of commending itself to the intelligent reader. The twenty-four astonishing plates would assure the success of any book they illustrated. Freedom for scientific research goes in waves, it ebbs and flows. These illustrations show what woman's inhumanity to woman in maintaining the taboos that surrounded childbirth has done; and again they illustrate experimental practices that are at the present day forbidden by English law or English public opinion, practices in which to take part would cost you your job in any of the civil services, and yet they are the subjects of lay lectures in Russia, which, no matter how it may be economically, is untrammelled and ahead in all the sciences of medical research.

These illustrations, gathered from many lands and the museums of many countries, are beautifully reproduced.

In conclusion, a word, personal though it may appear to be, must be said for the character of Harvey Graham, the savant who has written this vast commentary. The survey of long eras of history and the realisation of the oceanic weight of woe that has beset Man in his infirmity down to the period of the great redemption from pain and sepsis have engendered a calm and invulnerable serenity and a humanity broad enough to include his publishers, and even his agents, in his general acknowledgements.

Preface

"And if so be any man object unto me that this my discourse is only compilede together of certayne rapsodyes of the antique Chyrurgians, I willingly heere confes and acknowledge that in this Treatise there is verye little, or nothing at all, of myne own Inventione. . . ."

JACQUES GUILLEMEAU
A.D. *1594.*

THIS is a story book: a story of surgery itself made up of the stories of a thousand and one surgeons who all helped to bring the surgical art to its present stage of development. The story is a good one. This statement I can make without immodesty, for I have no more responsibility for the dawn of surgery in prehistoric times than I have for its development to-day. It has moments of great excitement, moments of ribaldry, moments of tragedy. There are bright patches and dull patches, but they make a pleasant pattern. At least it has pleased me, and I hope that it will please the reader.

The reader should be an ordinary man or woman—as distinct from that nebulous and rather awe-inspiring creature the intelligent layman. Ordinary men and women are found in all walks of life, and they include even doctors and medical students, who, for no good reason, learn nothing of the chequered careers of their innumerable predecessors. It is for the ordinary individual that this book is written. It is not a history book, for it has not a solitary footnote and only the most meagre references to original works. It is not a historical treatise, for it was never intended for the Olympian few who read and enjoy such things. It is not a contribution to knowledge, for it contains nothing that is not known. It probably perpetuates more mistakes than it corrects, but they are all venerable mistakes, which only the irreverent would want to see corrected. It is based on the more accessible authorities, but where two renowned medical historians have disagreed, perhaps on the interpretation of some ninth-century Arabian manuscript, I have accepted the version which pleased me most. I confess, without shame, that I could not begin to interpret a ninth-century Arabian manuscript.

I have tried to present in a form that is readable a fascinating but little-known fragment of history. To what extent I have succeeded—or failed—in this attempt is for the reader to decide.

Acknowledgements

MY acknowledgements are especially due to Dr. William Brockbank for his ready advice and helpful criticism throughout the preparation of this book; to Mr. T. J. Shields and Mr. G. Wilson, the librarians of the British Medical Association Library and the Manchester University Medical Library, respectively, for the unflagging energy with which they met my many demands; and to Miss Ann Pym for preparing the index and for her encouraging enthusiasm. To my wife I owe much more than an acknowledgement.

I am indebted to the Director of the Museum Boymans, Rotterdam, for permission to use the picture by Jan de Bray which forms the frontispiece to this book. Plate I is reproduced by kind permission of the Ferdinand Enke Verlagsbuchhandlung of Stuttgart, publishers of Professor E. Hollander's *Plastik und Medizin*. Plate II appears with the consent of the Editor of the *Chemist and Druggist;* it was reprinted in colour in the issue of this journal of June 25, 1932. Professor Charles Singer has allowed me to take Plate III from his *Greek Biology and Medicine,* published at Oxford in 1922 by the Clarendon Press. To the Clarendon Press I am also grateful for permission to reproduce Plate XXI, which is from the late Sir Rickman J. Godlee's *Life of Lord Lister.* Plate IV is from Walter Von Brunn's *Die Handschrift Des Schnitt- und Augen-Arztes: Caspar Stromayn in Lindau im Bodensee* published by Selle and Company of Berlin. The Director of the British Museum has afforded me every assistance in connexion with Plates V, IX, and XIV. Equally helpful has been Mr. P. Johnston-Saint, Conservator of the Wellcome Historical Medical Museum, by whose permission Plates VII and XVI appear. Plate VIII is published by permission of the Royal College of Surgeons of England; Plate XVII by the courtesy of the Director of the Louvre, Paris. Plate XIX is from the original engraving in Sir John Soane's Museum, by permission of the Trustees. For Plate XX I am indebted to the Director of the Boston Medical Library, and Plate XXIII is taken from the film, *War Without End,* by permission of King Edward's Hospital Fund. All the other illustrations are from books in the Manchester University Medical Library, to the librarian of which I must again express my indebtedness. These general acknowledgements would not be complete without some reference to my agents and my publishers, who have been very patient and very helpful.

Contents

List of Illustrations

[xv]

I.   The Dawn of Surgery

MAN LEFT HIS ANTHROPOID COUSINS SOME TWO MILLION YEARS ago.   The cleavage was not abrupt.   It is difficult to estimate just how long it was before the divorce was complete, but the most ancient remains of man date back only to about 350,000 years B.C., and it would seem that man has existed, as man, for not much more than half a million years.   Half a million years ago man began an endless struggle against disease.   Since the last glacier retreated man has had to fight for health, and the first weapon in the hands of the first surgeon was a flint.

It was a flint newly flaked by the surgeon's assistant.   The surgeon himself was very old.   The patient, a victim of the dreaded falling sickness, lay flat on his face on the beaten earth. All around were the men of the tribe, the skins they wore heaped about huge shoulders, great clubs ready to their hands.   In the darkness of the caves behind, crouching women, their long hair matted and their tiny, deep-set eyes reddened by the smoke from a fire in the depths of the caves, watched intently.   Abruptly the surgeon's assistant laid on one side the two great flints he had been striking together.   He took the long, keen flakes and handed them to the surgeon.   A grunt of approval rewarded him and the razor-edged flints were laid in a row.   The surgeon, squatting now, held his patient's head, fixed as in a vice, between his powerful, hairy thighs.   His assistant and another man knelt at either side of the victim, their hands on his arms and legs.   All the spectators came closer, even the women advancing from the caves, holding their children's hands.

With clawed fingers the old man parted his patient's tangled hair, and to each of his assistants he gave a great handful on either side of the short parting.   They pulled steadily.   The surgeon took up a flint in readiness.   His two assistants pulled hard on the coarse hair.   The flint knife cut cleanly from skin to bone, and blood spurted from the cut edges of the wound for a moment before the assistants' clumsy fingers nipped them and gained control.   With another flint the tough fibres that had escaped the first slash were scraped away until a wide ellipse of dull white bone was laid bare.

The tribe watched closely.   The falling sickness was always due to a demon entrapped in the skull and unable to escape from its bony prison.   Sometimes the demon died, and all was

[*17*]

well. Sometimes it could be placated and kept asleep. But if it grew and became enraged, it would beat against the walls of the skull, and the unhappy owner of the skull would howl with pain, or perhaps the movements of the demon would unbalance him and he would fall suddenly and on a clear path. These were silent demons. There were noisy demons, too, demons who mimicked the roar of the torrent and the noise of the wind whistling through bowed and swaying trees, so that the man whom they possessed heard nothing save the demoniacal roars within his own head. Attempts were made to propitiate all the demons who did not die a natural death. If the attempts made by the physicians and medicine-men failed, recourse was had to a surgeon. The belief in demoniacal possession was perhaps one of the first concepts of *homo sapiens*. The treatment for demons imprisoned in the bony vault of the skull was a perfectly rational one.

The surgeon was scratching busily with a strong, sharp-pointed flint. The great, bushy brows to which his low, almost invisible, forehead sloped were knit together, and his huge jaw was pushed forwards as he concentrated on his task. A series of scratches was soon converted into a shallow groove in the white bone. Other flints were taken up and the groove was deepened and widened. Steady scraping, which sounded to the unfortunate victim like the shrieks of the demon itself, angered by this attack on its sanctuary, soon converted the groove into a basin-shaped ellipse with sharply sloping sides. The hard outer shell of bone had gone, and the diploë, the soft middle layer of the bone, was scooped away quickly and easily. More slowly the surgeon began to scratch his way through the last thin layer of bone. He knew that beneath it was a thin, greyish membrane which must not be injured. If it should be hurt in any way, the demon would be enraged and the patient would die. So he proceeded cautiously till at length the grey covering of the brain, across which coursed thin red streaks, was exposed uninjured. The hole was not more than an inch across, but it was enough. The demon had escaped through it already, and all would be well. The men and women squatting in a close half-circle had not seen the demon emerge, but it must have done so, for the patient, who had been moaning and struggling, lay still and quiet. The two assistants released the tufts of hair. Blood began to ooze from the cut and wrinkled scalp edges. The old man pressed the two flaps together. Freshly gathered leaves were placed over the wound. Thin bark covered them and was bound in place by a length of twisted grass. The operation was over. The patient might die or he might live. It did not matter much what happened. What was important was that the right operation had been performed at the right time.

Actually, the patient probably did live, as did hundreds of other patients whose demons were freed by Neolithic surgeons. The operation they practised became known, thousands of years later, as trepanning. Immediately after operation the bone can be seen cleanly cut and showing three distinctive layers, thin red marrow being sandwiched between the outer and inner layers of bone. Later on, however, provided that the patient lives, a new outgrowth of bone rounds off the sharp edges and covers completely the marrow or diploë. Neolithic skulls with the trepan holes showing sufficient bony repair to make it clear that patients did survive operation have been found in many countries. In Switzerland, Bohemia, Poland, Denmark, Sweden, and particularly in France trepanned Neolithic skulls have been discovered. Not more than half a dozen of them have been found in England, and even fewer adorn the museums of other countries. None has ever been found in India or in China, and it is doubtful whether the Egyptians ever practised the operation. In America, though unknown to the Redskins in the North, trepanning was undertaken in the former empires of Mexico and Central America and in Peru. Until recently, in a few isolated savage communities, notably in New Britain and New Ireland, just off New Guinea, the same operation was practised almost exactly as it was half a million years ago. There the operation itself had not changed since the Neolithic era, but the indications for it had altered profoundly. In the early part of this century, trepanning was being done by a primitive and unlettered people in these islands specifically, and correctly, for the relief of pressure on the brain caused by a fragment of bone being driven inwards by the stone hurled from an enemy's sling.

Trepanning for the release of demons is the earliest surgical operation of which any evidence remains. Skulls have outlasted skeletons and borne mute witness to what was done æons before the dawn of civilization. It is hardly possible that the surgeons who undertook this hazardous operation did not know of many other lesser surgical procedures, but evidence of what has been done to human flesh moulders rapidly. Bones remain, and enough Neolithic bones of arms and legs have been found to show that Neolithic man suffered from broken limbs just as often as from demoniacal possession. The old bones have told their story of the trepanning of skulls. They have taught us, too, that something was done to assist the healing of fractures. Exactly what methods were used in setting the fractures and splinting them we do not know, but we can legitimately guess. To assist this admitted guessing we must leave the long dead and seek instruction from the still-living primitive peoples who have preserved minor surgical techniques since they came into existence. We may surmise that their methods of treating broken bones were known to Neolithic man. Some of them probably were, but we can never prove it.

The argument that the surgical practice of existing primitive tribes probably conforms closely to that of Neolithic man is an easy one to advance. Australian aborigines, for example, are culturally at about the same level as Neolithic man. It follows that the surgery they practise to-day is probably analogous to that practised by our beetle-browed and shaggy-haired forebears half a million years ago. Unfortunately, this thesis can be refuted as easily as it can be advanced. Anyone is at liberty to suggest that half a million years ago the most complicated operations were performed. There is no more evidence to disprove the suggestion than there is to support it. The most we can say is that existing tribal practices may be regarded as a mirror of Neolithic surgery. The degree of distortion of such a mirror it is impossible to estimate, but it happens to be the only mirror we have.

At least two existing races treat fractures in ways which may have been known to Neolithic man. American Indians have long used bark splints. These they bandaged round a broken limb with great care. Unhappily, as they never attempted to set the fractured bones before applying the splints, their results were rarely good. The native surgeons of Southern Australia for some centuries have been encasing broken legs and arms in soft clay which sets hard. The discovery of plaster of Paris, which has revolutionized modern fracture treatment, must have left them quite unmoved. One or other of these two methods may have been known to Neolithic surgeons. Karl Jaeger examined many Neolithic bones which had been broken in the lifetime of their owners. He found that 53.8 per cent. of these fractures had united well, as compared with 46.2 per cent. which had fared badly. Considering the state of fracture treatment all over the civilized world until the lessons of the Great War were learnt, this is an achievement of which our remote ancestors need not be ashamed.

As to the surgery that Neolithic man directed at parts other than bones or skulls there is no evidence at all. Not an ounce of flesh, nor even a scrap of scar tissue remain. We can only turn again to the tribal mirror, and see first of all how wounds were treated. An instinctive treatment, popular amongst all sorts of primitive races, is to apply the leaves of trees or plants. A little later befeathered medicine-men must have thrown in, for luck as it were, non-surgical and usually nonsensical incantations calculated to impress the patient and his anxious relatives. Anxious relatives always have been reassured, and probably always will be reassured, by words which mean nothing to them but sound very potent. A leaf or a cobweb and an incantation was as far as most primitive peoples went in the treatment of wounds. In one or two existing tribes, however, definite attempts at wound surgery have been recorded by modern observers. Here again there is a likelihood that one or more of these methods were known to Neolithic man.

North American Indians used to fill a bleeding wound with some dry powder, obviously intended as a styptic, and then apply firm pressure before bandaging it tightly with strips of bark. The Dacota Indians were even more advanced. They would swill a wound out, using the equivalent of a modern syringe, made of a bladder and the quill of a feather, and they actually inserted wicks of soft tree-bark into extensive wounds to provide a point of drainage. The modern surgeon drains wounds in exactly the same way, except that he uses a rubber strip instead of the original tree-bark. Another peculiar primitive technique which has its modern parallel is that used for the stitching of wounds by certain South American Indians. They press the edges of the wound together, and hold over it leaf-cutter ants, which have very powerful jaws. As the jaws close and hold the wound together, they cut off the ant's body, leaving the closed jaws as a perfect natural suture. The metal clips devised by a French surgeon, Michel, which are in use to-day work in exactly the same way. South Sea Islanders tie a tapa-cloth bandage tightly round an injured limb so that it acts as a tourniquet, and then in some cases they cauterize the wound with a red-hot sea-shell. Most native tribes know the obvious necessity for removing the grosser foreign bodies, such as arrow-heads and the like, from wounds. Where this cannot be done manually, they usually apply their lips to the wound and suck vigorously. These are only a few isolated instances, however, and in general the medicine-men of existing uncivilized races have none of the surgical boldness of Neolithic man. They leave most wounds severely alone. If the patient dies the gods have willed it, if he lives the gods have no feeling about it, and in either case one man more or less is neither here nor there.

Slanting the mirror a little brings into focus next the art of bleeding and the kindred practices of cupping, leeching, and scarifying. All are varieties of blood-letting, and all are based on the same theory. A demon is causing pain or swelling. An exit must be provided if the patient is to be relieved. A hole made in the skull frees a demon in the head. Surely a hole in the flesh, deep enough to cause bleeding, will as effectively deal with a demon in an arm or a leg. This may or may not have been a Neolithic line of thought, but it is certainly the idea which prompts these activities in the native tribes who practise them to-day. The natives of British Columbia, Northern Mexico, and Australia use ordinary suction with the lips so energetically on bites, stings, and even ordinary wounds that blood exudes from the unbroken skin near the site of the injury. This is the origin of cupping, in which the same effect is achieved mechanically by heating some form of a cup and applying it quickly to the skin. As it cools a partial vacuum is created and blood is drawn slowly through the skin.

Scarification is practised by different primitive peoples all over the world. Flints, thorns, fish-bones, sharp mussel-shells, and knives of all kinds are used to make a series of scratches over the affected part. The blood that flows from it is confidently expected to wash away the unhappy devil who started all the trouble. The Brazilian Karaya Indians use for scarifying a triangular piece of nutshell to which are attached fish-teeth protected by some kind of cotton-wool, so that the depth to which they scratch can be regulated. Leeching has been popular in Bengal and in parts of Asia for uncounted centuries. Its introduction to orthodox Western medicine was probably effected by Alexander the Great after his Indian expedition. Once known, it achieved an astonishing vogue as a method of treating any and all of the ills of man, and this popularity continued until quite recent years.

Methods of opening veins for the purpose of blood-letting are known to many quite uncivilized tribes. Evil spirits have ever haunted the Indians of South America, and these Mohseks, as they are called, can only be disposed of by drawing from the afflicted limb the blood in which they are residing. The technique employed is one befitting a warlike people. The surgeon shoots into the patient at close range a small arrow, which he holds near to the point so that it shall not penetrate too deeply. If the arrow opens a vein and the blood flows freely, all is well. If the arrow misses a vein, the surgeon tries again, probably in a strained silence guaranteed to convince the unhappy operator that the story about the demon side-stepping the arrow and taking the vein with him has been told too often. Central Californian Indians used to open the veins of the right arm for diseases of the trunk, and of the left arm for diseases of the extremities. South Sea Islanders, using a shark's tooth or a sharpened sea-shell, open veins widely and freely, often with fatal results. Certain Amazon tribes carried the theory of localized demoniacal possession to its logical conclusion. If the pain or swelling or whatever the symptom might be did not respond to repeated bleedings, the surgeon proceeded to amputate the affected limb, and thus made quite sure of disposing of the demon responsible. The Incas of Peru are believed to have had a well-defined surgical treatment for headache. The surgeon used a flint attached to a stick, and applied this between the eyebrows till the desired flow of blood was obtained. If treatment of this type did not actually cure the headache, it probably persuaded the patient to suffer the headache in silence.

All these methods of bleeding were direct attacks on pains, either as pains or as manifestations of demoniacal activity. It seems reasonable to suppose that the fact that such bleedings did not always succeed in allaying pain or curing disease directed the thoughts of primitive surgeons to other methods of approaching the same problems. One line of thought must have led to the Amazons' amputations—wholesale removal of the affected part complete with demons; another led to the cautery. If the demon could not be removed by bleeding, then it might possibly be driven away by heat, or perhaps counter-irritation. This concept of the surgical application of heat is undoubtedly responsible for the use of the cautery so far as existing native tribes are concerned. That Neolithic man thought along the same simple lines is at least possible, and if he did so, then, to judge from the practice of different tribes, he might have applied the cautery in a variety of ways.

The Andamanese, for example, treat skin diseases by the application of flat stones which have been heated in the fire. North American and Twana Indians have always had faith in the actual cautery, using red-hot needles, made of bone or flint or shell, for relieving rheumatic pains. A primitive race in Rajputana—the Bhils—have women surgeons who use the cautery for any and every kind of swelling. Dislocations receive the same treatment as tumours and cysts. Ruptures, which are only recognized when they show appreciable swelling, are dealt with in the same way. Belief in the efficacy of making parts of the patient's body too hot to hold even the toughest demon persists to this day in Tibet, where fire cures are still in vogue. The technique is improved, or perhaps advanced is the better word, but the principles underlying it are the same. The Tibetan treatment of lumbago is little less than heroic. The surgeon uses a blazing brand, which he applies at several points on the patient's back and abdomen. Having marked in blisters the proposed field of operation, he places on the same points cones of some crude mixture of sulphur and saltpetre. These are lighted with the torch, and the patient at this stage tends to degrade a major surgical procedure into a minor firework display. The result is a girdle of burns deep enough to banish any thought of afflictions as mild as lumbago.

The mildest application of the actual cautery led to the production of blisters. It was probably but a step from this to blistering by certain plasters. The oldest type of plaster was made of cantharidis, formed by crushing *Cantharis vesicatoria*, the so-called Spanish Fly which is actually a beetle. It is not known when cantharidis was first used, but Hippocrates in the fifth century B.C. mentioned it as if it were a well-known and long-established remedy. Even at that time its original surgical use externally to produce counter-irritant blisters was almost lost sight of. Instead it was given internally as an aphrodisiac or love-philtre. Cantharidis is excreted by the kidneys, and inflames all the mucous membranes with which it comes in contact. As a reflex effect of its inflammatory action on the urethral mucosa it causes intense sexual excitement. It often produced acute nephritis, which in many cases proved fatal; but it was such an effective aphrodisiac that despite this danger it was widely used, by both men and women, for many centuries.

Bleeding, cupping, leeching, scarifying, and applying counter-irritation were all primitive surgical procedures. That they are all as old as the first operation, Neolithic trepanning, is very probable, though it is not capable of historical proof. There is one other operation which has a well-established history of some six thousand years. This can hardly be compared in antiquity with the trepanny of half a million years ago, but it is the oldest operation on soft parts, as distinct from bone, of which we have knowledge. It was Elliot Smith who showed that the operation of circumcision was practised about 4000 B.C. He actually found a number of pictures of the operation which were carved at least 2,000 years before the time of Rameses II, and other evidence proving that it had been employed over a thousand years earlier. One of the best-known, though not the earliest, representations of the operation is in a bas-relief which was found in the small temple of Khons, which formed an annex to the great temple of Maut at Karnac. The upper part of the bas-relief is defaced, but the lower part shows clearly the surgeon, who was possibly a priest, kneeling in front of a child. The child is standing, supported by a matron who kneels behind him and holds both his hands firmly, while the operator has the prepuce held in his right hand and a knife, apparently of stone, in his left hand. It has been suggested that this bas-relief represents the circumcision of one of the children of Rameses II. At one time in ancient Egypt circumcision was limited to the priesthood, but later it seems to have been adopted by royalty, the nobility, and the warrior class. Later still, apart from the hygienic importance the Egyptians attached to the rite, it appears to have acquired a nationalistic significance. It is recorded that when Pythagoras visited the country he had to submit to circumcision before being allowed to study in the Egyptian temples. The demands made on foreign visitors even by our modern totalitarian states are not quite so stringent.

The first written record of the operation was made about 800 B.C. and is in the seventeenth chapter of Genesis.

9. And God said unto Abraham, Thou shalt keep my covenant therefore, thou, and thy seed after thee in their generations.

10. This is my covenant, which ye shall keep, between me and you and thy seed after thee; every man child among you shall be circumcised.

11. And ye shall circumcise the flesh of your foreskin; and it shall be a token of the covenant betwixt me and you.

12. And he that is eight days old shall be circumcised among you, every man child in your generations, he that is born in the house, or bought with money of any stranger, which is not of thy seed.

13. He that is born in thy house, and he that is bought with thy money, must needs be circumcised: and my covenant shall be in your flesh for an everlasting covenant.

14. And the uncircumcised man child whose flesh of his foreskin is not circumcised, that soul shall be cut off from his people; he hath broken my covenant.

Here, too, a reason for circumcision is implied for the first time. It is to ensure male fertility. There is no doubt that this reasonable explanation—for which there is no physiological evidence—was attached at a late date to a rite which had been practised, without any such reasons, many centuries before. It is impossible to say whether circumcision was done in Neolithic times, though there is some doubtful evidence for the belief that Palæolithic man knew and practised it. It is quite clear, however, that, excluding these possibilities, the operation originated in Egypt. Egyptian travellers and surgeons over five thousand years ago taught it to innumerable other more primitive peoples, including the Jews. These races were all in well-defined geographical areas believed to have been visited by the Egyptians, comprising the Levant, Mesopotamia, India, the entire African continent, North and South America, Polynesia, and Australia. Each of these peoples elaborated its own version of the same original operation. Actually the earliest procedure was not circumcision as we know it, but simply "incision", in which the foreskin is not removed in its entirety as in circumcision, but is slit longitudinally on the dorsal aspect. It was this operation which the Egyptians taught the Phœnicians, the Assyrians, and so many other races, among whom the Mohammedan peoples are notable. The Prophet, like Moses, attached a religious significance to it, and wherever the Crescent banners were carried, in Northern Africa, Eastern Europe, and in Asia, circumcision went too.

Delange, a French Army surgeon, described circumcision as he saw it practised in Algeria in 1868. The operation is performed on a group of boys at the same time, regardless of trifing differences in age. Feasting and general rejoicing for some eight days precede the ceremony. A banquet ends these festivities, and the next morning all the relatives of the children meet in the house where the rite is to be performed, the women going up to the second floor and looking down at the court-yard from behind screens which prevent them from being seen. The men gather in the courtyard, with the surgeon, his assistants, and the children, who are all dressed in ornate yellow silk. Each child is made to sit in a pan of sand, which has been exposed overnight to the rays of the full moon. An assistant squatting behind the boy fixes his hands and holds the thighs widely apart. The surgeon examines and cleans the prepuce and the glans, and slips on to the penis a compress with an aperture through which the glans protrudes. The operation is performed quickly and effectively, and except that no attempt is made at suture it resembles very closely modern surgical practice. The wound is then sprinkled with a powder made from juniper berries and a small cloth bandage is applied. Any further dressings are of powder and oil. During all the operations the women inside the house create an ungodly noise with cymbals, kettles, pans, and any domestic utensil which comes to hand. Finally, all the severed foreskins are gathered together and buried ceremoniously.

The records of Spanish explorers show that the operation had a religious significance in old Mexico. The child was taken to the temple, and there the priest-surgeon scratched the foreskin with a knife till it bled freely, blood-offering being in this way made to the gods. This was done usually on the twenty-eighth or twenty-ninth day of life. In female infants the priests usually made an incision in the ear. In Nicaragua, after the same type of operation, the blood was sprinkled on maize which was eaten with ceremony. Both the Mexican and Nicaraguan procedures seem to be ritual descendants of child-sacrifice. In Australia and Polynesia the incision operation is usually practised as an initiation into manhood when hair first appears on a boy's face. It is regarded as so important that tribal wars may be stopped and a temporary armistice declared so that the rite may take place.

The origin of even the most primitive operation lies in reason. The reason may be inaccurate, but there always is a reason. The theories advanced as to why circumcision should have been performed are innumerable. The popular theory, that it was done for cleanliness or hygienic reasons, was first propounded by Herodotus about 460 B.C. He wrote:

> The Egyptians . . . are the only people who practise circumcision. . . . They practise circumcision for cleanliness sake—for they set cleanliness above seemliness.

It is obvious that in this statement he ranges himself against those modern philosophers who have suggested that circumcision was done for the sake of seemliness. They say that circumcision produces a more æsthetic and less untidy appearance. They may be right, but Herodotus at least did not think so. Another theory often advanced is that the rite developed from the practices of primitive warriors. The man who was defeated in battle was unfit to bear the name of man, and so the victors made a habit of rendering the vanquished as much like women, externally, as possible—usually with fatal results. Gradually the fact that a live prisoner could do the victor's menial work was realized, and the entire ablation of the genitals was abandoned. It was still important, however, that the prisoner should be marked in some way as being less than a man. Something milder than complete ablation was called for, and so the practices of castration, either by the knife or by crushing, and later circumcision were substituted.

Æsthetic, hygienic, social, moral, and religious theories have all been evoked, as has the theory that the rite is an attenuated form of child sacrifice. There are objections to all of them. The most common-sense hypothesis of the origin of circumcision is that suggested by Dan McKenzie, from whose works on this subject I have borrowed freely. He suggests that the reason was a magical one, and magic is far and away the earliest form of human thought. A magical belief common in all races is that constrictions, actual or magical, prevent growth, meaning by growth increase in bulk. The foreskin is a constriction, and the native argues, according to McKenzie, that as a constriction it will have a magical effect on erection. No physical effect is seen, but magical influences do not have visible effects. The obvious course, then, is to cut the constriction, and so arose the original incision. Circumcision, in which the whole offending foreskin was removed, was elaborated on the same belief. This is pure hypothesis, but it has the merit of linking known facts without evoking standards of æsthetics and *h*ygiene which were probably unknown when the operation originated.

From the circumcision of males the so-called circumcision of females probably followed automatically. Pococke ascribes to Mohammed himself the words "Circumcision is an ordinance for men, and honourable in women". There is some evidence that excision of the external female genitalia was practised centuries before Mohammed, and that it was performed on all women irrespective of social rank when they were of age to receive their dowries, notably among certain Peruvian tribes, especially the Pano, the Campa, and the Tomagua. The mutilation or circumcision of girls by what is more properly called excision of the external genitals has almost as long a history as circumcision itself. It was certainly usual in Ancient Egypt, and to this day it persists in parts of Africa, Asia, and South America. In Arabia until quite recent times the profession of *resectricis nympharum*, or she-circumciser, provided steady and remunerative employment for elderly women, who would travel from village to village crying out their occupation rather like itinerant tinkers. Incidentally, "Son of a she-circumciser" is one of the unkindest descriptions that even the masters of Arab invective ever apply to a fellow-Mohammedan; almost equally virulent is the unhappy greeting "O Son of an uncircumcised woman".

It seems reasonable to assume, particularly amongst the tribes who regard women as domestic chattels, that this crude excision was intended to remove a known organ of sexual sensitivity, the clitoris, in the belief that a woman so mutilated would be more likely to remain faithful. Many primitive peoples, and many Orientals to this day, prizing the continence, chastity, and virginity of their females far above any considerations of health or comfort, invoked the aid of surgery and every other known science to this end. Surgical infibulation, or the so-called muzzling, with a metal ring formed an adequate prop for woman's wavering chastity till she reached an age for marriage or concubinage. The surgeons then undid their own work and gave up the unequal struggle. At this stage, failing effective isolation in harems or seraglios under the watchful eyes of faithful eunuchs, weird mechanical devices had to be enlisted on the side of the angels. Married women in certain parts of Africa and Asia were forced to wear a muzzle fastened around the body with a primitive padlock. There is no doubt that this was the early counterpart of the complicated mediæval girdles of chastity. These fantastic metal belts studded with sharp spikes were applied to their wives by crusading husbands, whose chivalry was always remarkable except where their wives were concerned. The only difficulty was that even the most formidable-looking iron cage had a lock of some sort, and there is no doubt that the love-laughs-at-locksmiths philosophy arose in this era. Many races still insist that virgins should wear some special kind of dress or some device that marks them off from the married women. Gradually a barbarous misuse of surgery has been replaced by minor modifications in dress. The virgins of Judea till quite recent years were distinguished by a mincing walk and the tinkling of tiny bells. They all wore a chain of these bells just below the knees, and the explanation given for their use is that they confine the lower limbs within certain limits and do not allow of any striding or running, which might "rupture" the maidenhead. Considering this wildly improbable explanation, which has been believed apparently for centuries, it seems clear that there must have lived in Judea at one time an erstwhile virgin sufficiently quick-witted to tell a good story and stick to it.

The surgical mutilation of males other than by circumcision has an even more ancient history than male or female infibulation. In Greek mythology Kronos emasculated his father, Ouranos, with a sickle said to be made of diamond. This was after Gää, mother of the Titans, of whom Kronos was the youngest, had incited them all to rebellion against their father. The severed male member was flung into the sea, and from the foam which resulted Venus was born. At the same time the blood that dripped from the wounded surface caused the Giants, the Furies, and the Melian nymphs to spring to life. The Egyptian Book of the Dead records rather similarly how Horus tore out the male organs of Set the god of evil. As a punishment castration was practised by the Franks on any man who violated a free woman. A like punishment was in vogue with the Early Britons, the Spaniards, and the Poles. The mere charge of rape, which has always been one of the easiest to make and most difficult to refute, was sufficient to bring the accused into the hands of the judicial surgeons. But castration never had the popularity as a punishment that it enjoyed for so long as a social custom in the East. There is no doubt that eunuchs

PLATE I

A bas-relief from the Necropolis at Sakkarah, showing the ritual
of circumcision in Ancient Egypt.

华陀醫師肖像

PLATE II

Hua T'o, a Chinese surgeon (*circa* A.D. *200*). Hua T'o was famed for his skill in acupuncture and moxibustion and credited with the ability to foretell the sex of unborn children.

were first employed as guardians of the harem. Their surgical asexuality was of first importance in this calling, but the mental changes which followed the operation had the further advantage of tending to create trustworthy and diligent servants. Thus it was that a menial class of eunuchs was created and maintained in ancient Assyria, and in China even up to modern times. The Jews are the only people of the East who specifically forbade castration. Herodotus records how in the Greek Archipelago there were operating centres or eunuch mass-production plants supplying their mutilated human material to the East. Even comparatively recently a Coptic monastery in upper Egypt was devoted to operating on Nubian and Abyssinian boys of about eight years to supply the Turkish demand for eunuchs.

In Rome three distinct types of eunuchs were recognized: those who had been completely emasculated, having had all the external organs removed; those who had been simply castrated, the testicles being removed but the penis being intact; and those *Thlassiæ* whose testicles had been destroyed by a crushing operation. No less an authority than Juvenal describes how a demand for the last two types was created by Roman wives whose husbands were perpetually empire-building. The operations were performed by the priests of Cybele, who were imported from Phrygia after the second Punic War in 205 B.C., and by a special class of barber-surgeons. The priests themselves were all eunuchs. A clamp found in the bed of the Thames in 1840 is almost certainly one of the instruments used by them to clamp the scrotum before the testicles were cut off, and presumably this was brought over to England at the time of the Roman conquest. Castration proper, as performed for purely surgical reasons, for cancer, tuberculosis, and other disorders of the testicles, has not nearly as long a history as castration and emasculation for social reasons. It was known to the natives of Tahiti, though their technique was so crude that many patients died after the operation, and it has been practised by other primitive tribes.

It is quite clear that surgery was in the beginning an attack on disease in exactly the same way as it is to-day. The Neolithic surgeon had no knowledge of pathology and not much more of anatomy. His instruments were crude, but his ideas were sound. His belief in demons was the only one possible in his time, and his attack on intracranial invaders was just as direct as the modern surgeon's approach to a brain tumour. The cupping and bleeding that his immediate descendants practised were just as logical. That the demoniacal premises on which their therapy was based were incorrect is not remarkable. After half a million years we have discarded the demons, but in the explanation of disease we still invoke certain concepts which will probably amuse surgical posterity much less than half a million days hence. In the same way ritual mutilations of men and women were an undoubted prostitution of surgery, but even so they had more social significance than gastro-enterostomy will ever attain. Surgery was born of a queer muddle of demonology, tribal ritual, and social necessity, but in the earliest civilizations it developed rapidly into a lusty infant art.

II.   Surgery of the Old World

SLOWLY, OVER MANY THOUSANDS OF YEARS, MAN BECAME CIVIL-
ized and rather more slowly his surgeons followed suit.   South-
West Asia was the first home of civilization.   The Sumerians
by 5000 B.C. were organizing an ordered civilization in Babylon
and over the whole delta of the Tigris and Euphrates in Sumer
and Akkad.   It was in Babylon itself, not quite 2250 years
before Christ, that the great law-giver Hammurabi drew up his
Code.   In it he regulated, among innumerable other things, the
exact fees that a surgeon was to receive for certain operations.
Hammurabi wrote:

> If a physician operate on a man for a severe wound (or make a severe
> wound upon a man) with a bronze lancet and save the man's life; or if
> he open an abscess (in the eye) of a man with a bronze lancet and save
> that man's eye, he shall receive ten shekels of silver (as his fee).
> If he be a free man, he shall receive five shekels.
> If it be a man's slave, the owner of the slave shall give two shekels of
> silver to the physician.
> If a physician set a broken bone for a man or cure his diseased bowels,
> the patient shall give five shekels of silver to the physician.
> If he be a free man, he shall give three shekels of silver.
> If it be a man's slave, the owner of the slave shall give two shekels of
> silver to the physician.

It is clear that where the Code speaks of a "man" a gentleman or a nobleman is meant.   The variation in fees according to
the social status of the patient has persisted to this day.   Certain
penal clauses calculated to discourage the rash surgeon have not
survived.   They laid it down that if, as a result of an operation,
"a man" lost his life, or his eye, the surgeon should have his
hands cut off by way of retaliation.

From the few medical and surgical references in works written
at the same time as this Code, it would seem that the surgery
practised by the Sumerians was of a fairly high order.   The
Babylonians were highly skilled in the mechanical arts and had
an extensive literature.   Of their surgical technique little or
nothing is known, simply because the systematic excavations
at Ur and elsewhere have not yet revealed any tablets or papyri
exclusively devoted to surgery.   Only one deduction is per-
missible about Sumerian medicine and surgery.   Their word
for a physician was "Asu".   This means literally "one who

knows water", and brings the Sumerians into line with their mediæval prototypes, who diagnosed every known ailment simply by gazing at the patient's urine. In Egypt, on the other hand, no less than four papyri of surgical importance have been found. Of these the earliest, and perhaps the most important surgically, is the Edwin Smith papyrus, which was written about 1600 B.C., and seems to be based on still older works.

It is a papyrus roll that Mr. Edwin Smith brought from Luxor in 1872. Only ten years ago it was finally deciphered and translated. It is the work of a surgeon who had seen service in the wars and whose whole outlook was scientifically advanced. So much so that he had no use for the charms, amulets, and incantations which completely ousted true surgery in later years. He is remarkable, too, in that he seems to have had a surgical conscience. He examined all his cases carefully, recording the pulse, which he knew might be affected by a head injury, and exploring with his fingers the depths of the wounds he treated. He knew that a patient might sustain a depressed fracture of the vault of the skull even though the scalp was not torn, and that such an injury, if it involved the brain, might cause loss of speech and paralysis of the limbs. He seems to have recognized aneurysms, that is, local enlargements of arteries —presumably of the type due to injury—and though he did not diagnose tuberculous abscesses as such, he did advise that they should not be incised. The papyrus describes forty-eight cases, all typical ones, and they are arranged systematically with head injuries coming first. Each case was considered in the same way. An examination was made, and on this the diagnosis was based. The surgeon then told the patient that he could cure the condition, attempt to cure it, or else that the condition was incurable, and in that event he would have nothing to do with it. In treatment he reduced dislocations of the jaw in exactly the same way as we do to-day. Wounds were closed by adhesive plaster, and when bandages were needed he directed his patients to obtain them from the embalmer. Splints were made of wood, or of linen soaked in glue. Fractures of the collar-bone, the upper arm, and the neck are described. The last case is that of a man who fell from a height and landed on his head. The accident was fatal, and the actual injury the man sustained, an impacted fracture of a neck vertebra, is described.

The technique this anonymous Egyptian surgeon advises

for the reduction of fractured collar-bones is sound, though his methods for retaining the fragments in position do not seem quite so good. He writes:

> If thou examinest a man having a break in his collar-bone . . . thou shouldst place him prostrate on his back, with something folded between his two shoulder-blades; thou shouldst spread out his two shoulders in order to stretch apart his collar-bone until that break falls into its place. Thou shouldst make for him two splints of linen, thou shouldst apply one of them both on the inside of his upper arm and the other on the under side of his upper arm. Thou shouldst bind it . . . treat it afterwards [with] honey every day until he recovers.

The treatment of fractures of the upper arm is described as being almost identical with that for the fracture of the clavicle. Splints arranged in this way would help to control the fragments of a fractured upper arm, but in the case of a broken collar-bone even if a figure-of-eight bandage was applied they would not be very effective. The method of reduction, however, is in the best modern manner. Many lovely ladies have spent uncomfortable weeks lying flat on their backs with a sand-bag wedged between their shoulder-blades, for if a perfect cosmetic result is to be achieved after the lady has sustained a broken collar-bone, no other method will so safely and surely produce the desired effect. Wounds which did not require suturing, and bruises of all kinds were healed quite simply. The anxious mother who applies a beef-steak to her belligerent son's black eye has only to use a honey ointment the next day and she will be following exactly the advice given nearly four thousand years ago. It is not surprising that in the general treatment of his patients the surgeon was just as modern—or is it just conceivable that we are becoming old-fashioned? Time and time again he uses a rather attractive idiom, "put the patient on his fingers", and explains that this means "to put him on his accustomed food without giving him medical treatment". All of which lends the policy of masterly inactivity considerable traditional support.

A papyrus discovered at the same time is the Ebers papyrus. It is some fifty years younger than the Edwin Smith papyrus and is in many respects a more comprehensive work. It was discovered by George M. Ebers in 1872 and translated into German by H. Joachim in 1890. It includes one large and several small works on the treatment of disease, and was probably written in 1560 B.C., just before the Syrians began to exert their influence on Egypt. Many of the prescriptions in it are supposed to have been concocted by the gods, although there is little that is sacred or mysterious about the ingredients. The patient was almost always expected to pronounce an invocation to the appropriate god while taking or applying a medicine. Ra, Isis, and Horus were most often called upon. The prescriptions are occasionally rational—in the use of opium, for example— and the prayers in these instances at least seem to correspond less to a magic incantation than to the reflex "Mud in your eye" of the orthodox modern beer-drinker. The gods were far from neglected, but the assistance they were asked to give was re-inforced by reasonably sensible general measures and a few drugs known to have a definite pharmacological action, even though they were mixed up with some regrettable god-given concoctions.

Most of this ancient book is devoted to the medicinal treat-ment of disease, and surgical interference is recommended in only a few conditions. A great deal of space is expended on cosmetic treatment. Methods of removing wrinkles and moles, dyeing the hair and eyebrows, correcting squints, and generally beautifying the body, are mixed quite indiscriminately with hints to the handyman on killing scorpions and lizards, keeping rats out of the granary, charming away fleas, soothing crying babies, sweetening the breath—without reference to the patient's best friends—and finally there is a remedy of considerable social value for sweaty feet.

The ingredients used in prescriptions range from the sublime excrement-of-the-gods—whatever this was and however pro-cured—to the by comparison ridiculous castor-oil tree. Every theme had the most ingenious variations. Beer, for example, which was a favorite vehicle for medicines, is variously pre-scribed as Plain Beer, Sweet Beer, Bitter Beer, Flat Beer, Cold Beer, Warmed Beer, Froth of Beer, Yeast of Beer, Beer-which-has-been-brewed-from-many-ingredients, and—happy thought!— Swill-of-Beer. Milk was presented in almost as many forms, and Milk-of-a-Man had ascribed to it all the virtues of its un-doubted rarity. Water was never advised *qua* water, but Plain Water, Well Water, Salt Water, Spring Water, and Cake Water all vie in popularity with Water-from-the-Bird-Pond, Water-from-the-Rain-of-the-Heavens, and, most potent of all, Water-in-which-the-Phallus-has-been-Washed. In organotherapy the mixtures used mark out their originators as direct ancestors of our modern manufacturers of hormonic cocktails. Male semen is used to flavour a preparation designed to relieve intestinal obstruction. For the Great Debility—to cure it and not to cause it—Excrement-of-the-Adu-Bird and What-is-in-the-ut'ait-fruit, cooked in Sweet Beer and Olive Oil, should be taken for four days. Tortoise-shell, Granite, and Trash-from-the-Knife-Stone cures certain abscesses. For the immediate cure of another obscure disease the unhappy patient is directed to Crush, Rub in Wine, and Drink The-Two-Testicles-of-a-Black-Ass. Vulva, Phallus, and Black Lizard mixed together formed a hair-restorer, and not a hair-curler, as might be imagined, and the schoolgirl complexion could be effectively attained by a face-cream of Bullock's-Bile and Ostrich-Egg beaten up with Fresh-Milk; hair could be dyed by a mixture which included a Tapeworm, Hoof-of-an-Ass, and Vulva-of-a-Bitch. This last cosmetic horror would turn even platinum blondes grey.

The first woman doctor to receive historical notice is mentioned in this papyrus. She was the goddess Tefnut, and she compounded a medicine for the Great God Ra. It gave him a headache, but the goddess Isis cured this by another medicine which contained Berry-of-the-Poppy-Plant. This is one of the very early records of the use of opium to relieve pain. In the papyrus itself the application of opium externally in ointments of Ass's Fat is mentioned. Many minor surgical conditions were treated "bloodlessly". The bites of crocodiles—and of men—were cured by the application of raw meat. Burns were dealt with by innumerable applications varying from A-Frog-Warmed-in-Oil to Goat-Dung-in-Yeast-that-is-Fermenting. Any lack in the therapeutic efficiency of these remedies was made up by an Incantation for a Burn:

> "O Son, Horus! There is Fire in the Land!
> Water is not there and thou art not there!
> Bring Water over the River-Bank to quench the Fire."
>
> To-be-Spoken-over-Milk-of-a-Woman-who-has-Borne-a-Son.

A series of ointments guaranteed to extract splinters seem equally guaranteed to make the patients keep quiet about any such accidents.

What To Do To Draw Out Splinters in the Flesh:

> The per-baibait-bird-with-Honey
> Apply thereto.

Another:

> Worms' blood, cook and crush it in Oil;
> Mole, kill, cook, and drain in Oil;
> Ass's dung, mix in Fresh Milk,
> Apply to the opening.

Another:

> Male-and-Female-Semen
> Apply thereto.

Another:

> Skull-of-the-Shadfish, cooked in Oil;
> Apply to the point of the splinter.
> Thereby it comes out.

"Stinking Ulcers" are dealt with lengthily, and to one prescription of thorns, ostrich-eggs, and tortoise-shell is appended the very necessary advice "Warm and anoint therewith, But Don't Get Tired Doing It". This advice might have been more generally tendered, without much harm resulting.

In major surgery the cautery was relied on to some extent.

> Instructions for a Tumour of the Flesh in any Part of the Body of a Person:
> When thou comest upon a tumour of the flesh in any part of the body of a person and thou dost find it like skin on his flesh; it is moist; it moves under thy fingers save when thy fingers are held still, then its movement is caused by thy fingers. So shalt thou say: "It is a tumour of the flesh. I will treat the disease since I will try to cure it with fire, as the metalworker cures."

In one case it is recommended that the surgeon should use the knife and then check the hæmorrhage by means of the red-hot cautery. Discussing the diagnosis of "Obstructions in the Abdomen" a perfect clinical picture is followed by a relatively pedestrian diagnosis.

> When thou Examinest the Obstruction in his Abdomen and thou findest that he is not in a condition to leap the Nile, his stomach is swollen and his chest asthmatic, then say thou to him: "It is the Blood that has got itself fixed and does not circulate."

When dealing with fatty growths in the neck the surgeon says: "I will treat the disease with the Knife, taking care of the Blood-Vessels the while". In connection with fluid swellings: "I will try to heal it with fire like the Cautery heals". Tumours in the head, tumours of blood-vessels, and lipomata, fatty tumours, were treated with the knife. In another instance:

> When thou meetest a Skin-Tumour on the outside part of the body above his Genitals lay thy finger on it, and examine his body, palpating with thy fingers. If his bowels move and he vomits at the same time, then say thou: "It is a Skin-Tumour in his body. I will treat the disease by heat to the bladder on the front of his body which causes the tumour to fall to the earth." . . . Heal it as the cautery heals.

The most dreaded of tumours is difficult to identify.

> When thou meetest a large tumour of the God Xensu in any part of the limb of a person, it is loathsome and suffers many pustules to come forth; something arises therein as though wind were in it, causing irritation. The Tumour calls with a loud voice to thee: "Is it not like the most loathsome of pustules?" It mottles the skin and makes figures. All the limbs are like those which are affected. Then say thou: *"It is a tumour of the God Xensu. Do thou nothing there against."*

Obstetrics and gynæcology are not neglected, though it might have been better for the patients if they had been. Douches of Garlic and Wine regulated menstruation. The Dried Liver of a Swallow in Sour Milk would protect the virgin who anointed herself with it from leucorrhœa—a white discharge. Dates, Onions, and the Fruit-of-the-Acanthus crushed with Honey and applied to the vulva would cause abortion. Strangely enough, this is the only abortifacient mentioned. We do seem to have progressed in some directions.

There are, however, many methods of accelerating the birth of a child. "Peppermint: Let the woman apply it to her bare posterior", is the simplest, and was probably no less effective than any of the other treatments suggested. To correct a displaced womb The-Film-of-Dampness-which-is-found-on-the-Wood-of-Ships rubbed in Yeast-of-Fermented-Beer was taken by mouth. For amenorrhœa a mixture of Caraway Incense, Uah-grain, and Berry-of-the-uan-tree in Cow's Milk which had been Put to the Fire with Thigh-Tallow was taken. An essential part of the treatment in those cases in which menstruation had ceased was that a Magic Formula should be spoken and coitus performed before the medicine was taken. There is possibly some confusion of cause and effect here.

The outstanding differences between the two papyri help to show the beginning of the end of Egyptian medicine and surgery. The Edwin Smith papyrus reveals a knowledge of true surgery.

clear-cut and worthy of the standards of civilization at that time.
The Ebers papyrus was written later, soon after the Eighteenth
Dynasty had established the New Kingdom and the First
Empire, after the fall of the Middle Kingdom and a long period
of anarchy. There is still much sound medicine and practical
surgery advised, but it is becoming overladen with charms and
incantations. The belief in demoniacal possession, though it
was never lost completely, has returned in full force. There
is no doubt that many of the prescriptions in the Ebers papyrus
have a dual purpose. Opium, iron, arsenic, calamine, and so
on seem to be prescribed according to the dictates of reason
and experience, but with them the entrails of moles and many
even more regrettable preparations were mixed, and were
presumably calculated to disgust the demons, which they almost
certainly would. Medicine and surgery had never been completely divorced from religion, but gradually the mystical incantation began to have far more significance than any rational
treatment, and surgery was slowly engulfed by exorcism, while
Egypt itself sank into comparative obscurity to become finally a
mere province of Imperial Rome. Egyptian surgery, at its
zenith, exerted a great and good effect upon the practice of this
art in other civilizations. The Greeks, for example, always
recognized this debt, and they identified Asklepios with Imhotep,
a god of medicine, who was probably the apotheosis of the chief
physician of Zoser, about 2980 B.C.

The Egyptian practice of mummification allowed the acquisi-
tion of a certain degree of anatomical knowledge which other
peoples did not possess, but at the same time such knowledge
was strictly limited. The Egyptians believed in the sanctity
of the body they embalmed, and so any detailed dissection was
probably regarded as an offence against the dead. Extensive
studies of mummified remains have been made, notably by Elliot
Smith and Armand Ruffer; many of their findings are of surgical
interest. They noted the prevalence of fractures of the forearm,
especially of the ulna about two inches above the wrist. This
was probably caused when the arm was raised instinctively
to try to ward off a blow from the flailing cudgel of a brutal
overseer. Their studies of the teeth of mummies are also
revealing. They showed that among the earlier Egyptians
teeth were perfectly preserved. In later and more luxurious
times their teeth were ravaged by decay. Tartar formation,
dental caries, and alveolar abscesses were probably more common

then than they are to-day. It is clear that dentistry was quite unknown.

According to Herodotus, Egyptian hygiene was of a much higher order than Egyptian medicine and surgery. There is no doubt that the Jews during their stay in Egypt absorbed hygienic ideals with much more of Egyptian culture. Surgically, the Jews' knowledge was very small. Circumcision is the only operation the Bible mentions apart from Adam's rib excision. The anatomical knowledge shown by the Jews was also rather sketchy. Writings embodied in the Talmud show a vague anatomy which features the Bone of Luz. This is the seed from which the body is to be resurrected, and is a sort of indestructible nucleus. Belief in this remarkable bone and in "Adam's missing rib" persisted until the sixteenth century, when Vesalius showed that both were myths.

Egyptian surgery, before mysticism destroyed it, inspired many other peoples, but the surgery practised in China seems to have resembled more closely Sumerian practice. Both the Sumerians and the Chinese used enemata, oil frictions, bleeding, and cupping in much the same way. A work comparable to the Egyptian papyri is the *Nei Ching,* which is traditionally ascribed to Huang Ti, who lived about 2600 B.C. More probably it was compiled perhaps fifteen hundred years later and deliberately antedated to enhance its appeal and authority. Anatomically this book divides the internal organs into five "Tsangs" and six "Fus". The "Tsangs" are the heart, liver, spleen, lungs, and kidneys, which were believed to be solid organs which stored up and did not eliminate. The hollow and eliminating "Fus" were the gall-bladder, stomach, large and small intestine, the bladder, and the "San Chiao". These last "three burning spaces" are purely imaginary organs, about the location or function of which no two authorities are agreed. The Confucian belief that the body is sacred prevented any anatomical dissections being undertaken. It has been stated that the first time human dissection was attempted in interior China was on April 22, 1915. It is small wonder that Chinese anatomical ideas do not bear inspection. Surgery inevitably suffered from being based on a system of anatomy in which the few coherent observations ever made were promptly twisted to fit an intricate natural philosophy laid down by Confucius.

One of the first records of Chinese surgery concerns a singularly versatile individual, Yu Fu, who was attached to the Court of the Emperor Huang Ti. It is said that he "Employed manipulation, baking, and radical excision. If necessary he made incisions through the skin, loosened off the muscles, identified the blood-vessels, sutured tendon fragments, exposed the spinal cord and brain and cleansed various viscera". Generally speaking, the early Chinese surgeons confined their activities to three minor procedures, massage, acupuncture, and moxibustion. The Japanese, who are still acknowledged experts, learnt the art of massage—as they learnt most other arts except that of war—from the Chinese, who had practised it from time immemorial. Tapping, kneading, pinching, chafing, and pommelling the body all over was advised, and was probably often effective, in the treatment of muscular fatigue, rheumatism, nervousness, insomnia, and so forth.

Acupuncture is practised in China to this day exactly as it was three thousand years ago. The life of man is said to be ruled by two great forces—a positive *Yang,* and a negative *Yin.* Normally these principles, which are always in a state of flux, balance each other and circulate through the body by means of twelve channels. The course of these channels is not strictly laid down and their anatomical relations are unknown, but they begin near the toes and fingers and radiate to different parts of the body. If the balance of these two principles is disturbed, disease follows. Acupuncture by means of driving a needle deeply into the flesh allows the excessive *Yang,* or it may be *Yin,* to escape, a normal balance is restored and health is regained. There are nine different needles, and 365 points along the twelve channels at which they may be inserted. One authority did specify 650 needle points, but this seems to be carrying things a little far. The patient, who is seated, is asked to cough, and then the selected needle is inserted by a twisting motion, by pressure, or by light taps with a hammer. The site of insertion, the direction of the needle, whether it is left in for minutes or days, whether it is hot or cold, whether it is twisted to the right or left—all these details are carefully worked out according to the nature and severity of the individual case. When the needle is withdrawn, firm pressure may be applied, or occasionally the moxa may be used. The moxa is a combustible cone of common mugwort. These cones are often arranged in geometrical figures, as in the fire cures of Tibet, favourite sites for applications being the epigastrium, the upper part of the sternum, and the nape of the neck. Once ignited, the moxa smoulders slowly and raises a painful blister. It may be used separately or in conjunction with acupuncture, and its effect is similar to that achieved by any other method of counter-irritation.

Of major operations, which may or may not have been carried out, a typical one is described as having taken place about 300 B.C. Pien Ch'iao is the writer.

> One day two men, Lu and Chao, called on him; he gave them a toxic drink and they were unconscious for three days. Pien Ch'iao operated and performed a gastrostomy and explored the heart; after removing and interchanging their organs he gave a wonderful drug and the two men went home recovered.

This is one of the earliest records of anæsthesia. Pien Ch'iao might have achieved a niche in the surgeons' Valhalla had his operation been nearly probable enough to lend authenticity to his "toxic drink."

China went the way of Egypt, and remained at a surgical standstill for much longer. The Japanese followed their neighbours blindly until the middle of the last century, then they broke away and were soon in the van of surgical progress. Chinese surgery was never of as high a standard as Egyptian or Sumerian surgery, though there are points of comparison with both schools. It was only in its degradation that the surgical art in China followed at all closely the Egyptian model. In each case the first step towards chaos was a gross over-specialization, though even here the Chinese did not attain the remarkable heights of Egyptian specialism. Senousret, who was one of Tut-ank-amen's ancestors, rejoiced in having one specialist for his right eye and one for his left.

It has been suggested that the feet of Chinese women may have suffered from the perverted application of what was formerly a knowledge of orthopædic surgery. This is unlikely. The deliberate mutilation which has been practised for so long in many, though not all, of the provinces of China is probably a form of "beauty culture". It is said to have been introduced by the Emperor Chen-Hon-Djon about A.D. 580. The emperor was a lascivious soul and wanted to introduce a new feminine charm in diminutive feet. Another possibility is that it derived from a form of courtly flattery by imitation of some imperial

[*43*]

personage who was born with club feet. A more probable
theory, put forward by Professor H. A. Giles, is that binding
the feet was begun because it necessarily increases the musculature
of the thighs and pelvis, and so greatly enhances a woman's
erotic attraction and ability. In any event, mutilation of feminine
feet to reduce them to a tortured immobility of not more than
four inches long is evidence against rather than for any orthopædic knowledge.

Surgery attained a remarkable development in ancient India.
Knowledge of early Aryan surgery has been gained for the most
part from three sacred books, the *Rig Veda,* the *Atharva Veda,*
and the *Sushruta Samhitá.* It is generally believed that the
original four vedas, *Rig, Yajur, Sama,* and *Atharva,* were compiled between 1000 and 2000 B.C., a date tentatively suggested
being 1400 B.C. The *Ayur Veda* is believed to have been
added as a sort of supplement on the science of life somewhere
about 900 B.C. This supplement is an elaboration of parts of
the *Rig Veda* so far as it treats of medicine and of parts of the
Atharva Veda in so far as surgery is concerned. Surgery is
dealt with in the first of the eight sections of the *Ayur
Veda,* and it is on this that Sushruta, the father of Hindoo
surgery, based his *Samhitá,* which was probably written about
600 B.C.

These are the facts of the origin of these medical texts so far
as can be ascertained. More interesting by far are the legends
which surround them. It is said that Brahma taught the
Ayur Veda to a certain sage, who in his turn conveyed it to the
Ashvini Kumars, "twin sons of the sun", who acted as physicians
to the gods. A legend in the *Rig Veda* pays tribute to their
surgical skill and ingenuity, which has never since been equalled.
The twins wished to learn the science of Brahma-Vedya, the
highest philosophy, from one Dadhyanchi, who had learnt it
from Indra. Unhappily Indra had promised to cut off his
pupil's head if he ever communicated this philosophy to anyone
else. This might have made things difficult for lesser men than
the Ashvini. They prevailed on the sage to expound the Brahma-
Vedya, and then, with his consent, cut off his head and replaced
on his trunk the head of a horse. Indra, in his wrath, cut off
the equine head as he had promised he would. The Ashvini,
who were proficient surgeons, restored the original head, which
they had preserved, and all was well. A difficulty arose when

the gods learnt of this prodigious feat. They decided that, despite the subsequent replacement, the Ashvini's act in cutting off the head of their preceptor was morally indefensible. The twins were cast out from among the gods. They went to see an old and decrepit sage who had recently married a young and charming princess. The Ashvini restored the holy impotent to full vigour. By way of thanks he had offered to them at the next sacrificial rites the libations which had been their due before they were cast out by the gods. Indra was greatly affronted at this and raised the inevitable thunderbolt. The bolt was never hurled because Indra's arm was suddenly paralysed. The Ashvini cured this paralysis, and were promptly restored to the company of the gods, where they continued their good work, and finally taught the *Ayur Veda* to Indra. It was by the pupils of Indra that many of the oldest surgical and medical books were supposed to be produced.

These early surgical books are remarkable for their comprehensiveness and systematic arrangement, and this may be said especially of the *Sushruta Samhitá*. It describes how surgery was of primary importance because injuries sustained in the wars between the gods and the demons had to be dealt with long before the art of medicine was needed to cure fevers and general diseases, which were then unknown. The qualities of character and temperament necessary in one who is to be a surgeon it gives in detail with the whole involved ritual of initiation. The need for anatomical knowledge, and the fact that this could only be obtained by careful dissection of the human cadaver, are stressed. Discrepancies in Hindoo accounts of human anatomy as compared with modern knowledge are probably due not to lack of observation, but to the fact that dissections were made on the bodies of children of less than two years, since older children and adults were cremated. The preparation of the cadavers, by immersion in water for up to seven days, must necessarily have prohibited the detailed study which is possible with modern methods of preservation and injection, particularly in a country in which decomposition is rapid. A clear-cut and logical classification of operations mentions eight general types: incising, excising, scraping, puncturing, searching or probing, extracting, secreting fluids, and suturing. One hundred and twenty-five different surgical instruments are minutely described, and the indications for their use outlined. The insistence on a correct training is remarkable, and the section

[45]

of the *Sushruta Samhitá* describing how the apprentice may try his hand on ingenious models bears quotation.

Now we shall discuss the chapter which treats of practical instructions in surgical operations (*Yogya-Sutra*).

The preceptor should see his disciple attends the practice of surgery even if he has already thoroughly mastered the several branches of the science of Medicine, or has perused it in its entirety. In all acts connected with surgical operations of incision, etc., and injection of oil, etc., the pupil should be fully instructed as regards the channels along or into which the operations or applications are to be made (*Karma-patha*). A pupil, otherwise well read, but uninitiated into the practice (of medicine or surgery) is not competent (to take in hand the medical or Surgical treatment of a disease). The art of making specific forms of incision should be taught by making cuts in the body of a *Pushpaphalá* (a kind of gourd), *Alávu,* watermelon, cucumber, or *Erváruka*. The art of making cuts either in the upward or downward direction should be similarly taught. The art of making excisions should be practically demonstrated by making openings in the body of a full water-bag, or in the bladder of a dead animal, or in the side of a leather pouch full of slime or water. The art of scraping should be instructed on a piece of skin on which the hair has been allowed to remain. The art of venesection (*Vedhya*) should be taught on the vein of a dead animal, or with the help of a lotus stem. The art of probing and stuffing should be taught on worm (*Ghuna*) eaten wood, or on the reed of a bamboo, or on the mouth of a dried *Alávu* (gourd). The art of extracting should be taught by withdrawing seeds from the kernel of a *Vimbi, Vilva* or Jack fruit, as well as by extracting teeth from the jaws of a dead animal. The act of secreting or evacuating should be taught on the surface of a *Shálmali* plank covered over with a coat of bees-wax, and suturing on pieces of cloth, skin or hide. Similarly the art of bandaging or ligaturing should be practically learned by tying bandages round the specific limbs and members of a full-sized doll made of stuffed linen. The art of tying up a *Karna-sandhi* (severed ear-lobe) should be practically demonstrated on a soft severed muscle or on flesh, or with the stem of a lotus lily. The art of cauterizing, or applying alkaline preparations (caustics) should be demonstrated on a piece of soft flesh; and lastly the art of inserting syringes and injecting enemas into the region of the bladder or into an ulcerated channel, should be taught (by asking the pupil) to insert a tube into a lateral fissure of a pitcher, full of water, or into the mouth of a gourd (*Alávu*).

Authoritative verses on the subject:

An intelligent physician who has tried his prentice hand in surgery (on such articles of experiment as gourds, etc.), or has learnt the art with the help of things as stated above, or has been instructed in the art of cauterization or blistering (application of alkali) by experimenting on things which are most akin, or similar to the parts or members of the human body they are usually applied to, will never lose his presence of mind in his professional practice.

Thus ends the ninth chapter of the *Sutrasthanam* in the *Sushruta Samhitá* which treats of Instructions in Surgical operations.

Leeching, bleeding, and cupping were well known, and the actual cautery was used extensively. In describing these and all other procedures the Hindoo surgeons were systematic. A good example is, "the chapter which treats of cauteries and the rules to be observed in their use". The "accessories to an act of cauterization" are first described, then the seasons in which it may be practised—"all seasons of the year except summer and autumn"—though there is a saving clause to the effect that "no such distinction [of seasons] shall be observed in cases of impending danger". It is next advised that the patient should either fast or take a special dietary, according to his or her condition, immediately before the operation. There follows a list of indications, and a description of the diseases which the actual cautery will benefit. Glandular inflammation, tumour, fistula-in-ano, scrofula, elephantiasis, hernia, and warts are given especial mention. Next the four techniques of cauterization are enumerated. They are: "The Ring, the Dot, the Lateral or Slanting Lines, and the Rubbing Modes". Dressings and post-operative care are dealt with, and the contra-indications are listed last. For instance, it is said that ". . . a weak or an old man, an infant, or a man of timid disposition . . . should be regarded as a subject unfit for cauterization". As a natural appendix to this chapter the treatment of burns other than those sustained surgically is outlined. Always the plan is the same, and is one that is still followed. Instruments and accessories, pre-operative preparation, indications for operation, operative technique, post-operative care, and contra-indications, all are dealt with and always in that order.

The mere fact of such an exact systematization betokens a long experience and a high order of skill. This is further evidenced by the remarkable extent to which these surgeons had developed plastic surgery. Hindoo children had their ears pierced for protection against the evil influences of malignant stars and spirits, or more prosaically for ornamentation. If the ear-rings were heavy or the piercing had been done badly, a fissure splitting the ear-lobe into two parts might result. The surgeon had no less than fifteen methods for ensuring the plastic repair of this cosmetic misfortune. One of these operations is known as *Ganda-Karna*. "*Ganda-Karna* consists in slicing off a patch of healthy flesh from one of the regions of the cheeks and in adhering to it one of the severed lobes of the ears which is more elongated on its anterior side than the other."

Since cutting off the nose and ears was a common punishment in India the surgeons had no lack of clinical material for their early attempts at plastic surgery. Even so it is surprising that they were able to bring to perfection the difficult operation of rhinoplasty, the more or less complete building up of a new nose by using sensible skin flaps moulded round wooden tubes which kept the nostrils open. The surgery of nerves, too, was not unknown. Division of the supra-orbital nerve was advised for supra-orbital neuralgia which did not respond to medicinal treatment, and there is some evidence that intracranial explorations were undertaken. The abdomen was opened in cases of intestinal obstruction, and suture of the bowel was practised when perforations of the gut followed abdominal injuries. A further indication of the skill possessed by these early surgeons is provided by the chapter in the *Sushruta Samhitá* on incurable diseases. Cases regarded as extremely hard to cure, and those which usually ended in death are not much more numerous than they are to-day. For example, Sushruta writes that: "A case of piles attended with thirst, aversion to food, colic pain, excessive hæmorrhage, local dropsy, and dysentery is soon relieved by death." The same patient to-day would die just as certainly and as quickly, though perhaps under some more exact label.

A surgical science as great as, if not greater than, that of Egypt and Sumeria began a gradual decline in the lifetime of Buddha. He and his followers in the sixth century B.C. gave great support to medicine and particularly veterinary medicine. The earliest Indian hospitals or "Houses of Benevolence" were founded at this time, as were the *Pinjrrapoles* or animal hospitals peculiar to India. Unhappily, the virtue which prompted this care for animals prohibited animal experiment and dissection. The followers of Gautama had the same aversion to sacrificial offerings, from which much anatomical knowledge had been gained in the early days. They shrank, too, from the contacts with blood and pus and diseased flesh which surgery demanded. The priests took into their own hands the existing medical treatises, and gave them religious authority by an accumulation of myths and mysticism, which rapidly obscured the fundamental surgical truths on which they had been based. There was pollution in disease and death. Animal experiment was a profane sacrilege. Surgery was lost in exorcism. As in Egypt, religion destroyed far more than it could ever create. A debased and bastard craft was bequeathed by priests abhorring surgery to the lowest castes, unfortunates so unclean that they could not further be contaminated by handling knives which had been allowed to become blunt and rusty.

To this day there are practising in India itinerant cutters for stone. These peripatetic specialists make the same meagre living as their forefathers and in exactly the same way. They are "experts" in this one operation of cutting for stone in the bladder, and know no other. The operator puts his finger in the patient's anus and hooks down the stone, which can be felt in the bladder, so that it presses hard against the perineal tissues. With an ordinary razor an incision is made over the flinty protrusion and deepened till the bladder is opened. The stone is extracted with a scoop, and that is all. There is no pre-operative preparation and no question of serious post-operative care. The wandering stone-cutter moves on to the next village and his next batch of patients. What happens to the patient is unimportant. Priests whose ancestors four thousand years ago were brilliant surgeons have progressed. To-day their hands are clean.

The Thakore Saheb of Gondal has written:

> ... circumstantial evidence has led some European writers—Louis Jacolliot among others—to affirm that if Egypt gave civilization to Greece and the latter bequeathed it to Rome, Egypt herself received her laws, arts, and sciences from India. There is nothing in the Egyptian medicine which is not in the Indian system, and there is much in the elaborate Indian system that is wanting in the medical science of Egypt.

It is difficult to assess the extent to which these and other great civilizations were dependent on each other's culture. It is easier to estimate the degree of surgical development attained in different countries, leaving on one side the vexed question as to whether such culture was borrowed or arose independently.

Old China never had any real system of surgery, nor had Japan. Of the Babylonians we know little except that they practised surgery in a fairly advanced form and that to them must be given credit for freeing surgery from the trammels of religion, at least for a time. Surgery in Egypt, and to an even greater extent in India, reached heights which only the Greeks equalled, and only our own civilization has bettered. Indian surgeons advanced far beyond their Egyptian contemporaries, but in medicine, in general therapeutics, and in hygiene, Egypt and India must have ranked equal. The decline and fall of surgery followed almost exactly the same lines in the two countries. In each case an over-specialization was the first step. There was next a tightening of the age-old links between medicine and religion. The priests invoked their gods, and made a haze of incantations and myths obscure true surgery, in order that their own authority might be enhanced. Surgery was no longer a profession, no longer an art. It was allowed to become a trade and a menial one. Demons that knives brilliantly wielded had dispossessed came into their own again.

III. Greeks and Romans

THERE WAS ONCE A CHIEF OF THESSALY WHO FOUGHT IN THE
Trojan Wars. He was born in the thirteenth century B.C. He
is believed to have invented an instrument for removing arrow-
heads from the depths of wounds, which he probed with another
instrument of his own devising. According to one authority
he was acquainted with the use of ligatures, and he certainly
employed bandages in various forms. His two sons, or perhaps they were sons in the sense of pupils, Machaon and Poda-
leiros, helped him to treat the wounds sustained by the Greeks
before Troy. The name of this chief was Asklepois, and the
Romans knew him later as Æsculapius. Homer's story of
Asklepois is a plain tale of a mortal man skilled in a rude
form of surgery. Pindar's story is that of a mortal whose skill
in the healing arts was great enough to distress Pluto. Pluto
complained bitterly that the work of Asklepios on earth had so
prolonged life that the population of Hell was diminishing.
Zeus promptly slew Asklepios with a thunderbolt. This had
the triple effect of restoring the balance of population and thus
redressing Pluto's grievance, reasserting the authority of Olympus
in matters of life and death, and allowing the immediate deifica-
tion of Asklepios.

The myths and legends that began to gather around the
Thessalian chief were legion. It soon became clear that no
mortal could have wrought such miraculous cures as were
attributed to him. He was deemed a god and the son of gods,
and the legends grew till it appeared to poets who lived only a
few centuries after the man himself that even a god could hardly
have achieved so much. The myth of a divine parentage of
pedestrian orthodoxy was discarded. It was first suggested
that his mother was Ascinöe and that she abandoned him as an
infant, but he was saved from starvation by a goat. This theory
was soon rejected in favour of a better one. Asklepios was the
son of a god, Apollo, and a mortal woman, Koronis. Koronis
died before he was born and Apollo himself cut his son from
out the womb of Koronis as she lay on her funeral pyre. Asklepios survived this startling entrance into the world long enough
to marry twice. His daughter by his first wife was Hygeia,
who was called Athene, and it was she who became the goddess
of hygiene. Her name has passed into every modern language,

while the symbol of Asklepios is still the most commonly used medical emblem. The caduceus, two snakes twined on a staff, may be found in one form or another in most medical arms and crests.

Temples of Asklepios were first built in the eighth or early seventh century B.C. and over three hundred of them were erected. Epidaurus seems to have been the centre of the cult which grew so rapidly, and the ruins there give some idea of the scale on which festivals were organized. A theatre which would hold twenty thousand people, and a stadium seating twelve thousand were just a part of the accommodation necessary for those who sought health at the Temple of Asklepios in Epidaurus. Votive tablets found in the ruins of this temple bear inscriptions in the nature of unsolicited testimonials. Many of them describe operations which must have been successfully undertaken by the priests, though all are attributed to the divine intervention of Asklepios, a belief which the priests themselves fostered. Typical of these cases are the records of abscesses of different types which the patients, on waking, found incised and drained. In a different class are the accounts of surgical miracles casually performed by Asklepios in person. There was Kleo, for example, who grew progressively larger and larger with child for a period of five years. She slept for one night in the Abaton, and the benign influence of Asklepios immediately had the desired effect. Next morning she bore a four-year-old boy, who washed himself at the fountain, took his mother's arm, and strolled placidly back home. Another patient, a man, was dying of dropsy. Asklepios cured him overnight by the simple process of cutting off his head, holding the body upside down so as to drain off all the dropsical fluid, and then neatly replacing the head. The stories of Kleo and this gentleman, and many others, must have emanated from that section of the priesthood responsible for propaganda. There is no doubt that the Asklepiadæ did exploit human weakness in this and other ways, but it was almost inevitable that they should do so. They had to live up to a truly god-like tradition, and the number of patients who flocked to them must soon have made them realize that their crude but rational methods of medicine and surgery could not possibly maintain the Asklepian standards. So they brought in the atmosphere of secrecy, the element of religious superstition, and the more material assistance of sacred serpents, which were trained to lick the patients' wounds. The Asklepiadæ had the great distinction of being the first and the only surgeons to have a death-rate which was exactly nil. Not one of the thousands of patients they treated died on their hands. At the first sign of approaching death patients were dumped in the woods near by, lest their death in the temple should suggest that Asklepios and his disciples were fallible.

In the course of time the priests devoted themselves more and more to the purely religious side of their work, and a school of lay assistants, or secular Asklepiadæ, grew up and took over the medical and surgical treatment of patients. There was an unbelievable wealth of clinical material passing through the temples with their huge Abatons, lofty buildings each designed to house perhaps a hundred and twenty patients. The laymen who were given charge of them must have been brought up in the Greek schools of philosophy and logic. It is hardly surprising that when their trained intellects were brought to bear upon the problems of human disease, they achieved more in a few years than the superstitious priests, trammelled by myths and mysticism, had achieved in centuries. So it was that a rational medicine and a clear-cut science of surgery grew gradually from a cult which had centred round a chief of Thessaly.

Inevitably, medical schools arose, and the first of these was in Cnidos, a Lacedæmonian colony in Asiatic Doris. It was founded probably in the seventh century B.C. The surgeons of this school ruthlessly discarded all the time-honoured elements of magic and superstition. They observed and described systematically facts relating to disease, facts and nothing but facts. To them, a lump in a man's abdomen was just a lump in a man's abdomen. It was of a certain size, a certain consistency, and a certain shape; it might or might not vary in size; but it was not the work of demons or devils, it was not the product of witchcraft, it was just a lump. The doctrines of this school were drawn up in a series of "Sentences" or Aphorisms. The influence the Cnidian surgeons exerted was of vital importance. They over-emphasized diagnosis, they over-elaborated their treatment, and they paid more attention to the patient's signs and symptoms than to the patient himself, but they insisted that a lump was a lump, which it was, is, and always will be. They based their surgery on a science of accurate and detailed observation. The rightness of their ideas and their ideals has never been questioned. They failed only in that they did the right thing to excess. They did not realize that the man who owned both the lump and the abdomen merited as much consideration as either.

The great rival school, on the island of Cos, founded perhaps a hundred years later, was just as exact in making clinical observations, but it regarded the man as more important than any lump he might have. The writings of the physicians and surgeons, pupils of these two schools, of the fourth and fifth centuries B.C. were collected together by an Alexandrian Commission of scholars in the third century B.C. Some of these sixty or seventy works show the influence of Cnidos, but most of them are from Cos, and all these latter seem to have been inspired by one man, who himself wrote at least two of the major works. He was born in 460 B.C., the son of a lay Asklepiad, and was a pupil and later a teacher in the school of Cos. He died about 370 B.C., after having wandered far and wide through Thrace, Abdera, Delos, Thasos, Thessaly, and elsewhere. His name was Hippocrates and he is known as the father of medicine. He and his fellows seem to have absorbed all that was good from the cultures of older civilizations, but they brought to such culture a clearer insight and a broader rationalism than the older civilizations ever knew. They never distinguished between medicine and surgery, but practised both as integral parts of a single liberal art.

Of Hippocrates as an individual it may be said that he was the embodiment of all that a physician should be. He was a close observer, a humane scholar, and a man filled with the desire to help his patients and to ensure that by his teaching and experience others should benefit. High ideals are set forth simply in the Hippocratic oath. This oath has been respected by physicians and surgeons of every race and creed for two thousand years. To this day it is the simplest expression of a complicated ethical code that has always been based on it:

> I swear by Apollo the healer, and Asklepios, and Hygeia, and Panacea and all the gods and goddesses . . . that, according to my ability and judgement, I will keep this Oath and this stipulation—to reckon him who taught me this Art as dear to me as those who bore me . . . to look upon his offspring as my own brothers, and to teach them this Art, if they would learn it, without fee or stipulation. By precept, lecture, and all other modes of instruction, I will impart a knowledge of the

Art to my own sons, and those of my teacher, and to disciples bound by a stipulation and oath according to the Law of Medicine, but to none other. I will follow that system of regimen which, according to my ability and judgement, I consider for the benefit of my patients, and abstain from whatever is deleterious and mischievous. I will give no deadly medicine to any one if asked, nor suggest any such counsel; nor will I aid a woman to produce abortion. With purity and holiness I will pass my life and practise my Art. . . . Into whatever houses I enter, I will go there for the benefit of the sick, and will abstain from every act of mischief and corruption; and above all from seduction. . . . Whatever in my professional practice—or even not in connexion with it—I see or hear in the lives of men which ought not to be spoken of abroad, I will not divulge, deeming that on such matters we should be silent. While I keep this Oath unviolated, may it be granted me to enjoy life and the practice of the Art, always respected among men, but should I break or violate this Oath, may the reverse be my lot.

Clinically, Hippocrates and his followers always adopted the same careful routine, whatever the condition or whoever the patient they were called upon to treat. First came a detailed consideration of *phenomena,* the symptoms the patient complained of and the signs they themselves elicited by a close examination. Second, *judgement,* which to-day is prognosis. What is the probable course of the disease, and how long will it be before the patient either recovers or dies? Third, *general propositions*—that is, general treatment as to rest, diet, climate, and so forth. Lastly, *craft,* or treatment of a more specific nature—what drugs should be given or what operation should be performed.

As may be imagined, the surgery practised by Hippocrates was just as rational and just as effective as his general medicine. The Greeks excelled in the observation of facts and the acute relation of cause to effect. They knew, for instance, that curvature of the spine was due to injury in some patients, while in others it was associated with tubercles in the lungs and spine, was in fact tuberculous disease of the spine. They filtered or boiled the water in which wounds were washed, and directed that dressings should be of new linen. Wine and oil were the most usual applications for wounds, and they expected clean wounds to heal promptly. They insisted that the surgeon's hands and nails should be kept clean. In *Concerning the Surgery,* and in the more elaborate *On the Physician,* there are the most minute directions as to the organization of an operating theatre; the arrangment of the lighting, whether natural or artificial, the care that must be taken of instruments, the position in which the patient is to be placed—all these and many more things are dealt with at length.

A patient who had an accumulation of pus within the pleura—the membranes covering the lungs—was treated almost exactly as he would be to-day. The chest was opened and the contents of the abscess allowed to drain. Fractured skulls were trepanned, and it was directed that the surgeon should be careful not to injure the brain, otherwise convulsions and palsy would ensue. Diseases of the eye were studied and certain conditions, such as ectropion, in which an eyelid is turned outwards and the delicate lining exposed, were treated by operation.

Arteries were not ligatured—which would seem to place the alleged use of ligatures by Asklepios himself on the same plane as the myth of his god-like origin—but the red-hot cautery was used to stop bleeding and for other purposes. For example, in *Airs and Places,* one of the best-known works in the Hippocratic collection, the writer speaks of a "Scythian nation", referring perhaps to the Amazons, and says that their women have no right breast:

> . . . for while still of a tender age their mothers heat strongly a copper instrument, constructed for this very purpose, and apply it to the right breast, which is burnt up, and its development being arrested, all the strength and fullness are determined to the right shoulder and arm.

Greek knowledge of the structure and function of the body was surprisingly small. The surface form of the body was studied minutely, as were separate bones if not complete skeletons. But no dissection was done except on animals and, very wisely, the Greeks placed little reliance on animal anatomy as a guide to human anatomy. Even so the Hippocratic descriptions and treatment of fractures and dislocations show to what good use limited anatomical material was put.

In the treatment of fractures the principle of extension is of vital importance if the broken bone is to be set accurately. In a fracture of the humerus—that is, of the upper arm—the broken ends of the bone override each other. If the bone is to be set in correct alignment, the two fragments must be drawn apart, or extended, and then manipulated into correct position. Usually the shoulder is fixed and the elbow is pulled strongly downwards, and this traction is only released when the two fragments, after being first separated, have been adjusted so as to fall accurately together again. How Hippocrates recognized and applied this principle is well shown in an account of the treatment of a broken upper arm. A stout piece of wood was suspended by two chains from the ceiling of the operating theatre. It would look rather like a clumsy trapeze. The patient's broken arm was placed over this in such a way that to all intents and purposes he was suspended by the armpit from the wooden crossbar. This effectively fixed the upper fragment of the broken bone. The arm was bent at right angles, the wrist being supported by an assistant. A broad silk scarf was placed loosely over the bent elbow and to its tied ends a heavy weight was attached. This weight pulling on the lower fragment drew it down and into line with the fixed upper part of the broken bone—that is, weight extension brought down the overriding broken bone and kept the two fragments roughly in a line with each other. It was then easy for the surgeon to manipulate the two broken ends of bone into exact position. The same principle of fixing one end of a broken bone so that traction could effectively be exerted at the other end was applied also in setting a broken thigh or a broken leg. A stake was driven firmly into the ground, and the patient was placed with one leg to either side of it, so that his own weight fixed his body against the immovable stake. Pulling on the ankle or knee would then separate the ends of the fractured bone and allow of its being set. In fractures of bones below the knee an ingenious use was made of the natural elastic springiness of twigs from the cornel tree. Thickly padded rings, one just above the ankle and the other just below the knee, were placed around the injured leg. Four twigs a little longer than the distance between the padded rings were then cut and forced into position between the rings. The slightly bent twigs by their tendency to spring into a straight line constantly forced the padded rings apart, and so transmitted the body-weight from ankle to knee without allowing undue strain on the broken bone.

Dislocations of the hip, shoulder, and jaw are described exactly in the Hippocratic works and treated almost as we would treat them to-day, except that an anæsthetic was not used. The reductions of a dislocated shoulder and of a dislocated jaw are shown in a ninth-century manuscript of Apollonius of Kitium believed to have been copied from the pre-Christian manuscripts of surgeons in the direct line of Hippocratic descent.

(*See plate facing* p. 64). The patient with a dislocated jaw is seated. An assistant stands behind him fixing his head. The surgeon is in front, both his thumbs inside the patient's mouth pressing the jaw-bone downwards, while his fingers are outside and reaching behind the angle of the dislocated bone to rotate it back into position. The modern surgeon faced with the same dislocation varies the technique depicted by Apollonius in only two minor particulars. A modern surgeon hates to have his thumbs bitten as a dislocated jaw snaps back into position, so he puts a thick pad of lint round each thumb. That is one slight difference, the other is in the rather more formal attire expected of the modern surgeon.

The patient with a dislocated shoulder is lifted on to the surgeon's back. An assistant drags his body downwards while the surgeon, whose shoulder is beneath the patient's armpit, is forcing the dislocated bone upwards into its natural position. This is an application of a simple lever principle, but it is important to notice the position of the patient's dislocated arm. The surgeon is holding it firmly above the elbow, which is bent at right angles with the hand palm-upwards and the forearm rotated outwards. If a dislocated arm is forced into this position and then abruptly released from it, the dislocation will be reduced. To-day we use this method without applying the upward lift in the patient's armpit. Usually it succeeds, but when it fails some variation of the old Hippocratic method must be tried.

Dislocation of the shoulder was a common injury in the time of Hippocrates, and it has been suggested that certain of the wrestling throws depicted in painting and statuary were deliberately designed to disable an opponent by producing this injury. Wrestling must also have been responsible often for dislocations of the thigh. Nowadays an outward dislocation is most commonly met with, but Hippocrates described an inward displacement as being the commonest type of dislocation in his experience. This again may perhaps have been due to some wrestling trick of which we have no knowledge. His description of the appearance of a wrestler who had sustained this injury has never been bettered. The treatment of it has, as he wrote himself, "something masterly about it, pleasing to those who like to make some display in such matter". The patient's arms were bound by his sides. A broad, soft strap encircled his legs just above the knee, so tied that the limbs were "four-fingers' breadth or even less" apart. These preliminaries completed, the patient was lifted till his feet were to either side of a stout beam, some six feet from the ground. Strong but soft bands about his ankles suspended him head downwards from this miniature gallows. In this position the weight of his body would tend to reduce the dislocation of the hip. Actually the reduction was effected by an assistant inserting his forearm between the patient's thighs, and abruptly suspending his whole weight from the already suspended patient. A dexterous twist of the forearm was then all that was needed. The dislocated bone slipped back into its socket with a sickening crack, and the reduction was completed. Bandages were applied, and at length the patient was lifted down and restored to his bed. For success to be certain "the suspended assistant must be an intelligent and extremely powerful man". Hippocrates knew and described surgical conditions varying from congenital club foot to fracture of the spine. We have never improved on his clinical pictures. That we should have improved on his theories and his methods of treatment was inevitable. Hippocrates lived many centuries before microscopes and X-ray plants, round which our modern pathology revolves, were even thought of. It is not remarkable that he should have been wrong. It is more than remarkable that he was so often right.

For nearly four hundred years after the death of Hippocrates his teachings were followed. Alexander the Great, after he had conquered Egypt, founded in Alexandria a great seat of learning in which Greek physicians and surgeons learnt all that old Egypt could teach them. They advanced the Hippocratic teachings especially in anatomy and surgery. Notable in this advancement were Herophilus and Erasistratus, who taught in Alexandria in the third century B.C. They dissected human corpses, and there are good reasons for believing that they also vivisected prisoners who had been condemned to death and who were placed at their disposal by the Ptolemaic monarchs. This charge of human vivisection is made by at least two reputable writers and strongly supported by the evidence of others. Whatever their methods, Herophilus and Erasistratus were the first to distinguish between nerves and tendons, and they demonstrated the fact that all the peripheral nerves were linked to the spinal cord. Herophilus described very accurately the anatomy

[59]

of the brain, and to this day the point where four great venous sinuses meet inside the skull is known as the *torcular Herophili*— the winepress of Herophilus. Herophilus named, too, the prostate, a gland at the neck of the male bladder, the duodenum, that part of the alimentary canal immediately beyond the stomach, and the hyoid, a tiny bone in the neck just above the Adam's apple. Erasistratus it was who first made it clear that the windpipe and the gullet are two distinct passages. He disapproved of bleeding and, like Herophilus, counted the pulse by a water-clock and studied its rate and rhythm.

Alexandria was establishing a great university while Rome was building a great empire. The ancient Britons were just beginning to imagine that dabs of woad might improve their rather shaggy appearance, and America simply did not exist so far as Europe was concerned. The Roman religion forbade any scientific medicine, so until the arrival of the despised and hated Greeks, in the second century B.C., Rome had neither medicine nor surgery worthy of the name. Despised the Greeks might be, and many were the diatribes directed against them, but it was not long before Pliny wrote ruefully:

> . . . it is a well-known fact that those physicians, who, without being able to speak Greek, attempted to build up a practice in Rome, failed to gain the confidence of their patients, even those who were not at all familiar with that language.

The first Greek surgeons in Rome were probably charlatans and adventurers for the most part, but because they were Greek they were employed to look after the all-important gladiators and gymnasts. Gradually Greek medicine and surgery were taken more seriously and one Asclepiades of Bithynia—no relation to Asklepios of Thessaly—went to Rome about 90 B.C. and became a successful physician and a close friend of Cicero. He introduced Greek medicine to Rome not nearly as effectively as he might have done simply because he regarded the Hippocratic doctrine as a "meditation upon death". He introduced in its stead a somewhat woolly theory out of which arose the School of Methodists—a surgical and not a religious school of thought. The only remark of his that merits the attention of posterity was to the effect that "the inhabitants of Britain"— which Cæsar had visited in 54 B.C.—"were long lived because the climate prevented the dissipation of the 'innate heat' of their bodies". Stubbs and Bligh, who give this remark the prominence it deserves, suggest mildly that it is "a theory but poorly supported by observation". The same authors describe how quacks abounded in Imperial Rome, for at no time was there any regulation of medical or surgical practice. Many of them "specialized" in diseases of the eye, though there were of course many reputable practitioners in this speciality, one of whom was formally appointed to the Roman Fleet in British waters, and was styled "Oculist to the British Navy". There were many other public appointments, and the physician to the Emperor Claudius received a salary equivalent to about £10,000 a year. Other lesser appointments involved the care of various classes of workers. Unhappily, the physician who was blessed with the care of the vestal virgins found no time for writing.

The earliest scientific medical work in Latin is the *De Re Medica*. If it is not a pure translation from the Greek it is at least a compilation from Greek works. In many ways reminiscent of the Hippocratic collection it is the work of Aurelius Cornelius Celsus, who was not a medical man, and appeared in A.D. 30. It is one of the best text-books of this period. It is divided into eight parts, of which the last two are concerned with surgery.

An appreciable section is devoted to dental practice. Methods and reasons for extracting teeth are described, indications for wiring the teeth, as in fractures of the jaw, are outlined, and there is an account of what must have been one of the earliest dental mirrors. Plastic operations on the face and mouth very like the Hindoo procedures are mentioned, as is a method for removing nasal polypi—small fleshy growths inside the nose. Cutting for stone in the bladder was practised, and there is a description of the technique adopted for the removal of the tonsils. Collections of fluid in the scrotum and ruptures were treated successfully by operation, and a long section is devoted to the cure of penetrating wounds of the abdomen. Piles and fistulæ—abnormal sinuses between the skin and the rectum— were also dealt with surgically. The most remarkable operation described by Celsus is one that has only been perfected by the present generation of surgeons, excision of the thyroid gland in the neck for the treatment of goitre.

Celsus died about A.D. 50, and for a hundred years after his death there are no Latin surgical works worthy of notice. Scribonius Largus, who had the dubious distinction of being

physician to the Empress Messalina, is perhaps notable in that
his is the first written record known of the Hippocratic oath.
Previously it must have been handed down from teacher to
pupil by word of mouth, or if it was written down the manuscripts have been lost. Scribonius is to be blamed for reverting
in his works to the unscientific method of regional classification,
starting at the head and working solemnly downwards to the
feet. This was the method used by the Egyptians, who may
be forgiven for their disregard of the relations and functions of
organs about which they knew relatively little. The same
method was popular in the scientific murkiness of the Middle
Ages, but Scribonius should have known better.

A distinguished member of the Methodist School was Soranus
of Ephesus, who lived in the second century A.D. He was one
of the earliest authoritative writers on infant hygiene and nutri-
tion, and was famous as a specialist in the diseases of women.
He designed the first obstetric chair for facilitating the birth of
a child. He is also believed to have been the first man to
practice the turning or version of an unborn child in the womb
in order to bring it round from an abnormal to a normal position.

At Pergamos, in Asia Minor, in A.D. 131 there was born a
man whose name was to be remembered and virtually worshipped for centuries. Galen was the man, and when he
arrived in Imperial Rome, in A.D. 162, Marcus Aurelius had
just become Emperor. Hippocratic calm and Hippocratic
liberality of thought were lost. Methodists and Dogmatists
heaped abuse on each other, and Empiricists reviled both sects
soundly. Galen was caught up in this factious warfare and
seems to have been a bonny fighter. Living and dead authors
and theories, friends and enemies, surgical sects of this, that,
and the other kind, he castigated impartially. His polemics,
like some of his surgical works, were written in highly polished
Greek, but his polemics alone are of no importance, for it was
his medical and surgical works which were to influence every
act and every thought of unborn generations of surgeons.
Had Galen been a second Hippocrates, the surgery we practise
to-day might have been achieved almost in its entirety centuries
ago. Galen was a genius, a born physiologist, a brilliant
exponent of experimental methods, and a first-class anatomist,
but he was not another Hippocrates. He was the Dictator,
while the great Asklepiad of Cos was the Father, of Medicine.

A dictator with anything remotely resembling the visionary qualities of Hippocrates has yet to arise.

Much of Galen's surgery was learnt on the battered bodies of gladiators, for their care was entrusted to him by the Pontifex of the Games in Pergamos. This honour was granted him after he had devised a successful dressing for the treatment of ruptured tendons and nerves. Ligaments, nerves, and tendons were frequently confused at that time, despite the work of Erasistratus and Herophilus, and it was only later in life tha Galen demonstrated—as they had already done—that nerves arose from the brain or spinal cord. Ligaments he described, correctly, as "for the purpose of binding parts together". Tendons he erroneously believed to be made of equal parts of nervous and ligamentous tissue, and capable of contraction. Before Galen's time rupture of a tendon almost always led to paralysis of the muscle involved. Galen was fortunate in using a dressing which did not promote infection or suppuration, and so a proportion of the cases he treated resulted in union of the severed tendon and the restoration of full movement to the injured limb. As he gained experience of these injuries, which were apparently very common among the gladiators in his charge, he began to suture the ruptured ends of the tendons in certain cases, and again had good results. In Rome it is doubtful if he had any connexion with the gladiatorial schools at first, but the reputation that had been his at Pergamos prompted Marcus Aurelius to place him in charge of young Commodus, who when he became Emperor entered the arena and himself fought as a gladiator. It is hardly likely that the young Emperor should have done this without availing himself of Galen's long experience, and so it is probable that the Roman arenas provided many of the surgical cases which Galen described in his later works. Wounds of the abdomen with protrusion of the intestines he treated rationally, by repairing the gut, replacing it, and suturing the abdominal wall. Fractures of the skull he trepanned and dressed with the blood of a dove, though he records on several occasions, without comment, cases treated in the absence of this particular remedy—no dove being available—which did quite well. Not all the surgery Galen practised was that of injuries. He removed nasal polyps, excised varicose veins, sutured hare-lips, and in patients complaining of a persistent cough removed the uvula. The operation of removing this small tongue of flesh which can be seen at the back of the throat seems to have been as popular then as tonsil-lectomy is to-day, and was just as indiscriminately undertaken. For the relief of pain he gave opium and mandragora, and may possibly have administered these narcotics to patients about to undergo operations. Warts he removed with a special scalpel, though most of his colleagues bit them off their long-suffering patients.

He practised vivisection extensively, starting his work on pigs, in which he studied the processes of digestion. He gave the animals a certain diet, and then opened up the stomach to see what changes had taken place after a known period of time. He observed the action of the diaphragm and of the muscles lying between the ribs in breathing, and tried to see how these actions were affected by the division of different nerves, among them the recurrent laryngeal nerve which controls the vocal muscles. Galen demonstrated that division of these nerves in whatever species of animal had the same effect. Immediately it was severed the pig stopped squealing, the dog barking, the horse whinnying, and so on. A surgeon of his acquaintance in removing a goitre cut the same nerves in an infant and made the child mute. His interest in the function of nerves aroused by these experiments, Galen took up further work on the spinal cord, dividing it at different levels and recording the degree of paralysis which resulted. This particular investigation was so thorough that it was not superseded till sixteen centuries later— actually in 1807. For these physiological experiments he used pigs, goats, and sheep. He also dissected apes, cows, mules, asses, dogs, lions, wolves, lynxes, stags, camels, and on at least one occasion an elephant.

Thanks to his employment of what to-day we would call an expert stenographer, Galen wrote some five hundred treatises. About ten years before his death many of these were destroyed in a fire at his *Apotheke* on the Sacred Way. His intention was to present a sort of universal encyclopædia of all Greek and Roman medicine. He was much more than a translator and compiler, however. He based his work on the Hippocratic doctrine of humours. The theory which Hippocrates put for-ward was that the whole life-process was the resultant of two sets of forces. Those working externally—that is, the environ-ment of the individual—and those working internally. The internal elements or humours were four in number. They were the blood, the phlegm, the black bile, and the yellow bile.

PLATE III

Reducing a dislocated shoulder.   Reducing a dislocated jaw.

From a ninth-century manuscript of Apollonius of Kitium, which was copied
from a pre-Christian original.

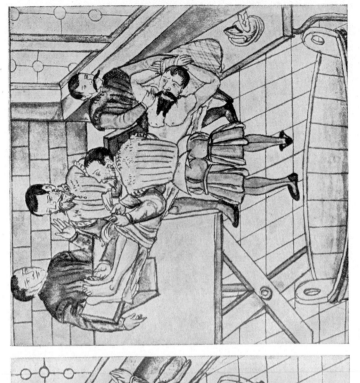

PLATE IV

A sixteenth-century surgeon, his four assistants, and his patient, at pre-operative prayer.

Tying down the patient in readiness for operation.

When these humours were properly balanced the patient was in a state of health, when one or other was in excess then ill-health followed. Four basic "temperaments" were recognized in this system—sanguineous, phlegmatic, melancholic, and bilious. Bilious, melancholic, and phlegmatic people are all well-known types. The sanguine are always with us, but might be a little shaken if they were ever referred to as sanguineous. Hippocrates regarded this theory of humours as a good working hypothesis, which it was. Galen worked out all the possible combinations and permutations of excess or lack of the four humours and elevated this system, in a way which was as far removed as anything could be from Hippocratic intention, to a dogmatic authority which was to shackle surgical science for centuries. To challenge the sanctity of Holy Writ was at one time tantamount to self-immolation on a burning fiery furnace. The penalties attaching to any similar challenge of Galen's authority were nil. Penalties were unnecessary. Challenging the work of Galen simply was not done. Galen was a great scientist and he made many discoveries of vital importance to anatomy and physiology, but the inflated importance that later ages gave to his every word almost completely negated the good that this aggressive and efficient rationalist would otherwise have done.

The writings of several surgeons who lived and worked after the death of Galen are still in existence. They all tended to copy Galen's works, but were not sufficiently remote from him to fall completely under the spell of his posthumous dictatorship. Notable among them were Ætius of Amida, who was born in the early part of the sixth century, Alexander of Tralles, who was born in A.D. 526, and Paulus of Ægina.

Ætius, who was physician to the Emperor Justinian I at Constantinople, described carefully fatty tumours, or lipomata, and their treatment. He recommends that they should be removed through a straight or a "myrtle-leaf shaped" incision, and differentiates them from enlarged tuberculous glands. He completes his treatise on the steatomas, as he called them, by mentioning rather doubtfully a plaster of "soft flowers of oxeye, together with wax, and oil" which was said to absorb fatty tumours. Ætius suggests, very properly, that this plaster might be better reserved for cases other than those in which operation is possible. He also put forward an ingenious if improbable explanation of the causation of aneurysms. He

THE STORY OF SURGERY

knew that these dilations of arteries often followed an injury to the blood-vessel, but in certain cases they arose without any wound having been inflicted. He suggested that in women this last type of aneurysm might be due to forcible holding of the breath during childbirth causing the arteries to rupture. Whether the aneurysms he saw arose in this way or not, he described the signs and symptoms they produced very exactly, and he treated them rationally. At operation the artery was severed between two tight ligatures of twisted flax above the site of the aneurysm, and the swelling itself could then be opened without fear of hæmorrhage and the blood-clots turned out of it. Ætius warns, however, against any surgical interference in aneurysms of the head or neck, because the bleeding from them was violent and could not be controlled. In describing this and other operations Ætius quoted largely from Galen, but he had strayed far from the teachings of Hippocrates. Never expecting wounds to heal by first intention—that is, cleanly and quickly without any septic infection—as both Hippocrates and Galen did, he "had recourse to the suppurative treatment". Pus was allowed to form in the wounds, and if by any mischance it did not appear, plasters and salves were applied with the avowed object of promoting its formation.

Ætius was a credulous soul much addicted to charms and amulets, with which he supplemented orthodox surgical treatment. A fishbone in the throat, for example, was addressed politely but firmly and conjured to come forth, "as Lazarus came forth from the sepulchre, as Jonah came out of the whale's belly". The chief value of his works is that they describe operations performed by earlier surgeons whose own writings have been lost. Cancer of the breast he treated along the lines suggested by a first-century surgeon, Leonides, doing a wide amputation of the entire breast with a red-hot iron. A surgeon of the second century who wrote on the causation of difficult labours and the extraction of the dead fœtus from the womb is also quoted. This writer described in detail the fowl-like trussing of men or women for operations upon the genital and urinary passages. The unhappy patient was placed upon a table with the thighs drawn up on to the abdomen and the knees widely separated. The left wrist was then tied firmly and the cord was brought beneath the knee, up round the patient's neck, down under the other knee, and so to the right wrist, thus securing excellent exposure of the field of operation

[66]

and a guarantee of non-intervention on the part of the patient.
In general use at that time in the diagnosis and treatment of
diseases of women was a speculum very like the modern instrument. It was made of bronze, blunt-ended and three-pronged,
and so constructed that it could be inserted closed into the
vagina. A simple screw attachment allowed the three prongs
to be opened gently, exposing in this way the neck of the womb
and the dome of the vagina. Medicated tampons could then
be applied or ulcers, cysts, abscesses, and the like affecting
these regions could receive the appropriate surgical treatment
after the patient was duly trussed. Ætius's work shows the
advances that had been made since the time of Hippocrates,
and even of Galen and Celsus. Thus Celsus recognized thirteen conditions affecting the eye and requiring surgical treatment, Ætius thirty. In the same way the catalogue of general
surgical operations had increased appreciably, and the surgical
treatment of diseases of women in particular had been elevated
to a distinct branch of surgery, Ætius devoting no less than one
hundred and twelve chapters to it.

Ætius never pretended to be anything other than a compiler,
and fortunately he was undiscriminating enough to make his
compilations comprehensive, but he does show one or two
sparks of originality. He was the first to mention the magnet
as a therapeutic agent: "They say that those who are afflicted
with gout in their hands or feet, or with convulsions, are relieved
by holding a magnet in their hands." This may or may not
have been so, but the suggestion was no more remarkable than
another magnetic idea put forward a thousand years later. This
was that a rupture might be cured by covering it with iron
filings and feeding powdered magnet to the patient, so that
the swelling in the groin would be attracted back into the
abdomen. Another original contribution from the pen of
Ætius was an addendum to Galen's version of the humoral
theory. This was already complicated enough for any ordinary
mortal, but Ætius introduced another factor, the saliva, the
properties of which he believed to vary according to whether
the individual had been fasting or eating. This enabled him
further to subdivide Galen's classification of types and temperaments. Whatever his faults, Ætius did his compiling conscientiously and thoroughly, and in his own day was sufficiently
distinguished to be granted the title of Lord High Chamberlain
of the Court at Byzantium.

Alexander of Tralles was contemporary with Ætius, and his work, which is also based on Galen's writings, shows the last degradation of Græco-Roman medicine and surgery. Much of his treatment was rational, but green lizards and live dung-beetles had crept into therapy again, and henbane, which was given for the cure of gout, was only effective if dug with the thumb and third finger of the left hand, with the moon in Pisces or Aquarius, and while intoning a suitable incantation.

Paulus of Ægina was another compiler of Greek works—in fact, the last of the Byzantine period. There is nothing that is original in his manuscripts, but much that reveals the catholicity of his surgical interest. He operated upon the eye, removed polyps from the nose, drew teeth if teeth needed drawing, removed tonsils, cured ruptures, and extracted stones from the bladder. He was the first to point out that arrow-heads and other foreign bodies of the art of war could best be removed if the patient was placed in the same position as the one he was in when injured. The arrow-head or whatever it might be would then be found buried somewhere along a straight line drawn from the point at which it had entered the body. This fairly obvious trick for indicating in what direction to probe a wound was to be forgotten for a thousand years. Paulus seems to have been a clever operator and manipulator. The operation he performed for the removal of tonsils was a model of simplicity. The patient was seated, facing the sun, with his mouth held wide open by the surgeon's assistant, and the tongue was depressed by a spatula. A hook was passed quickly through the tonsil, pulling it forwards. A curved scalpel slid through its base, and one tonsil was dealt with. A scalpel curved in the opposite direction amputated the other tonsil, and the operation was over. The patient, if still conscious, was then made to gargle with cold water.

The death of Paulus in A.D. 690 marked the end of one era and the beginning of another. Even as he finished the seventh volume of his *Epitome,* and explained briefly that there was nothing original in all his work because all that could be said about surgery or medicine had been said, the Dark Ages were being ushered in. For centuries after his death this belief in the ancients was to be perpetuated and original thought ranked with original sin.

Roman surgery, though it was Greek in origin and in practice, never quite reached the Hippocratic heights, largely because the Romans themselves were never capable of Greek modes of thought and philosophy. The bitter sectarianism which characterized much of Roman surgical practice did nothing to advance the science, and Galen, the last of the great Roman surgeons, unwittingly did it untold harm. Even so, the Romans did bring something of their own culture to the surgery of their period. The health of their conquering legions was all important, and in consequence their Army Medical Service reached a stage of detailed organization which was remarkable. It was inevitable that surgeons practising amongst the Roman armies should concern themselves with amputations, so there were elaborated two distinct operations. The least used was the amputation of the leg, usually after severe fracture, in which flaps were cut and sewed up to give the stump of the leg a complete circular covering of skin. More commonly, they employed the circular method. Limbs were cut off above the site of injury as if by a guillotine, skin, muscles, and bone all being cut through at the same level. For a variety of reasons army surgeons had to revert to this ancient form of amputation as recently as 1914. More important still, these Roman surgeons built up a form of hospital organization. The idea of hospitals was not new. The Egyptian and Greek Temples were really hospitals and so were the Hindoo Houses of Benevolence. Roman military hospitals, however, approximated more nearly to the hospitals we know to-day than did the temples of earlier civilizations, and on them were modelled all the early Christian hospitals.

One other legacy of the Roman domination of Europe was the cult of the bath. Bathing was first undertaken with the idea of refreshing the body after exercise. Later, huge baths were built near mineral springs, and people bathed there in the hope of relieving all kinds of affections. At Baiae, for example, the baths were supposed to be a potent cure for female sterility, and in England the Romans built what was almost a city around the mineral springs of Bath. In Imperial Rome itself great baths were built resembling in many respects the modern Turkish baths. These were divided into *frigidaria, laconicum, tepidaria,* and *calidaria.* Venesection was practised at them and many types of massage, but gradually they took on a social rather than a therapeutic rôle. They became amusement centres on a grand scale, and almost the permanent abiding-place of

[*69*]

gossips of both sexes. Lovers began to meet there, and before long licensed baths became unlicensed brothels. A corps of young men was available to help restore the shattered tissues of jaded Roman matrons. Painters were employed to depict in the baths scenes as brilliant as they were obscene. A chorus of lovely masseuses practised an art much more ancient than mere massage for the delectation of retired consuls, who to-day would lapse automatically into the ranks of the tired business men. The Roman baths, however, suffered a prostitution no greater than that to which Roman writers finally subjected Greek ideals in surgery and medicine.

Hippocrates made of surgery a liberal art. Galen tried to make it a dogmatic science, and the misinterpretations of later compilers, who had neither the vision of the one nor the genius of the other, made it a pseudo-scientific hotch-potch of every art and every science from black magic to botany. Only philosophy and reason were excluded from the mad mixture. Goth and Visigoth overran the ruins of Imperial Rome, and in the year A.D. 640 they scattered the books in the great library of Byzantium. Their onslaught was not the abrupt and brutal end of all surgery and medicine. It was simply the final crumbling of a noble structure of thought which was created first on the island of Cos. Galen with his well-meant attempt at a mathematical systematization placed on the pillars of pure reason, which Hippocrates had erected on a foundation of accurately observed facts, a burden of doctrine and dogma. Slowly the whole edifice began to crumble, and the fasting spittle of Ætius was of just as little help in staying the decay as the compilations of Oribasius and Paulus Æginata. The coming of the barbarians simply marked the final eclipse of a sun of surgery which had begun to grow dim five centuries before.

IV.   Surgery in Eclipse

IN A.D. 431 A RELIGIOUS QUIBBLE WHICH BECAME A SCHISMATIC squabble did more to assist surgery than any priestly support that the art has received either before or since that time. Ironically enough, the quarrel which saved surgery from complete eclipse had nothing to do with surgery.   Nestorius, who had become Patriarch of Constantinople three years previously, taught a heretical doctrine.   He believed that the Virgin Mary should be styled "Mother of the Christ" and not "Mother of God".   A General Council of the Church excommunicated him, and Nestorius and his heretic followers fled to Mesopotamia.   At Edessa they established a seat of Greek learning and built up a medical school, which centred round the two hospitals there.

Some sixty years later the orthodox Bishop of Cyprus expelled all Nestorians from Edessa.   They fled to Persia and established at Jundeshapur a famous school which was the true starting-point of Mohammedan medicine and surgery.   There they kept alive a knowledge of Greek surgery for a long two hundred years till, in the seventh century, the banners of triumphant Islam were flying over the whole of the Near East.   Then a sudden passion for culture possessed all Islam.   A frenzy of translation began.   Greek works which were in the possession of the Nestorians were all translated into Arabic.   Later on the Arabic was translated into Latin, and it was these Latin versions of the Arabic translations of the works of Galen, Hippocrates, and other writers that penetrated slowly into Europe.   For a long time this orgy of culture was a purely academic process. The Arab physicians would have tremendous wordy battles about the exact shades of meaning conveyed by one of the Hippocratic aphorisms, but if a patient was rash enough to interrupt their discourse, he would be told merely that whatever his condition God had willed it, and Mohammed was his prophet. Except in its most primitive form, surgery was hardly practised for two hundred years.   Islam was too busy conquering the world in the first of these centuries, and too intent upon parading its culture to practise it in the second of them.

At length a few men began to unlock the storehouse of surgical knowledge which the Nestorians had guarded.   One of the first of these men was a Nestorian teacher, Hunain ibn Isháq, or

Johannitius, who was born seven years after the death of the great Harun al-Rashid in A.D. 809. Hunain began his studies in the school of medicine at Jundeshapur as a pupil of John ibn Masawayh. Hunain was thought stupid, and after some more than usually bitter comments from his master he left Persia for Greece, where he studied the language for two years. On his return he settled in Baghdad and began the translations which were to bring him fame. Bar Hebraeus, a friend of Hunain's, tells how Hunain brought him on one occasion a translation of the Aphorisms of Hippocrates:

> And he asked me to show it to John ibn Masawayh without mentioning his name. When Masawayh had read it, he was filled with astonishment, and declared that it must have been written by the inspiration of the Holy Ghost. "Not at all," said I. "It is by the pupil whom you drove away some time since." Then he begged me to reconcile him to Hunain, which I did, and they lived in great harmony together as long as I stayed in Baghdad.

Hunain was soon selling his manuscripts for their weight in gold, and quite apart from his innumerable translations he produced the oldest known treatise in Arabic on diseases of the eye. In this he had a diagrammatic representation of Galen's "sight-spirit". The spirit proceeded from the brain and out along the nerves to envelop any object which was seen. It then returned to the lens of the eye to complete the act of vision. Soon Hunain was famous enough to attract the attention of Al-Mamun, the Caliph of Baghdad. He was summoned to Court, and the Caliph bade him concoct a poison which would destroy one of his enemies. He was promised rich rewards if he produced the poison, severe punishment if he refused. Hunain did refuse, and was thrown into prison. A year later he was brought before the Caliph again, and again given a choice, this time of compliance and a reward or refusal and the executioner's sword.

"I have already told the Commander of the Faithful that I have skill only in what is beneficial, and have studied naught else."

Satisfied at last of his complete integrity, the Caliph appointed Hunain Court Physician. In this position it is probable that Hunain was at least partly responsible for persuading the Caliph to institute a College of Translators, with his old friend John ibn Masawayh as its first president. From this college there grew up a school of medicine, and finally no less an institution than a Board of Examiners. Then in A.D. 931—exactly five hundred years after the heretic Nestorius had been driven from his see in Constantinople—a royal decree forbade the practice of medicine except to those authorized by the president of the Board, a position which was filled by a delegate of the Caliph's.

A man who would have rejoiced in this legislative triumph was a great Arabian clinician who, though in theory a follower of Galen, was in practice a true disciple of Hippocrates. This was Abu Bakr Mahomed ibn Zakariyyá, who was born in Ray, near Teheran, in A.D. 852. Persia was at that time dominated by Arabia, and so "of Ray" became Ar-Razi, and the mediæval Latinists construed this as "Rhazes". Rhazes in early life was a skilful lute-player and an indifferent philosopher. His interest in medicine was aroused at a mature age, and he studied at a hospital newly founded at Ray, and ultimately became its chief physician. It was proposed to build a great hospital in Baghdad, and the Caliph consulted Rhazes about it. Rhazes selected the site by a simple but effective experiment. He had pieces of raw meat hung up in different parts of the city. The hospital was built at the point where the raw meat had decomposed least rapidly, and finally Rhazes was brought from Ray to be chief physician to the Baghdad hospital. Persian tradition credits him with the authorship of no fewer than two hundred and fifty works. Actually his description and differentiation of measles and smallpox would alone have sufficed to assure him of lasting fame. Another monograph was on stones in the bladder and kidneys. Interesting, too, is an entertaining discussion on the success of charlatans and quacks in securing a popularity often denied to the competent and qualified physician. In addition to his many monographs, Rhazes was responsible for at least six general works on medicine apart from his monumental *Hawi,* or *Continens,* an encyclopædia of medicine the compilation of which was completed by his pupils, after his death, from the many unfinished notes and papers which he left. Like the Hippocratic writings, this contains innumerable detailed reports of actual cases illustrating various points in diagnosis and treatment. It was published in twenty-five volumes, and a European edition of 1486 weighs 17 lb., so that the work could hardly become a *vade mecum.*

The extent of Rhazes' practice may be judged from the fact

that he treated no less than a thousand cases of sciatica, usually by bleeding from the leg. He describes all the four methods of bleeding in vogue at that time—namely, by cupping, by opening a vein, by incising an artery, or by applying a leech. He was a bold surgeon, and caries of bone which was common among his patients he treated by removing the affected parts. Only in caries of the head of the thigh-bone or of the spinal column—in which the bone is the seat of a disease causing it to crumble and collapse—did he admit himself helpless.

A story about Rhazes which illustrates his clinical acumen and his application of a heroic method of treatment concerns a young man of Baghdad. He came to Rhazes complaining that he had vomited blood. No cause could be found and no ordinary treatment seemed to cure the condition. Rhazes questioned the young man carefully as to the food he had taken and the water he had drunk on a recent journey. He elicited the information that at one stage of the journey water from a stagnant pond had been drunk. Rhazes then said he could effect a cure if the young man would order his servants to do just what they were told. The young man agreed, and Rhazes brought to his house two huge vessels filled with water-weed. The patient swallowed a great deal of it, but finally said that he was quite unable to take any more. Rhazes ordered the servants to sit on their young master and hold his mouth open. They did so, and Rhazes went on pouring the nauseous stuff down his throat till the young man vomited violently. In the vomit was a leech which had been causing the trouble.

Two other stories, which like the previous one may or may not be authentic, concern perhaps the earliest applications of psychotherapy. Violent emotion may occasionally cause disease, or occasionally cure it. Rhazes in the first of these anecdotes deliberately provoked violent anger in his patient in the course of treating him for a rheumatic affection. The patient was the Amir Mansur, and, after obtaining from him the best horse and the best mule in his stables, Rhazes had him placed in a hot bath. Making sure that the horse was near by and ready saddled, Rhazes went to see his patient with a large knife in his hand. He reviled the Amir soundly, and concluded by raising the knife and promising to kill him. Convulsed with fear and anger, the Amir, who had previously been unable to walk, leaped out of his bath. Rhazes fled to the waiting horse. Some days later he wrote to the Amir explaining what he had done and why he had done it. The Amir when he calmed down had found himself cured. He tried to get Rhazes to return but, perhaps wisely, the physician refused. The Amir then had sent to him many rich presents, and some female slaves, and he also assigned to Rhazes a yearly pension and two hundred ass-loads of corn.

The second story refers to an unnamed King's physician, who may or may not have been Rhazes. The patient he was called upon to treat was a woman in the King's household, who while bending down to lay the table found herself suddenly unable to straighten up into the erect posture again. This was probably a hysterical manifestation, but, whatever its nature, the physician's treatment proved effective. He removed the lady's veil, hoping that the emotion of shame would cure her. It had no effect, however, so the physician went rather further and removed her skirt. The lady immediately stood upright, quite cured and probably highly indignant.

Rhazes would not have been ill-equipped for practice a thousand years before his time in the Isle of Cos or practice a thousand years later in a modern hospital. Though essentially a physician, Rhazes must have exerted a great influence on contemporary surgery, quite apart from his own contributions to the art. He was perhaps one of the first men to use sutures of animal gut for the repair of abdominal wounds. It may have been his early musical training which suggested the diversion of harp-strings to this end. In the field of chemistry his discovery of sulphuric acid and his distillation of alcohol from starch are noteworthy. Another essay of his that is of interest describes how he gave mercury to an ape and observed the effects on the animal before trying it on his patients. Of this experiment he wrote:

> I do not suppose that any great harm would happen to a man who should drink metallic mercury, except some severe pains in the stomach and intestines. I gave some to an ape which I had, nor did I see any evil befall him beyond that above mentioned, which I concluded from the fact that he twisted about and kept biting at his stomach and pawing it with his hands.

Towards the end of his life Rhazes became blind from a cataract. His biographers have invented a series of apocryphal explanations of this affliction. The most popular is that Rhazes found a formula for the philosopher's stone and presented his discovery to the ruler of Bukhara. The great man rewarded him with a thousand golden coins and bade him put his theory into practice and convert some lead into gold. Rhazes was unable to do so, and by way of punishment the ruler ordered that the book Rhazes had written about the subject should be beaten about his head till either it or the head was broken. The book yielded first, but Rhazes lost his sight as a result. Less imaginative authors ascribed the blindness to a surfeit of beans, of which Rhazes was excessively fond. Whatever the cause of the cataract, it is believed that for some time Rhazes refused to undergo an operation because he desired to see no more of a world with which he was disgusted and disillusioned. Later, he did approach a surgeon, but on questioning the man and finding him entirely ignorant of the gross anatomy of the eyeball, he not unnaturally refused operation.

Nearly fifty years after the death of Rhazes another great man was born. It was in August of the year A.D. 980, in the village of Afshana near Bukhara. Avicenna was the man who was to become known as the Prince of Physicians. Avicenna was a convivial soul, a lover of wine and women, and occasionally addicted to song. Thanks to his considerable activities in these directions, he died at the age of fifty-eight, after a life packed with incident. His early education was religious, but at the age of sixteen he turned to the study of medicine. He was soon so proficient that when a prince of the ruling house fell ill he was called in to treat him. His success was rewarded by permission to make free use of the royal library. By the age of twenty-one he had produced a commentary on law, and a synopsis of all the known sciences.

After the death of his father at about this time, Avicenna offered his services to the Shah of Khwarazm, who had already attracted many men of fame and learning to his Court. The Sultan of Ghazna, envious of the brilliance of a lesser potentate's entourage, demanded that a number of the men who were in the service of the Shah should be sent to his own Court. Avicenna was one of the men named. The Shah could not refuse this request, but he gave Avicenna and the others the option of going quietly to the Sultan's Court or making good their escape. Avicenna, always an independent spirit, chose the latter course, and after a most hazardous journey made his way to Nishapur. The Sultan was aggrieved at having lost the man he most wanted. Portraits of Avicenna were painted, and copies of them distributed widely. The much-sought-after physician fled to Jurjan, and took up practice there. In Jurjan a relation of the ruling Prince fell ill, and the local physician, unable to effect a cure, suggested calling in the stranger who had been practising there for some time. Avicenna was recognized, but the Prince allowed him to remain in his household and treated him with great honour.

Later he wandered to Ray, the birthplace of Rhazes, and from there went on to the Court of Prince Shams-ul-Douleh at Hamadan. Colic seized the Prince one day. Avicenna cured him, and was promptly appointed Prime Minister. The army, which was then, as always, politically powerful, brought all its influence to bear, and soon the appointment was rescinded and Avicenna was forced into exile. Fortunately for the physician, the Prince's colic recurred, and since the army could do nothing about it, Avicenna became Prime Minister again.

On the death of Prince Shams-ul-Douleh, his successor offered to re-affirm Avicenna's appointment, but the Prime Minister physician refused this offer and began a treasonable correspondence with the ruler of Ispahan. His intrigue was discovered, and the one-time Prime Minister was flung into prison. He escaped and reached Ispahan in safety. It was here that his fame reached its zenith. He wrote on subjects ranging from medicine and music to metaphysics and mechanics. In his last illness he treated himself unsuccessfully, and his detractors, who were many, were in the happy position of being able to say that his physic could not save his body nor his metaphysics his soul. A wit wrote one of the couplets on his tomb:

"What he attained by *Healing* did not secure his Health; nor did he escape Death by his *Deliverance*."

Two of his most famous works were *Healing* and *Deliverance*, and altogether no fewer than ninety-nine books are known to have been written by him. Many of his works were in verse, and one quatrain at least, which has long been ascribed to Omar Khayyam, is believed to have been written by Avicenna. It is the one which Fitzgerald translated as:

Up from Earth's Centre through the Seventh Gate
I rose, and on the Throne of Saturn sate,
And many Knots unravel'd by the Road;
But not the Knot of Human Death and Fate.

Within only a few years of his death Avicenna was referred to as the "Chief of Chiefs", or the "Second Teacher", Aristotle or perhaps Galen or Hippocrates being the First Teacher. This fame was almost wholly due to the greatest of his works, the *Canon*. Only a hundred years after his death an Arabian authority wrote quite firmly:

> The Lord of the two Worlds and Guide of the two Material Races saith: "Every kind of game is comprehended in the Wild Ass." All this, together with much more, is to be found in the *Qanun* [*Canon*], and from him who hath mastered the first volume thereof nothing will be hidden concerning the general theory and principles of Medicine, so that could Hippocrates and Galen return to life, it would be proper that they should do reverence to this book. Yet have I heard a wonderful thing, to wit that one hath taken exception to Abu 'Ali [Avicenna] in respect to this work, and hath embodied his criticisms in a book which he hath entitled the *Rectification of the Qanun*. It is as though I looked upon both, and saw how foolish is the author and how detestable his work. What right hath anyone to find fault with so great a man, when the very first question he meets with in a book of his which he comes across is difficult to his comprehension? For four thousand years the physicians of antiquity travailed in spirit and spent their very souls in order to reduce the science of Philosophy to some fixed order, yet could they not effect this; until after the lapse of this period that pure philosopher and most great thinker Aristotle weighed out this coin in the balance of Logic, assayed it with the touchstone of Definitions, and measured it with the measure of Analogy, so that all doubt and uncertainty departed from it, and it was established on a sure and critical basis. And during these fifteen centuries which have elapsed since his time, no philosopher has won to the inmost essence of his doctrine, nor travelled the high road of his pre-eminence save that most excellent of the moderns, the Philosopher of the East, the Proof of God to mankind, Abu 'Ali Husayn ibn 'Abdullah ibn Sina [Avicenna]. Whosoever, therefore, finds fault with these two great men will have cast himself out from the fellowship of the wise, ranked himself with madmen, and revealed himself as fit company only for fools. May God by His Grace and Favour keep us from such stumblings and vain imaginings!

In Europe the Latin translations of the *Canon* were held in nearly as great an esteem, and it remained a standard text-book till the early seventeenth century. This was probably because Avicenna excelled as a philosopher, while at the same time being a great physician. His views were exactly those of Galen, but were presented with an elaborate classification and codification which even Galen never attained. Critics of the *Canon* have stigmatized it variously as "a methodic inanity", "a huge, unwieldy storehouse of learning, in which the author attempts to codify the whole medical knowledge of his time and to square its facts with the systems of Galen and Aristotle", and as the work of "a professional scribbler who had stupefied European physicians by his misinterpretation of Galen". With all its deficiencies, there is no doubt that the *Canon* preserved the work of Galen and Hippocrates through the long period in which European surgery was not much more than a minor branch of witchcraft, and so helped to pave the way for the intellectual revolution which was to take place in the sixteenth and seventeenth centuries.

There are many important original observations scattered throughout Avicenna's works. His is the earliest mention of obstetric forceps, but they were toothed instruments used only for the extraction of dead children. He discovered and described the points at which the muscles responsible for the movements of the eyeballs are inserted. He also taught a new theory of vision for which he was severely criticized. He wrote that:

> It is not a ray that leaves the eye and meets an object that gives rise to vision, but rather that the form of the perceived object passes into the eye and is transmitted by its transparent body, that is, the lens.

Avicenna was right in this instance and his critics were wrong. To parallel Rhazes' harp-strings for the suture of abdominal wounds, Avicenna suggested that sutures of linen thread in operations on fistula-in-ano should be abandoned. Linen thread rotted quickly, and he advised instead the use of pig's bristles, which were much less likely to putrefy. From the plates illustrating certain later editions of his works it seems clear that he knew and practised the Hippocratic method of forcible reduction for the treatment of spinal deformities. In its simplest form this consisted in tying the patient to the top of a ladder, which was held upright by two men and then very abruptly dropped, complete with the patient. Avicenna advanced surgery in some ways, but he did it great harm by first propounding the doctrine that surgery was a separate branch of medicine, and a very inferior one. This belief took centuries to overcome, as did his teaching that the cautery was always to be preferred to the knife.

After his death many stories were woven around this Prince of Physicians. Several of them have the same theme, and illustrate his psychological acumen. They all describe a young man who is mortally ill from some mysterious malady. Avicenna comes along and holds the patient's wrist, feeling the pulse, while a series of questions are put by his assistants. One of them will introduce into his questions the names of all the neighbouring towns. At one name the pulse quickens. All the streets in that town are then mentioned till the same quickening of the pulse is felt. Then the names of all the inhabitants of that street are recited, till at last Avicenna says that young man is in love with such a girl, who lives in a certain street in a certain town. The girl is sent for, and the young man recovers. Nowadays a physician attaches a blood-pressure recording instrument to a criminal's arm, and watches the flickering of a pointer as he asks about the weather, and the crops, and where was who on the night of the murder. This lie-detector may be a technical advance on Avicenna's method of taking the pulse, but at least it is not applied to quite such beneficent ends.

Rhazes and Avicenna were ornaments of the Eastern Caliphate. The Western Caliphate, which included Southern Spain, was graced by Albucasis. He was born near Cordova in A.D. 936 and died in A.D. 1013 at the ripe age of 77. He is remarkable for a work called the *Altasrif* or *Collection*, which became a leading surgical text-book, though it was never held in quite the same reverence as Avicenna's *Canon*. It is made up of three books based on the work of Paul of Ægina, and has many illustrations of surgical and dental instruments. The first book is devoted to the use of the actual cautery, which Avicenna had advocated, and describes its application to no fewer than fifty diseases. The second discusses very fully many different operations performed not with the cautery but with cutting instruments. The treatment of wounds with dressings of wine is dealt with at length. Two distinct operations are described for stone in the bladder, lithotomy in which the stone was cut out, and lithotrity, a method of crushing the stone into fragments so small that the patient could pass them in his urine. A few amputations are also mentioned, particularly those called for in cases of gangrene. Certain dental operations, such as fastening loose teeth by means of gold wire, are believed to have been recorded by Albucasis for the first time, if they were not actually devised by him. The third and last volume is devoted to the treatment of fractures and dislocations and the cure of sprains.

Albucasis and Avicenna established the actual red-hot cautery as being a cure for practically all the ills with which Allah had seen fit to afflict mankind. It was to be used for apoplexy, epilepsy, headache, toothache, piles, pleurisy, dropsy, sciatica, melancholia, and most other real or imaginary conditions. There were all sizes and shapes of cauteries, and an amazing variety of geometric patterns of dots, spots, and dashes, the number and size of which varied according to the condition being treated. Most of the cauteries were of iron, but a few—for the more obscure cases—were of gold. It was perhaps because amputation could rarely be performed with the cautery he so enthusiastically advocated that Albucasis hardly ever undertook this operation. He tells the story of a man who had a spreading gangrene of the foot. This hero placed his foot upon a block of wood, and with a razor-sharp scimitar sliced neatly and accurately through his own ankle joint. The disease next attacked his hand, and at this stage he hobbled to Albucasis and asked him to perform the necessary amputation. The surgeon refused, for fear that the man might not be able to endure the operation. Somewhat disgusted, the doughty individual took up his scimitar again, lopped off the offending part, and lived to a ripe old age.

Albucasis was a Spaniard, but his writings were in Arabic, as were those of Rhazes and Avicenna, both Persians. His work represents the only independent surgical book produced during the whole of this period. Rhazes and Avicenna made minor contributions to the art, but the religion of Islam forbade dissection, and surgery was relegated by Avicenna to an inferior position. Operative surgery and even venesection were left to wandering practitioners. To the Nestorian inheritance of the works of Galen and Hippocrates, which they translated with such vigour, the Arabians brought little that was new. They relied implicitly upon the Greek teachings. Their own translations of these early works were regarded as the Law and the Prophets. If they stumbled across something new, they discarded it unless they could fit it into some debatable aphorism which had been mistranslated. They would discuss for weeks the exact shade of meaning to be attributed to any one word of the original Greek writings, but any novel ideas would be disposed of in the space of minutes. Avicenna's own theory of vision was never really accepted, simply because Galen had never thought of it. They confirmed future generations for several centuries in the habit of regarding as near blasphemy any departure from the ideas and ideals of the Greek fathers of medicine. This much disservice the Arabs did, but had it not been for them, the Greek ideals and practice might have been lost for ever. Surgery they preserved from complete eclipse, if they did no more.

Credit must also be given to the Moslem world for the hospitals they founded—hospitals far in advance of the Hindoo establishments, or even of the Roman army hospitals. As early as A.D. 707 a hospital was built at Damascus by the Caliph El Welid. This hospital must have had some surgical wards, but most of its activities were concentrated on the treatment of lepers, and of patients with diseases of the eye. The "New Hospital" at Baghdad was built in A.D. 977. It had a staff of twenty-four physicians, and there were special departments for fevers, eye diseases, and for accidents. There were many other famous hospitals in both Eastern and Western Caliphates, and it is not unlikely that the knowledge of these highly organized institutions gained by the Crusaders was put to good use in Europe in later years.

What the Crusaders learnt from the Saracens supplemented the knowledge gained from the flow of translations, which transmitted all the accepted ideas of many centuries before from East to West. On the other hand, what the Saracens learnt from the Crusaders provides an interesting commentary on the state of surgery in Europe. A Saracen Amir named Usama ibn Munquidh, who was born in A.D. 1095, spent most of his life fighting the crusading Franks. Great bitterness of feeling there must have been on both sides, but in the intervals of fighting there was as much fraternizing then as in any other war. Usama, in his memoirs, discusses many of the Frankish customs which interested him, and tells several stories of their surgical practice. The Frankish warden of a besieged castle asked Usama's uncle for the loan of a physician. The physician went to the castle, but returned only ten days later. Usama and his friends congratulated him on the rapidity with which he must have cured the people who were known to have been lying ill within the gates of the beleaguered citadel. The physician explained that there was neither need nor cause for congratulation. He had been shown first a man with an abscess of the leg. To this he applied poultices, and the patient seemed to be making satisfactory progress until a Frankish surgeon intervened. He denounced the poultices as useless and asked the man whether he would prefer to die with two legs or live with one. The patient said he would rather live. The Frankish surgeon assured him of the wisdom of his choice, and summoned a man-at-arms who bore a huge battle-axe. Calmly, the surgeon instructed the soldier to chop off the offending leg at one blow. The axe fell, but the leg was not completely severed. The surgeon directed his stalwart assistant to try again, higher up. At the second blow the patient died. Another patient was a consumptive woman, whom the physician was treating with the appropriate drugs and diet. In a second uncalled-for consultation the Frankish surgeon diagnosed positively the presence of a devil within the woman's head. The physician's diagnosis of consumption was laughed at, and the surgeon ordered all the woman's hair to be shaved off and restored her to a dietary of garlic and oil. When she rapidly grew worse he embarked on more active treatment. He made a deep cross-incision through her scalp right down to the bone, and rubbed salt violently into the cruciform wound. Having watched the woman die, the physician asked if his services were further required, and in his own mild words: "Receiving a negative answer, I returned home having learned of their medical practice what had hitherto been unknown to me."

Frankish surgery was just an accepted barbarity. Great Britain at this time had not even achieved these surgical heights. Danish and Saxon leeches were perhaps even more ignorant than the Druids whom they had succeeded. The Druids practised human sacrifice, and must have acquired in these religious exercises at least some anatomical knowledge. Surgically the practice of the early leeches before the Norman Conquest can hardly have exceeded those few primitive proceedings which are barely removed from barbarism. Venesection was undoubtedly employed, and the lancet used was known as "oeder seax" or the vein-knife, but its application was governed almost purely by superstition. Leechdom, wortcunning, and starcraft were the basic divisions of Saxon medicine, and only a brief survey of the works of early Saxon and Danish authors is needed to show the low level of medical thought and practice in England at a time when Baghdad was building its great hospitals. The *Leech-book of Bald* is perhaps one of the best known of Saxon leech-books. It was written in the latter part of the tenth century, and was deciphered and republished in the Rolls series by the Rev. Oswald Cockayne. Among the few surgical references is one concerning the treatment of hare-lip. The operation described is simple but rational:

"For hare-lip, pound mastic very small, add the white of an egg, and mingle as thou dost vermillion, cut with a knife the false edges of the lip, sew fast with silk, then smear without and within with the salve, ere the silk rot. If it draw together arrange it with the hand; anoint again soon."

For the treatment of a broken leg, minute directions are given for the preparation of a salve of bone-wart and egg-white, and it is also mildly suggested that a splint should be applied. Through all the many leechdoms runs the primitive idea that eating some part of an animal corresponding to that part of the patient which is affected will ward off evil and cure disease. For example:

In case that a man may not retain his urine . . . burn to ashes the bladder of an unprolific, that is a gelt, swine, put it into wine, administer it to drink. For the same, fry a goat's bladder, give it to the man to eat. . . .

Again:

If a man cannot mie [pass urine] . . . let him eat a ram's bladder sodden. . . .

Leechdoms without number are listed for every conceivable condition from cancer to demoniacal possession. Incantations and prayers of different sorts are often invaluable, particularly against snake-bites. Racking pains in the joints called for the powdered skull of a wolf. For a worm-eaten and mortified body "dust of elder rind, taken on the north of the tree" together with ship's tar and a host of other things worked wonders. "Leechdoms if a man be too lustful or too unlustful" were curiously alike. In the first case "water agrimony" was to be boiled in foreign ale and drunk at night. In the second case the desired effect was achieved by boiling the same herb in milk. Much of the Saxon lore was borrowed from Greek and Roman sources, but the aphrodisiac learning of the Mediterranean peoples was perhaps not comprehended.

Throughout this long period only the Moslem Empire knew and practised something of a true surgery, and this Empire, like others before it, was soon to crumble. It did crumble, but it left behind a legacy of translations and compilations of medical and surgical works which were to pave the way for a surgical Renaissance.

V. Surgical Renaissance

IT WAS GALEN, WHO TOUCHED NOTHING THAT HE DID NOT ornament with his learning and injure with his theories, who first laid down the dictum that "surgery is only a mode of treatment". Avicenna pushed this doctrine to the extent of treating the surgeon himself as an inferior being. The Arab commentators and copyists gladly spread this idea, because it fitted so well their religious obsession as to the uncleanliness of human flesh. Quite typical was the attitude of one Moslem writer who deprecated the operation of cutting for stone in the bladder, because it involved the exposure of parts upon which the eye of the true believer could not rest without sin. This fundamental error was finally epitomized in 1215 by the famous ordinance of Pope Innocent III—*Ecclesia abhorret a sanguine*. Bloodshed was incompatible with the divine mission, and so any surgical procedures which involved bloodshed were relegated to men unlikely to be afflicted with divine missions. Barbers, bath-keepers, executioners, mountebanks, and sow-gelders were chief among them. In Prussia, up to the time of Frederick the Great, it was the army surgeon's duty to shave the officers. In Egypt and India surgery had been strangled in the toils of religion. It seems paradoxical to find that in that part of Southern Italy known as Magna Græcia surgery was re-born in a monastery.

In A.D. 529 St. Benedict of Nusia founded a monastery on the site of an old temple of Apollo at Monte Cassino. Of all who came to this cloister he asked only that they should "pray, study, and help sick brethren". St. Benedict himself was responsible for some remarkable cures. Henry II, Emperor of Bavaria, was one of his patients. The Emperor had a stone in his imperial bladder. St. Benedict put him to sleep, removed the stone from the bladder, and healed the wound instantaneously. In fact, the Emperor would not have known that he had been operated on, had he not found a stone in his hand when he awoke! In the course of years other monasteries grew up around the original one, and to each was appointed a "medicus", and in each cloister was a place where the sick could be treated. At first only the sick poor received the simple ministrations of the monks, but later the benefits of these early infirmaries were extended to all who applied for admission. Gradually, medical duties took precedence over religious ones as the "medicus" was even allowed to leave the monastery for long periods in order to treat the sick and injured in nearby towns. Bertharius, for example, who died in A.D. 884, wrote two long treatises on diseases and their remedies while abbot of Monte Cassino, and often journeyed far from his monastery to heal the sick. The medical and surgical activities of the priests—though not of the secular branch—were at length restricted by a decree of the Council of Tours in A.D. 1163, forbidding monks to leave their monasteries for longer than two months and prohibiting the teaching or practice of physic. All that happened, however, was that the patients were brought to the monastery instead of waiting for the "medicus"—now more usually a secular clerk —to come to them. Finally, in 1215 Pope Innocent III issued his Decretal which prevented priests, deacons, and sub-deacons from performing any operation involving the shedding of blood. By that time, however, the monastery at Monte Cassino had sheltered Constantinus Africanus long enough for him to complete his literary labours and die quietly, and other Benedictine monasteries at Salerno had slowly evolved a school of medicine.

Constantine the Moor, as he was called, was born in Carthage in A.D. 1010. His extensive travels gave him a wide knowledge of Oriental languages. Perhaps because of this, on returning to Carthage he was regarded as a magician and persecuted till at length he fled to Italy. He is known to have spent some time at Salerno, but whether he actually taught there or not is uncertain. At all events, about A.D. 1072 he made his way to Monte Cassino, and in the monastery there he spent the last fifteen years of his life translating into Latin, which had become the recognized language of such science as there was, the Arabic versions of many famous Greek works. Thus tortuously did Europe achieve its classic text-books. Constantine knew Arabic well and so, though not very learned in either Latin or medicine, he was able to paraphrase with more or less accuracy the works of Hippocrates and of Galen. That his mistakes superadded to those of the Arabian translators should have made occasional havoc of the original Greek text is hardly remarkable. At the same time the influence of Constantine, in Latinizing and making available to Western Europe the Greek culture which the Arabs had preserved and other purely Arabian works, was far-reaching.

The most important Arabian manuscript, so far as surgery

was concerned, which Constantine translated was the *Pantegni* of Hali ibn al Abbas, known originally as the *Liber Regius* or Royal Book. Haly Abbas, as Constantine called him, died in A.D. 994, sixty years after Rhazes, and very little is known about the man himself. The *Pantegni* comprised some twenty Discourses, each subdivided into many chapters. The first ten Discourses deal with the theory, and the last ten with the practice of medicine. The nineteenth Discourse, of one hundred and ten chapters, is devoted entirely to surgery.

In this section a method for removing barbed arrows is described in detail. Wounds are to be closed by sutures. Suppuration and pus formation are unfortunately still regarded as essential to healing, and if by some mischance a wound should heal without the appearance of pus, then salves and ointments are prescribed which will promote suppuration. Severed arteries should be tied with ligatures of silk to stop their bleeding, according to Haly Abbas, and here he was far in advance of Avicenna, whose works displaced his. One of the most interesting surgical procedures concerns the treatment of broken bones which had set badly. To-day the bones in such cases are refractured, and then set a second time in a more correct position. This is exactly what Haly Abbas advised, though he used rather crude instruments. The way in which Haly Abbas treated adhesions joining the eyelids to the eye was simple but effective. The eyelid was lifted by a blunt metal instrument, and the fleshy adhesion was divided by a small scalpel. While the surgeon was doing this he masticated a mixture of salt and herbs. The operation ended, he spat this vigorously into the patient's eye. A pad of wool soaked in white of egg was then applied to the eye and bound in position.

Constantine the Moor died in A.D. 1087 at a time when the School of Salerno was fast becoming something approaching a university. He had translated no fewer than thirty-seven medical and surgical works, and of these the Salernitans made good use. Constantine's reputation was a great one, but he built it up on other men's work, and he was not above giving the names of original authors falsely with the deliberate intention of deceiving his readers and enhancing his own fame. Constantine's literary depredations and deliberate plagiarisms were extensive. He leaned most heavily on a Jew—one Isaac Judæus —who practised in the tenth century and wrote some voluminous works in Arabic. Constantine's feet of clay have been badly undermined by both Charles Singer and Moritz Steinschneider. A literary rogue he undoubtedly was, but rather an attractive one.

The ancient city of Salerno, thirty-five miles to the south-east of Naples, was first known as a Roman colony in 194 B.C. Situated as it was on the Gulf of Pæstum, it rapidly became known as a health resort. In A.D. 1075 Robert Guiscard, the Norman, forced Salerno to capitulate after a siege which had lasted eight months. It is believed that Constantine the Moor during at least part of his stay in Salerno, before he went to Monte Cassino, was a sort of secretary to Robert Guiscard. Even at that time the city was of importance and had some fame as a centre of healing. The Normans brought a century of peace to Salerno and made it a great centre of trade. Latin, Greek, Arabic, and Jewish cultures were mingled by the currents of trade and war in a city ruled by Normans. Monasteries which the monks of Monte Cassino had founded became centres of learning. A medical school arose. Probably, like Topsy, it "just growed", but for centuries tradition had it that the School was founded in the middle of the seventh century by four physicians, a Greek, a Jew, an Arab, and a Latin. The story may have been an allegory, for the School of Salerno did borrow impartially, if not always too discriminatingly, from the medicine of all four races. Or it may be, as Charles Singer suggests, that the four physicians were really one man, a Jew named Donnolo. He wrote at Salerno a medical treatise largely in Hebrew and partly in Arabic, based on Greek methods of treatment but describing also some herbs first used by the Latins. In any event, the story, like so many good stories, was so firmly believed that it was never thought necessary to give documentary proof of it, and now such proof, if it ever existed, is lost.

The medical school at Salerno was the first institution in Europe to bear any resemblance to a university. The physicians there not only compiled and re-compiled encyclopædic texts from the works which Constantine had either translated or appropriated, they also published many individual works. About thirty writers are known. Their works were many and various, and among them was the *Regimen Sanitatis Salerni*. This was one of the most popular medical works ever written. The author was supposed to be one John of Milan, head of the faculty of the School of Salerno at the time it was written. John's name is not to be found in any of the lists of the learned men connected either with the School or with the monastery at Monte Cassino, and Arnald of Villanova, who had studied at Salerno and was the first man to comment on the *Regimen*— and quite possibly himself its author—ascribed it simply and modestly to the doctors of Salerno. The edition Arnald wrote about consisted of three hundred and sixty-three lines, and was the earliest known. A later spate of editions and copies swelled the lineage up to one thousand in more than one instance.

The best-known English text is that of Sir John Harington, a godson of Queen Elizabeth. Harington invented the modern water-closet, which he described under the heading of "A New Discourse of a Stale Subject called the Metamorphosis of Ajax" (London, 1596). "A jakes" was the accepted term for a privy in Elizabethan days. Harington was a great favourite of the Queen's, though he received the royal displeasure on one occasion for circulating among the ladies of the Court a translation of the story of Gioconda. After this impropriety he had to retire to the country for a while. The two most quoted couplets in his version of the *Regimen* are probably:

> Use three physicians still: first Doctor Quiet,
> Next Doctor Merry-man, and Doctor Diet.
>
> Joy, Temperance, and Repose
> Slam the door on the doctor's nose.

Surgery is "that skill which death loves not", and that is about the only reference to it. The rest is amusing rhyming advice on food and drink and the use of herbs. Sound common sense and purely Elizabethan ribaldry rub shoulders throughout the whole of Harington's version.

> Great harmes haue growne, & maladies exceeding,
> By keeping in a little blaft of wind:
> So *Cramps & Dropfies, Collickes* haue their breeding,
> And *Mazed Braines* for want of vent behind:
> Befides we finde in ftories worth the reading,
> A certaine *Romane Emperour* was fo kind,
> *Claudius* by name, he made a Proclamation,
> A *Scape* to be no loffe of reputation.
> Great fuppers do the ftomacke much offend,
> Sup light if quiet you to fleepe intend.

The reference to the Emperor Claudius is probably taken from Suetonius, who wrote that the Emperor had in mind at one time the issuing of a proclamation justifying the emission of flatus wherever and whenever the need might exist.

[89]

Garlic, pepper, sage, pennyroyal, rue, and many other simple remedies are advised for different purposes:

> If in your drinke you mingle *Rew* with *Sage*,
> All poyfon is expeld by power of thofe,
> And if you would withall Lufts heat affwage,
> Adde to them two the gentle flowre of Rofe:
> Would not be fea-ficke when feas do rage,
> *Sage-water* drinke with wine before he goes.
> *Salt, Garlicke, Parfly, Pepper, Sage, and Wine*,
> Make fawces for all meates both courfe and fine.

Two further references to rue Sir John may have written with his tongue in his cheek:

> Rew is a noble hearbe to giue it right,
> To chew it fafting, it will purge the fight.
> One quality thereof yet blame I muft,
> It makes men chafte, and women fils with luft.

> Faire Ladies, if thefe Phyficke rules be true,
> That Rew hath fuch ftrange qualities as thefe,
> Eate little Rew, left your good husbands (REW).

Advice is given on every conceivable article of diet—soups, fish, meats, fruits, nuts, and all else. Vaguely surgical is:

> A plaifter made of Figges, by fome mens telling,
> Is good againft all kernels, boyles and fwelling,
> With *Poppy* ioyn'd, it drawes out bones are broken,
> By *Figges* are lice ingendred, Luft prouoken.

Just as vaguely obstetrical is:

> The worms that gnaw the wombe & neuer ftint,
> Are kil'd, and purg'd, and driuen away with *Mint*.

Purely utilitarian are other couplets:

> She that hath hap a husband bad to bury,
> And is therefore in heart not fad, but merry,
> Yet if in fhew good manners fhee will keepe,
> *Onyons* and *Muftard-feed* will make her weepe.

> Greene *Leekes* are good, as fome Phyficians fay,
> Yet would I choofe how er'e I them beleeue,
> To weare *Leekes* rather on Saint *Dauids* day,
> Then eate the Leeke vpon Saint Dauids Eue.

The last part of the poem is devoted to a description of the different humours—sanguine, melancholy, phlegmatic, and choleric—and finally there are some indications for bleeding and directions as to how it should be performed. The poem opens with a dedication to "England's King", and much ink has spoiled more paper in identifying this king with Robert, Duke of Normandy, the eldest son of William the Conqueror.

In about A.D. 1096 Robert was seized by the crusading urge. The Conqueror had died, and after much fraternal strife Robert's younger brother had become King. Robert was a penniless scapegrace, and he had to mortgage his dukedom to raise enough funds for a crusade. On his way to the Holy Land he passed a winter at Salerno as the guest of Duke Ruggiero, a relative of his who reigned over the Duchy of Apulia, of which Salerno was the capital. Before sailing, Robert received the benediction of the monks of Monte Cassino, and some months later he aided in the capture of Jerusalem. In A.D. 1099 he returned to Salerno to see if he could obtain a cure for a poisoned arrow-wound, which had become fistulous and refused to heal. There he fell in love with, and married, Sybilla, daughter of the Count of Conversano. According to one version of the legend, the physicians told him that the only chance of recovery was to have the poison sucked from the wound. Sybilla volunteered for this hazardous service, but her husband sternly forbade her to attempt it. The fair lady waited till he was asleep one night, and then proceeded to suck the wound, which healed immediately. Salerno's advice and Sybilla's love had saved him, and lest any further mishap should befall, the *Regimen* of general advice was composed especially for him.

Unhappily, this seems to be just another good story. In the first place, the earliest known manuscript of the poem in its accepted form dates from the early fourteenth century, and Robert had died in captivity in A.D. 1134. In the second place, other manuscripts are dedicated just as fulsomely to the "King of the Franks," to the "King of Aragon," and so on. Mediæval dedication to a reigning monarch was just a smooth piece of propaganda, calculated to assist the sale of manuscripts in whatever country owed allegiance to the particular monarch.

There is another age-old story of Salerno, the explosion of which has not yet reverberated through the nurseries. Dame Trot of nursery-rhyme fame was traditionally believed to be Trotula, a woman of noble family who was a teacher at Salerno in the middle of the eleventh century and wrote a series of works known as the *Trotula*. The *Trotula* were not very good books.

For example, the procedure recommended for the treatment of difficult labour is rather barbarously regrettable:

> When there is difficult labour with a dead child, place the patient in a sheet held at the corners by four strong men, with her head somewhat elevated. Have them shake the sheet vigorously by pulling on the opposite corners, and with God's aid she will give birth.

Then, as in these days, the man or woman who could prognosticate correctly the sex of an unborn child was certain of fame. The method suggested in the *Trotula* is simple and sounds impressive. Two or three drops of milk, or of blood if milk was not yet available, were drawn from the woman's right breast and dropped into water taken from a spring. If they sank, the child would be a boy, if they floated, a girl. It is sad to relate that these compilations on obstetrics, hygiene, and other medical subjects seem to have been the work of one Trottus, a male. According to the custom of the time, they were spoken of collectively as the *Trotula*. They dealt with aspects of women's life ranging in rather Peeping Tom fashion from patchouli to parturition, and that they should have been wished on to a non-existent woman professor is not very surprising.

All these legends that grew up about the School of Salerno by their very existence testify to the high regard in which the School was held. For many centuries it was sufficient to state that a book was written by the doctors of Salerno to guarantee its success. Actually about fifty books did emanate from Salerno in the century following the death of Constantine. Surgery as taught there was a queer but probably not ineffective mingling of the old Greek practices and the Arabic lack of them. Anatomy was taught according to Galen, but in a very simplified form. As indicated in the *Regimen,* even though it was written after the School had lapsed from its high estate, pathology was that of the four humours: blood, phlegm, yellow bile, and black bile. Bleeding was done cautiously and fairly rationally:

> Phlebotomy is the beginning of health. It strengthens the mind and memory, purges the bladder, dries out the brain, warms the spinal cord, clears the hearing, restrains tears, relieves anorexia, purifies the stomach, invites digestion, induces sleep, is believed to favor longer life, and drives away disease. Phlebotomy should be done with caution, and the amount of blood withdrawn is large or small according to the strength and age of the patient, the time of year, and the state of his bodily heat. If the blood runs black at first, bleed until it becomes red; if thick or greasy,

bleed until it has the consistency of water; but the bleeding should
not be allowed to run until the patient is overtaken by lassitude or weakness of the stomach.

Consideration of the urine played a large part in diagnosis,
in fact the expert physician could work out the diagnosis and lay
down the lines of treatment to be followed without considering
anything other than the urine. Hippocratic ideals and methods
were almost lost. Such few case-reports as are authentically
Salernitan are merely lists of relevant and irrelevant symptoms,
bearing no resemblance to the clear-cut and exact Hippocratic
clinical pictures.

Treatment by diet was perhaps excessively systematized, and
drug treatment was rather complicated, though it was almost
free of astrological and superstitious taints. Disagreeable
substances of animal origin, in which the Egyptians revelled,
are rarely mentioned and then only for external application.
For example:

> For hæmorrhoids, take some of the little worms which are found under
> stones, the kind that are rough on the outside with a great many feet
> but roll up into a ball when you disturb them. Boil them in linseed oil
> and apply the oil to the place.

One of the most delightful things about these Salernitan
physicians and surgeons must have been their approach and their
bedside manner, which same manner will often compensate
for a lack of either knowledge or skill, as they shrewdly realized.
The following passage is taken from a work of general guidance
as to medical conduct written about A.D. 1100 by one Archi-
mathæus:

> When you are called to a patient, may the name of God be your help,
> and may the angel who walked with Tobias be the companion of your
> mind and body. At your entrance inquire of him who greets you from
> what disease the sick man suffers and how his illness progresses; this is
> advisable in order that when you come to him you may not seem entirely
> uninformed as to the illness. . . . Again when you reach the house
> and before you see him, ask if he has seen his confessor, and if he has not
> done this, arrange for him to do so, or have him promise to do so, for if
> the sick man hears talk on this subject after he has been examined and the
> signs of his illness studied, he will begin to despair of his safety, because
> he will think that you despair of it. Entering the sick-room you should
> have neither proud nor greedy countenance; you should repeat the greet-
> ing of those who rise as you enter, and with a gesture seat yourself when
> they sit down. Next you may resume the conversation with a few remarks

in which you praise the neighbourhood, commend the arrangements of the house, if it seems appropriate, or compliment the liberality of the family.

Then turning to the patient you may ask how it goes with him, and have him put out his arm. At first there may be differences between your own state and that of the patient, either because he is excited at your arrival, or because he is worried about the size of your fee, so that you find the pulse rather confusing; therefore you should consider the pulse only after the patient has become steadier. Take care that he does not lie upon his side nor has his finger over-extended or flexed against his palm. Support his arm with your left hand and observe the pulse for at least 100 beats in order to feel all its variations, and thus you will be able to satisfy the expectant bystanders with words which they are glad to hear.

Next have the urine brought to you, that the sick man may see you study his illness not only from the pulse but from the urine. When examining the urine you should observe its color, substance, quantity, and content; after which you may promise the patient that with the help of God you will cure him. As you go away, however, you should say to his servants that he is in a very bad way, because if he recovers you will receive great credit and praise, and if he dies, they will remember that you despaired of his health from the beginning. Meanwhile I urge you not to turn a lingering eye upon his wife, his daughter, or his maid-servant, for this sort of thing blinds the eye of the doctor, averts the favor of God, and makes the doctor abhorrent to the patient and less confident in himself. Be therefore careful in speech, respectable in conduct, attentively seeking Divine aid. If the people of the house invite you to a meal, as often happens, do not seem too much gratified, and do not seek the first place at the table, although it is the custom to give this to the priest or the doctor. Do not criticize the food or drink, and when in the country do not show distaste for country food, for example millet bread, even though you can scarcely control your stomach.

While you eat you may inquire as to the condition of the patient from any one who is present, for in this way the sick man will confide in you all the more, since he sees that you do not forget him while seeking your own comfort. When you rise from the table you may mention that you have been well looked after; this too will give pleasure to the patient.

Another writer, Cophon the Younger, who produced a treatise on the anatomy of the pig, was also responsible for a guide to practice. In this he explained a state of affairs which unfortunately still holds to-day. Prescriptions for the rich patients differed appreciably from those for the poorer classes, not because the rich man received better treatment or more powerful drugs, but because he could afford to have the nicest and most expensive kind of medical jam all round his gilded pills.

In the year A.D. 1224 the Emperor Frederick II formally instituted a university at Naples. Salerno went on conducting its examinations, to be eligible for which a candidate had to have studied medicine for at least seven years, and to have produced evidence of the legitimacy of his birth, but as the new university at Naples gradually increased in importance, Salerno began to decline. The last token of respect paid to the once great medical school was in 1748. The Faculty of Medicine of Paris referred the question of the relative status of physicians and surgeons in France to the Faculty of Salerno, since French professional opinion on this subject was so heated that some outside aid was necessary. The School of Salerno became a place where dubious degrees could be obtained for a consideration and a prescribed period of residence. Finally, in 1811, the School was formally abolished by decree of the Emperor Napoleon. For many years before that, however, Salerno had been moribund. It was but a withered corpse that Napoleon slew.

Salerno gave to Europe nothing original save perhaps its legends. But Salerno did perform great service. Such of the old Greek traditions as it had it held. With them it mingled all the culture of Arabia and the Greek and Roman teachings which Moslem ratiocination had twisted perhaps a little. A Greek, a Latin, an Arab, and a Jew each contributed something, and a Moor plagiarized them all. Salerno took these things and savoured them with a naïve common sense and a kindly sympathy, adapting all the learning of the East to fit the needs of awakening Europe.

Universities at Bologna, Naples, and Montpellier were gathering strength. Salerno was their model. Saxon leech-books were being put away. Long treatises from Salerno took their place. Surgery had been asleep. Roger Frugardi of Salerno awakened it.

VI. Surgeons in Europe

ROGER FRUGARDI OF PALERMO WAS A SURGEON OF SALERNO. A friend of his, one Guido Aretino, published in A.D. 1170 the *Practica Chirurgiæ,* which represented the teaching of Roger as noted down by Guido, partly from lectures and partly from private conversation.   Roger was one of the founders of modern surgery. His book had a tremendous vogue, and about A.D. 1230 a famous pupil of his, Roland of Parma, edited and added to the *Practica,* producing a book which was soon well known as the *Rogerina.*   At Salerno, Bologna, and other centres copies of the *Rogerina* were annotated by different surgeons, and finally about A.D. 1270 there was written at Salerno the *Glossulæ Quatuor Magistrorum Super Chirurgium Rogerii et Rolandi.*   This commentary by the "Four Masters", whose names are unknown, was for generations regarded as the most authoritative surgical work in existence.

Roger's *Practica,* on which the two later works were based, completely displaced the *Pantegni* of Hali ibn al Abbas, which Constantine the Moor had translated, so far as its surgical section was concerned.   The book was divided into four parts. Of these, the first was concerned with wounds of the head and fractures of the skull; the second dealt with diseases of the neck; the third with conditions affecting the upper limbs, the chest, and the abdomen; and the last section covered diseases of the lower limbs, the use of the cautery, and the treatment of leprosy and of convulsions.   Roger introduced the use of the seton, a method of stitching a bundle of linen threads through a fold of skin and leaving them to act as a counter-irritant.   He was also the first to suggest that torn intestines, which had always presented difficulties to contemporary surgeons, might be sutured more easily over a hollow tube of elderwood.   Roger ligatured blood-vessels which had been ruptured, if cauterization and styptics failed to check the bleeding; and, like Albucasis, he re-fractured and set again bones which had been broken and had united in bad position.   One of the most remarkable sections of Roger's *Practica* describes clearly and rationally the treatment of wounds and fractures of the skull.

In any scalp wound a finger was to be inserted and run gently over the underlying bone ". . . . because there is no better method of recognizing a fracture of the skull. . . ."

PLATE V

These pictures are taken from an edition of the *Surgery* of Salerno which appeared in A.D. 1240. The upper row of illustrations depicts: (1) the treatment of a fractured skull; (2) bandaging the head; (3) an arrow wound of the neck. The middle group shows the treatment for: (1) dislocation of the shoulder; (2) fracture or dislocation of the elbow; (3) fracture of the leg. The lower pictures represent the diagnosis of (1) some condition affecting the left breast; (2) an abdominal injury; and (3) a gross enlargement of the scrotum.

PLATE VI

The title-page of *The Frenche Chirurgerye* of Jacques Guillemeau. Imprinted at Dort in 1597.

Once the extent of the fracture had been ascertained, the wound was to be enlarged by cross-incision with a razor, and the scalp lifted up from the bone by means of a blunt instrument so as to expose clearly the whole fracture. Bleeding from the scalp was controlled, and any fragments of bone were removed. Only then were the flaps pressed together and the wound bound with a linen cloth, which had previously been soaked in white of egg. (*See plate facing* p. 96.) Roger must have had many opportunities of treating fractured skulls and other injuries, thanks to the almost continuous warfare between the Norman overlords of Salerno and their neighbours. The methods of warfare at that time were those of the joust or tournament. The lance, the mace, and the battle-axe were favourite weapons, and since most of the warriors were mounted and heavily armoured, the head was the part to be aimed at, and head injuries must have been numerous. Another procedure peculiar to military surgery which Roger described in detail was a method for removing barbed arrows by inserting an iron or copper tube into the wound, so that it slipped over the barbs and allowed of their extraction. This was only done if the barbs were too strong or too deeply placed for the surgeon to flatten them with forceps. If the metal head of a lance or an arrow was very deeply embedded, it was usually left alone. Roger said that he had seen more harm result from ill-advised attempts at extraction in these cases than was ever due to the weapon itself. Roger knew the surgery of war well enough to realize the limitations of his art. "If a man is wounded in the heart, lung, liver, or diaphragm we do not undertake his treatment." Just as hopeless were spinal injuries, which he believed were "scarcely or never cured by surgery". Worst of all were wounds of the kidneys, which were committed without comment "to the grace and goodness of God".

Roger erred greatly in only one particular. He did not believe that clean healing, by first intention, was possible. He thought it natural that wounds should become infected and suppurate before finally healing. This being so, he inserted drains in many of the wounds he treated, but since the drains consisted of strips of bacon, they were as likely to promote the formation of pus as to drain it away. He was neither the first nor the last surgeon to insist that wet dressings and ointments should be applied to wounds in order to produce the "laudable pus" which was thought necessary to healing, but his authority

[97]

was such that in later years his teachings were adduced as holy writ, to restrain any heretic who might have allowed simple wounds to heal of themselves without any interference. In this respect, too, Roland, and later the Four Masters, contented themselves with adding to, and elaborating, the concoctions which Roger advised for promoting pus formation.

The Four Masters and Roland described in detail many bold operations which Roger had suggested or had himself outlined. On only a few points did they differ appreciably from the teaching of Roger. For example, Roger said that any patient with a fractured skull must be regarded as in danger for at least one hundred days. This period, which was perhaps too long, the Four Masters reduced to a fortnight, which was perhaps too short. They operated on aneurysms, removed stones from the bladder, excised anal fistulæ, and their treatment of goitre—the enlargement and over-action of the thyroid gland in the neck—has been improved on only in the details of technique. Medical treatment was always tried first. To-day these patients are given small doses of iodine. The Four Masters achieved the same effect by giving ashes of seaweed, which has a high iodine content. If this failed, then resort was had to surgery. Very simple is a method for dealing with a goitre which is "single", that is, when only one side of the neck is enlarged. A few strands of linen thread were inserted with a hot iron as setons running longitudinally and horizontally.

Every day, morning and evening, the setons are drawn towards the outside until finally the flesh is cut through. When this is done if any part of the goitre remains, powder it with powder of asphodel and, purified in this way, the wound will heal like other wounds.

The Four Masters in other cases abandoned the seton and took up the knife. The enlarged gland was grasped firmly, and the skin over it was cut "lengthwise". The tumour was then grasped with a hook, and the skin was dissected away. A finger hooked up behind the gland completed the removal, and the wound was dressed with a linen cloth. It was pointed out by the Masters that the larger a goitre became, the more difficult it was to remove, and in general the surgeon was advised to leave severely alone cases in which the goitre was very large. There is a saving clause, however, which is also a grim reminder that anæsthetics were quite unknown: ". . . when it becomes necessary to treat these patients, we tie them to a table and have them held firmly in order that we may see exactly what we are doing".

Roger and Roland and the Four Masters were succeeded by other surgeons, who followed their teachings and assisted in placing surgery on a firm foundation again. Most of these surgeons travelled from country to country, learning their craft from the famous surgeons at the universities of Bologna, Padua, Montpellier, and so on. Their practical experience was gained in the wars, and then, as now, war was a good school for budding surgeons. Theodoric, a chaplain of the order of Preaching Friars, was one of the outstanding surgeons of this generation. In a treatise he wrote, about A.D. 1266, he categorically denied the doctrine that wounds could only heal successfully in the presence of "laudable" pus—that is, if they became infected. He wrote:

> For it is not necessary, as Roger and Roland have written, as many of their disciples teach, and as all modern surgeons profess, that pus should be generated in wounds. No error can be greater than this. Such a practice is indeed to hinder nature, to prolong the disease. and to prevent the conglutination and consolidation of the wound.

Theodoric was quite right. Any wound which is not grossly infected will heal quickly and simply without any aid other than from a clean, dry dressing. In this case the healing is by first intention. If this first natural intention or tendency to heal fails because the wound has become infected, then pus will form and the wound will heal slowly by second intention. The old teaching was that this pus was "laudable" and necessary, and if a wound did show any signs of healing normally, the surgeon applied salves and ointments, which would provide a medium for the development of infective germs and so delay the first healing, but make sure of achieving the laudable pus and the union by second intention. Theodoric must have been as great an original thinker as Lord Lister, but he lived six hundred years too soon. The Galenic copyists had taught the value of "laudable" pus. Roger and Roland had taught the same doctrine, so Theodoric's heresy was as great as, if not greater than, that of the excommunicated Bishop Nestorius. Like many another pioneer, Theodoric flung himself vainly against the entrenched advocates of pus formation. For his pains he was criticized by later authors as a plagiarist, and a poor one at that, and his contemporaries were even less restrained in their comments on his surgical sacrilege.

In England at this time the leech-books were gradually being abandoned. Barbers added a few minor operations to their bleeding repertoire and became barber-surgeons. Some physicians were beginning to devote themselves particularly to the compounding of medicines, and they became known as apothecaries. One of the first of these apothecaries was appointed to the Court of Henry II. This was Richard Fitznagel, who became Bishop of London, and died in A.D. 1198. His duties cannot have been light, for the prescriptions in vogue at that time were remarkable alike for the number and variety of their ingredients. Notable amongst them was theriac, a compound with a fantastically chequered history.

Mithridates, ruler of Pontus, is supposed to have started it all. He had some reputation as a pharmacist, and Pompey, who conquered him, preserved all his manuscripts, which included one or two simple prescriptions. So it was that there appeared in Rome some years later a much-propagandized preparation of "two dry walnuts, twenty leaves of rue, and two figs, pounded and strewn with a little salt". The simplicity of this prescription was more than balanced by the magnificent title of *Antidotum Mithridatium*. The body physician of Nero improved things not a little by sandwiching a spot of viper's flesh between the rue and the figs. Other physicians threw in squills and opium for luck, and mixed in enough honey to keep the mixture palatable. At this stage theriac, from the Greek word meaning a wild beast, against the bites of which it was particularly recommended, became its name. Pliny then raised his voice and roundly criticized the mixture. He had as much success in his campaign as would any modern physician who tried to convince the great newspaper-reading public that nineteen out of every twenty of them were not constipated. Theriac was advised by everybody for every known ailment, and everyone who ever dispensed it added a little extra something. Fifty, sixty, or seventy ingredients were soon accepted as necessary to the preparation of true theriac, and one German pharmacist managed to include one hundred and fifty different substances in the prescription he favoured. Richard Fitznagel never reached these heights, but even in his time this sovereign remedy must have necessitated the maintenance of something more than half a dozen stock bottles. It is fairly certain that Richard Fitznagel, whatever else he did, never wielded a scalpel. England in the early thirteenth century had still no surgeons worthy of the name. It was in Italy and in France that the work of Roger and Roland was being continued.

In Italy, Guglielmo Salicetti, or William of Salicet, was born about A.D. 1210, and won his surgical spurs on the battlefield rather than in the hospital. He became a professor at Bologna, and later at Verona, and for the benefit of his son, who was also to take up surgery, he wrote his *Cyrurgia*. William of Salicet did not mention in this book the theory of the treatment of wounds of which Theodoric had written, but he did treat injuries reasonably. He advised simple dressings of white of egg and rose-water, instead of the complicated salves and ointments which were then in vogue. More important than this, he upset badly two important Arabic doctrines which had done much harm to the progress of surgery. To the Arabs surgery was an inferior branch of treatment effected by the red-hot cautery. William of Salicet taught that the knife was a cleaner and surer instrument than the cautery, and he insisted that surgical diagnosis could not be rudely separated from medicine. Both depended in the same way and to the same degree on a careful recording of the patient's history and the results of examination. Only when these things had been judiciously weighed and considered was it possible to say that the patient needed a physician more than a surgeon, or surgery more than physic.

Two minor points of diagnosis William of Salicet laid stress on: he taught that bleeding from an artery could always be recognized immediately by the intermittent spurting of blood, and that a broken bone could be diagnosed if on gentle manipulation a crackling noise, or crepitus, was heard. He taught, too, that in extensive wounds severed nerves and tendons should be sought for and stitched together again. He followed Hippocrates in pointing out that injury to either side of the skull, if sufficiently severe, will cause a paralysis of muscles on the other side of the body. Arrow wounds and their treatment he described at length. His book also throws an interesting sidelight on the low esteem in which surgery was held at that time, and from which he did much to raise it. For example, he remarks deprecatingly, "A wise surgeon will refrain from stealing while he is actually in attendance upon a patient", and he comments mildly upon the unwisdom of employing as assistants notoriously bad characters. William of Salicet died in A.D. 1277, but one of his pupils, Lanfrank, carried his teachings and his ideals to Lyons and later to Paris.

Lanfrank was the founder of French surgery, but not by choice. Being a politically-minded young man, he involved himself in one of the perpetual quarrels of the Guelphs and the Ghibellines. He gave his allegiance to the wrong party, whichever one it was, and was hounded from his native Milan. He went to Lyons and achieved some fame there after writing a *Chirurgia Parva*. Paris he reached in A.D. 1295, and found to his dismay that his early marriage had wrecked his hope of a professorship at the university. All the teaching staff were celibate clerics. So he went to the College de Saint Côme, and it was there that he wrote his *Chirurgia Magna*. Both his books, which were dedicated to Philip the Fair, were translated into English and were later to become surgical classics. Like his teacher, he wrote that the division between medicine and surgery was an unreal one. A knowledge of medicine was as necessary to the surgeon as a scalpel. He was the first surgeon to describe concussion of the brain, and he pointed out clearly that the trepanning operation was not indicated in all cases of injury to the skull; it was only necessary to remove fragments of bone when they were pressing on and irritating the brain or its coverings. He was also the first surgeon to distinguish clearly between simple enlargement of the female breast and cancer. He gave, too, careful directions for bleeding, which he thought should never have been allowed to fall into the hands of barbers.

Paris he believed to be an earthly paradise, but for French surgery and surgeons he had nothing but contempt. His writing was forceful, particularly on the theme of surgery being a part of medicine.

> Good God, why this abandoning of operations by physicians to lay persons, disdaining surgery because they do not know how to operate, an abuse which has reached such a point that the vulgar begin to think the same man cannot know both surgery and medicine? I say, however, that no man can be a good physician who has no knowledge of operative surgery, a knowledge of both branches is essential.

A pupil of Lanfrank's who became well known was Jehan Yperman, and Lanfrank's most famous French contemporary was Henri de Mondeville, who was born in A.D. 1260 and died about A.D. 1320. De Mondeville made a last stand for the clean treatment of wounds. He advised that all flesh wounds should be washed clean and left alone, "since wounds dry much better before suppuration than after it". He wrote on this subject: "If they are treated on Theodoric's and my instructions every simple wound will heal without any notable quantity of pus. Many more surgeons know how to cause suppuration than how to heal a wound. Keep your needles sharp and clean or they will infect the wound."

De Mondeville was one of four body-surgeons of Philip the Fair, and he gave lectures on anatomy at the University of Montpellier. He was unorthodox again in disregarding the accepted practice of reducing to a starvation diet patients who had been injured. He advised that they should be assisted to recovery by good food and good wines. In addition, the "music of viols and a ten-stringed psaltery" would help in maintaining the patient's morale. De Mondeville was insistent on the importance of keeping the patient's spirits up, and the better to stress this point he wrote cheerfully that he was quite prepared to forge letters announcing the death of the patient's enemies or the exaltation of an ailing cleric to a bishopric, if he thought it would promote recovery.

His description of the ideal surgeon has never been bettered. The first quality of a good surgeon is boldness tempered with enough wisdom to avoid undertaking a really dangerous operation, unless he is certain that it is the only way to avoid "a greater danger". The surgeon's hands should be well shaped, with long, delicate, and supple fingers, which should not tremble. A cure should always be promised to the patient, but the parents or some trusted friend should be told if there is any danger. The surgeon should "refuse as far as possible all difficult cases and never interfere with desperate ones. He may give advice to the poor for the love of God only, but the rich should be made to pay well." De Mondeville had much to say on the subject of fees and how to collect them. "Never dine with a patient who is in your debt, but get your dinner at an inn, otherwise he will deduct his hospitality from your fee." An original thinker with great gifts of wit and sarcasm, Henri de Mondeville deserves to be remembered if only for perhaps the most illuminating remark one surgeon ever made about another: "God did not exhaust all His creative power in making Galen!"

Jehan Yperman, who was born in A.D. 1280, was a pupil of Lanfrank's in Milan and afterwards in Paris. In A.D. 1308 he was appointed surgeon to the *Ospial del Belle* at Ypres. His house and the hospital near it remained a monument to him until their destruction by bombardment during the last war. He taught that bleeding should be arrested by applying styptic powders, but when this fails: "Take a triangular needle, arm it with a stout waxed thread, and pass it under the artery; tie the two ends of the thread together securely and take care not to pierce the vessel with the needle." He pointed out that the cautery could be applied to large blood-vessels, but that there was always some danger of the scar falling off and the bleeding starting again. An ingenious but simple method for protecting the flesh around the artery to be cauterized is described by him. It consists simply in the use of a sheet of iron perforated with holes of varying size. These perforations just covered vessels of differing sizes, and allowed the red-hot iron to be applied to them without undue injury to the surrounding flesh. Jehan Yperman also gave a good account of trepanning, and of the treatment of arrow wounds. After the edges of a hare-lip had been stripped of skin and sewn together, he advised that the patient should be fed through a silver tube until the repaired hare-lip had healed satisfactorily. At this time, as for some hundreds of years later, it was firmly believed that the touch of a Royal hand would cure what was known as the "King's Evil"—that is, scrofula, or tuberculosis of the skin and superficial lymphatic glands. Jehan Yperman was not the first surgeon to mention this belief, but he was the first to suggest that curable cases recovered with or without the Royal touch.

It was in the thirteenth century that surgery bid fair to come to life again in Europe. Roger and Roland and the Four Masters had done their task well. Theodoric and Henri de Mondeville had done all they could to show in treatment as well as in words that Galen's work was a contribution to surgery rather than a crown. They battled very valiantly, and the defeat they suffered was at the hands of no less a personage than the Prince of Surgeons, Guy de Chauliac, the greatest surgeon of the fourteenth century. Europe was fast awakening from its surgical sloth, and even sleepy England stirred. An occasional Englishman went over to Montpellier to study. One

Scotsman at least went there, and Bernard de Gordon, for that was his name, wrote a book in which occurs one of the earliest descriptions of a truss, in the modern sense of the term.

The hospitals of St. Bartholomew and St. Thomas were coming into existence in London. St. Bartholomew's was founded as part of a priory of Augustine Canons, on a site at Smithfield given by Henry I in A.D. 1123. The man responsible for its foundation was a Norman, Rahere. He was born about A.D. 1080 and as a youth frequented the King's Court. He was famed for his wit, and soon achieved the status of a sort of licensed amateur jester. He remained at Court for several years, then left abruptly, and soon afterwards joined the Order of St. Augustine. At the age of forty he went on a pilgrimage to the shrines of St. Peter and St. Paul in Rome. While there he had a severe attack of malaria and was nursed back to health in a hospital on the island of St. Bartholomew, which lies near the mouth of the Tiber. In gratitude for his recovery he vowed to found a hospital for the relief of the sick poor. He had another attack on the way home, and at the height of his illness saw a vision of St. Bartholomew. The Saint commanded him to found a church in his name at Smithfield, a suburb of London. Bartholomew, so legend has it, suffered martyrdom by being flayed alive, and in Milan there is a grim statue of him carrying a flaying knife and his own skin. Rahere slowly made his way to London, arriving there early in A.D. 1123. He announced his intention of fulfilling the vow he had made and the command he had been vouchsafed by building both a church and a hospital. A grant of land, which was part of the Crown property known as the King's Market in Smithfield, was made to him by Henry I. Once the priory and the hospital were erected, Rahere assisting himself in the building and persuading men of all sorts and conditions to help him, he was appointed the first Prior and Master of the hospital. The hospital was managed by a warden, eight brothers, and four sisters of mercy under the general supervision of Rahere. It was simply a rest-house for the sick poor till such time as they recovered, and to it flocked sick and wounded men, poor women who were ill or pregnant, children with sore eyes, and all the poor who were sick in any way.

St. Thomas's was founded in the latter part of the twelfth century, burnt down in A.D. 1207, rebuilt five years later, and again on a fresh site in A.D. 1228. It was dedicated to St.

[*105*]

Thomas à Becket, but the dedication was changed later to St. Thomas the Apostle. There were, too, at least two hundred lazar-houses in England for the reception of lepers, and when the leprosy epidemic which had raged throughout Europe for nearly three hundred years died down, many of them became alms houses and later hospitals.

So in England there were hospitals, there were physicians, and there were apothecaries. Surgeons had yet to appear, but the barbers, who undertook what surgery there was, were quietly creating a guild to protect their own interests, a guild which was to have a considerable influence upon the rise of surgery in England.

VII.   The Black Death

AS THE THIRTEENTH CENTURY ENDED GUY DE CHAULIAC, THE son of an Auvergne peasant, was born.   Guido de Cauliaco, as he was called then, became in the middle of the fourteenth century the Prince of Surgeons, the greatest authority on surgery in Europe of that time.   He studied first in his own country, at Paris, Montpellier, and Toulouse, and later he learnt anatomy in Bologna.   He was a canon of the church of St. Justus, and surgeon to three popes, Clement VI, Innocent VI, and Urban V, at Avignon.   His chief disservice to surgery—and it was not recognized as such till five hundred years later—was his denunciation of the teaching of Theodoric, his insistence that suppuration and the formation of pus were essential to the healing of wounds.   Against this must be weighed many things that he did well, much teaching that was good, and not a few technical advances.   His interest in the details of surgical after-care is evidenced to this day by the rope or chain which hangs always over the hospital bed.   He suggested that this simple device would allow the patient more easily to raise himself or change his position in the bed.   One of his most important contributions to major surgery was in rescuing the treatment of rupture from the hands of quacks.   Just as there were many quack cutters for stone, so there were quacks who specialized in the treatment of ruptures.   They would apply a cautery, which did little harm but less good, or, worse still, make some flourishing incision, which was more likely to cut across the intestine than to cure the rupture.   Guy de Chauliac described an operation for the radical cure of hernia, or rupture, and made it clear that the treatment of this condition should not be left to itinerant quacks and peddlers.   His comprehensive text-book of surgery appeared about A.D. 1363.   No less than one hundred and twenty-nine editions are said to have appeared in manuscript form, and it was translated into English, French, Provençal, Dutch, and Hebrew.   It showed that healthy iconoclasm which surgery had so long needed and which had been first evidenced by Theodoric and Henri de Mondeville. Surgeons, physicians, and those practising all the kindred arts and sciences were at last beginning to realize that the age of a theory or a statement was not necessarily directly proportionate to its validity.   Guy de Chauliac was not quite as rude as De

[*107*]

Mondeville in speaking of the older writers generally and of their works, of which so far as the Greeks and the Arabians were concerned he had a considerable knowledge. He said, "We are like children sitting on the neck of a giant—who see all that he sees and something besides."

An English translation of his work was presented as *The Questyonary of Surgeans* and written in the form of question and answer. How much importance Guy de Chauliac attributed to a knowledge of anatomy is shown by the reply to a question whether the "scyence of nathomye be necessary and nedefull to the cyrurgen or not?" It is: "The same manner that the blinde man worketh in hewynge of a log, so doth a cyrurgen that knoweth not the nathomye." The Prince of Surgeons advised that amputations of limbs should never be undertaken except in those cases in which a battle-axe or two-handed sword had already done most of the work and it remained only for the surgeon to complete the severance of the limb. This advice was prompted simply by the ever-recurrent difficulty of controlling bleeding, a difficulty which was not really overcome until the middle of the sixteenth century, though not a few surgeons even in De Chauliac's time had drawn attention to the use of the ligature. In treating broken limbs, however, De Chauliac excelled. In the case of a compound fracture he advised that "arrows or pieces of bone" or other foreign bodies should be removed, then the separated ends of the bone should be brought together and the flesh wound "deeply sutured and closed firmly". Bandages were applied in various ways, but always so that the wound could be dressed regularly with the minimum disturbance of the splints which were next applied. Splints were made of willow, "Sword-handle wood", leather, horn, or even iron, so arranged that while supporting the fracture they neither touched nor injured the joints above and below it. Round the splints he often wrapped cloth soaked in the white of egg, which presumably stiffened and gave in some degree the effect of plaster of Paris. The limb was then placed in a "cradle" or otherwise suspended so that it remained in a position which was comfortable yet likely to produce good union of the broken bones. Bony healing was assisted by a diet of wheat cooked in water, boiled feet, rice, and the viscera and heads of animals, with a strong wine—a rather Egyptian mixture.

Union was thought to take forty to fifty days for most long

bones, and if it did not seem to be proceeding as it should, then it might be aided by "frictions and embrocations"—or, in other words, massage. Fractures of the jaw and of the clavicle were treated by the Hippocratic methods. Completely modern was his treatment of broken thigh-bones. Albucasis had advised binding the leg to the thigh so that the heel touched the buttock—that is, using the intact lower leg as a splint for the broken thigh. This position, though probably effective, must have been intolerably uncomfortable, and it was perhaps for this reason that Guy de Chauliac abandoned it. Instead he applied six or seven strong splints tightly to the thigh, and then prevented the tendency of the broken bones to override each other by simply tying a weight to the foot and suspending it over a pulley at the end of the bed. This method of continuous weight extension is still in use, though it is not as commonly employed as it was five or six years ago, and as with many other treatments the principle remains unaltered, though there has been a perhaps over-enthusiastic elaboration of the necessary apparatus.

Guy de Chauliac was to preserve his position as a leading surgical authority for some two hundred years—till, in fact, his most famous countryman, Ambroise Paré, displaced him from it. Two pages of his book were devoted to formulæ for salves and ointments, to be applied to wounds and to broken limbs to help promote the formation of "laudable pus". Only these reactionary recipes reflect anything other than credit on his teaching, and he erred in this respect with a vast and noble company.

Guy de Chauliac described five surgical schools of thought, which could be differentiated in his time according to their treatment of wounds. First were those who, like Galen and himself, deliberately applied salves which would promote suppuration and the formation of pus. This was the orthodox and popular school. Quite unorthodox were the few surgeons who followed Theodoric's teachings and tried to heal wounds by first intention. Less unorthodox were a third group who applied mild unguents and plasters. Orthodoxy regarded these surgeons as being less vicious than the followers of Theodoric, but thought their methods feeble, in that the ointments they used only caused pus to be formed in a proportion of their cases. A fourth and still large group comprised the men who relied on charms and incantations, possibly assisted by the odd cabbage leaf. Last of all came "Women and silly folk" who, according to Guy, sat and folded their hands, doing nothing but accept the will of God. Unhappily, a comparison of the results of treatment by these five different methods was never undertaken. If it had been, Theodoric and his followers would almost certainly have headed the list, with the "women and silly folk" a close second.

It was at Avignon that Guy de Chauliac saw and suffered from the Black Death. This great pestilence first reached Europe in the autumn of A.D. 1347, after having raged in the Far East for over three years. In China thirteen millions of people died; India was almost depopulated; Mesopotamia, Syria, and Armenia were ravaged. Slowly, the pestilence spread westwards. Near Constantinople the city of Caffa was besieged by Tartars. The Black Death seized the invading army, and thousands died each day. Bacterial warfare was born then as the survivors catapulted into the city from the engines of war the putrefying bodies of their friends. Within the space of days the last of the besieged had died as horribly as had the last of the besiegers.

The disease was bubonic plague, and its features were characteristic and unmistakable. Swellings, or buboes, appeared in the groins and armpits in fortunate individuals, many of whom recovered. In the less fortunate there was a superimposed pulmonary form of the disease, with or without the buboes, and before they died these patients had violent pains in the chest and they spat and vomited blood, thanks to a rapidly spreading gangrene of the throat and lungs. Guy de Chauliac divided the disease clearly into these two categories, and pointed out how often those who had only glandular swellings recovered, while in the second type there was "constant fever and blood-spitting, and from this the patient died in three days".

Boccaccio in his introduction to the *Decameron* describes how the Black Death came to Florence. There was no known cause and no hope of cure. "The contagion was communicated not only by conversation with those sick but also by approaching them too closely, or even by merely handling their clothes or anything they had previously touched." As to prevention there were two chief schools of thought. One group of people would fly to the country and shut themselves away from the world, refusing to have contact, or even converse, with anyone.

Another group adopted the attitude that they might or might not be struck down, but, since the representatives of law and order undoubtedly were struck down, the opportunity for a debauch sustained as long as life might last was too good to be missed. Since neither line of action prevented or even mitigated the incidence and effect of the pestilence, the licentious realists may be said to have chosen the better way. A plague-stricken Genoese ship brought the Black Death to Marseilles, and from there it spread northwards throughout France. In Avignon one thousand eight hundred people died in the first three days, and in the next seven months there was a roll of a hundred and fifty thousand dead in this territory alone. Writing of this time, De Chauliac describes how barely a quarter of the population of Avignon survived. He tells how such physicians and surgeons as remained alive dared hardly visit the plague-infected for fear of contracting the disease themselves. Then he writes, with perhaps more honesty than many of his contemporaries, "As for me, to avoid infamy, I did not dare to absent myself, but still I was in continual fear". His fears were justified, for he did contract the infection, but fortunately survived after being almost mortally ill for a long six weeks. The plague was conveyed to England from France and from the Channel Islands in the autumn of A.D. 1348. In England its effects were as far-reaching and as terrible as they had been in Europe and Asia. At first the dead were hurled into huge pits. Later, even this semblance of a burial was omitted, and putrefying corpses cumbered the streets of all the cities.

The population of the earth was reduced by a quarter in the space of a few years. Sixty millions of people died. Surgeons and physicians were flung into the same graves as their patients. The measures they had adopted to try to combat the plague were unavailing. The disease was thought to be due to evil miasms or corrupt vapours, which entered through the patient's skin, attacking particularly the heart, the liver, and the brain. Bathing, which opened the pores of the skin, was forbidden, a light diet was deemed essential, and acid fruits and drinks, notably vinegar, were given. Juniper branches were burnt in the rooms to purify the air. Mixtures of aromatic oils were taken internally and applied externally. If, despite all these things, an individual was struck down by the plague, then bleeding was resorted to, more as a pious gesture than for any hope of a successful cure. This great pestilence had an almost incalculable effect upon social evolution in England as in other countries, an effect which indirectly was to benefit all the arts and sciences, all the crafts and professions, and not least among them surgery.

The spread of leprosy in the Middle Ages, and particularly in connexion with the Crusades, had reached its height in Western Europe in the twelfth and thirteenth centuries. It was customary at this time for the bodies of Crusaders—who had died either from leprosy or by the sword—to be taken back to their native country for burial. The better to preserve them, these bodies were eviscerated and then boiled, a practice which a Papal Bull of A.D. 1300 solemnly interdicted. Whether the boiled bodies conveyed leprosy from one country to another is doubtful, but certainly those who survived the Crusades did so.

Innumerable leper hospitals, or lazar-houses, were set up all over Europe, and with them as many bathing-houses. The bath-keepers were for the most part opportunist barbers who undertook shaving, massage, bleeding, and minor surgery. So many were these establishments that in England the barbers who ran them banded together into a closely constituted guild or confraternity. There is evidence of the existence of such a guild as early as A.D. 1308, and the same evidence shows the doubtful character of at least some of the bathing establishments. It is recorded in that year that "Richard Le Barbour, dwelling opposite to the Church of Allhallows the Less, was chosen and presented by the Barbers of London, on Tuesday next after the feast of St. Lucy the Virgin [December 13] to have supervision over the trade of the barbers. And he was admitted and made oath that every month he would make scrutiny throughout the whole of his trade, and if he should find any among them keeping brothels or acting unseemly in any other way and to the scandal of the trade, he was to distrain upon them and cause the distress to be brought before the Chamber. . . ."

What happened to the disreputable folk when they were brought before the chamber is not known, but it seems certain that for the first half of the fourteenth century there continued the belief that it was not unnatural for those who dealt with minor pathological states to expand their businesses to cope with major physiological needs. Came the Black Death, afflicting reputable and disreputable alike. When it had gone there were great gaps in the ranks of the barbers. Those who were left realized slowly that an old social structure had crumbled. All the guilds which had tried vainly to keep in order too many members now had too few members for the work which was required of them. Artisans found that their work was at a premium, and began to demand better payment and better conditions of life. The guilds became tremendously powerful. Two other factors contributed to the growing importance of the old guild of barbers. The Black Death shocked the ecclesiastical and lay authorities out of their comparative indifference to the public health. The guild of barbers could be, and was, adapted as a sort of rough-and-ready public-health service. Barbers were expected to detect cases of leprosy, for example. Secondly, the pestilence had so reduced the number of craftsmen attached to any one guild that there arose the custom of linking together in one great organization all the crafts which were even remotely connected. So it was that the ranks of the bathers and barbers and one-time brothel-keepers were swelled by the inclusion of surgeons and apothecaries. These new recruits raised the standards of practice so much that only five years after the Black Death had disappeared, the Mayor, Aldermen, and Sheriffs of the City of London—whose predecessors only fifty years before had been concerned with a plague of brothel-keepers—were asked to investigate a charge of professional negligence.

Thomas de Shene had an "enormous and horrible hurt on the right side of the jaw". John le Spicer of Cornhulle "took the same Thomas under his care to heal the wound aforesaid". Thomas complained that he had not been treated with the skill and care he had a right to expect. His plea was upheld by four independent surgeons, "who say upon their oath that if the aforesaid John le Spicer at the time when he took the said Thomas under his care had been expert in his craft or art, or had called in counsel and assistance to his aid, he might have cured the injury aforesaid; and they further say, that through want of skill on the part of the said John le Spicer the said injury under his care became apparently incurable."

Surgeons, as distinct from both barbers and "barbers exercising the faculty of surgery", belonged originally to a small Guild of Surgeons within the City of London, which was officially recognized in A.D. 1368 by the appointment of Master Surgeons, who were given authority over their brethren of the craft. The Master Surgeons continued their work of over-seeing the other surgeons and dealing with any negligence or misconduct without let or hindrance till the end of the century. Then professional jealousy prompted the barbers to try to restrict the activity of the Master Surgeons. The barbers considered surgery a part of their craft, but found that they had little or no authority over the surgeons. These surgeons did not shave nor did they practise "polling or lousing"— more ponderously, trimming hair and disinfestation—and so they were regarded as of better standing than the barbers who engaged in these arts. Quite apart from this, the Guild of Surgeons, though small and relatively unimportant, was entirely separate from the greater and much more powerful Craft of Barbers, which had no jurisdiction over it at all. The dis-gruntled barbers at last had the opportunity of asserting them-selves when the Master Surgeons, unwisely, took it upon themselves to interfere with some of those barbers who prac-tised surgery. So in A.D. 1409 the barbers petitioned the Court of Aldermen, and it was unanimously agreed by the Court that "the barbers, who are for themselves and their successors barbers of the City of London, should for ever peaceably enjoy the privileges contained in the ordinance with-out scrutiny of any person of other craft or trade than barbers. And this neither in shavings, cutting, bleeding, nor other thing in any way pertaining to barbery or to such practice of surgery as is now used or in future to be used within the craft of the said barbers."

The ratification of this petition enhanced the powers of the barbers at the expense of the surgeons, against whom it was clearly directed, but the barbers' next difficulties came from within their own ranks. It was reported to the Mayor of London "that certain barbers of the City of London, inex-perienced in the art of surgery, very frequently take charge of sick and wounded persons with the intent of fraudulently acquiring their goods; whereby the sick were often worse off at their departure than at their incoming, and on account of the unskilfulness of these barbers were oftentimes maimed, to the scandal of the skilled, and the manifest harm of our Lord the King". The system of appointing two Masters, which had worked so well with the small body of surgeons, was applied to solve the problem that faced the barbers. Two Masters were selected to superintend all the barbers, to report any negligence or lack of skill, and to assist and advise the barbers in treating any difficult cases. The Master Barbers, unfortunately, were not as successful in controlling their brethren as were the Master Surgeons. Henry V was at war with France, and barbers no less than surgeons were pressed into the service of his army. The barbers who escaped the press-gang were few enough to be held in high esteem by their neighbours and clients. They soon developed an exalted idea of their own importance, and disdained to call into consultation the Master Barbers. This arrogance on the part of the ignorant was dealt with summarily. The Mayor and Aldermen, rather bitterly, ". . . seeing that many persons in these times dread the loss or payment of money more than the rule of honesty and of a safe conscience . . ." ordained and established "that no barber practising the surgical faculty within the liberty of the city should presume to take under his charge any sick person in actual danger of death or maim without shewing him to the overseeing masters". If a barber did take such a patient in his charge and did not report the fact to the Masters within three days, he was fined six shillings and eightpence.

The fourteenth century saw the mediæval period drawing to its close and the Renaissance being ushered in throughout all the Western world. In this century lived the first three Englishmen to contribute anything at all to the art of surgery. They were John of Arderne, John of Gaddesden, and John of Mirfield.

VIII.   Three Englishmen

THREE ENGLISHMEN, ALL BEARING THE NAME OF JOHN, AT VARY-
ing periods in the fourteenth century made their individual contributions to surgery.   The first of them, John of Gaddesden,
was more of a physician than a surgeon.   John of Arderne was
more of a surgeon than a physician.   John of Mirfield was
neither physician nor surgeon, but rather a priestly bibliophile.

John of Gaddesden was born in A.D. 1280.   Of his mother
nothing is known.   His father John described briefly as being
of a choleric temperament and fond of fruit and milk, either of
which qualities may or may not have been responsible for the
stone in the salivary duct which John had to remove late in his
father's life.   John was a student of Merton College, Oxford,
where there was something of a medical curriculum.   A Master
of Arts had to study there for some four years before being
admitted as a doctor of physic.   Most of this time was devoted
to reading and debating the works of Hippocrates and Galen
and others.   It was possible, and even usual, for the fully
qualified doctor to leave Oxford without ever having laid hands
on a patient.   Never cursed with false modesty, John of Gaddesden no sooner qualified than he descended upon London, a
city of not less than thirty thousand souls.   There he quickly
made up any defects there may have been in his practical education.   A doctor of physic he undoubtedly was, but he dabbled
in surgery, and according to one authority was quite prepared,
if paid for it, to act as dentist, chiropodist, and even delousing
attendant to his patients.   These activities must have been put
aside, however, when he was formally appointed physician to
His Majesty Edward the Second.   Prince Lionel, the King's
son, whom John of Gaddesden must also have had as a patient,
had among his retinue of personal attendants a young man
named Chaucer.   Chaucer may perhaps not have met John,
but at all events he knew of him, for in the *Prologue* to his
Canterbury Tales he wrote of his "doctor of physic" that "Wel
knew he the old Esculapius and"—among a long list of other
authorities, which included Dioscorides, Hippocrates, Haly
Abbas, Galen, Rhazes, and Avicenna—"Gatesden".

The work which made John of Gaddesden famous was the
Rosa Anglica.   As a rose has five sepals, so the *Rosa* had five
parts, dealing respectively with fevers, injuries, general hygiene,

diet, and materia medica and treatment by drugs. The analogy was carried further by John himself, who informed his readers that as a rose excelled all the other flowers so the *Rosa* excelled everything previously written on the subject of medicine. Actually, it was chiefly a repetition of less flowery but well-established works embellished with a few of his own cases. One of these was a princely case of smallpox. John had his patient wrapped in the mediæval equivalent of red flannel, had red carpets laid down, and red curtains hung about the room. The theory of this treatment is that the red cloth lowers the temperature of the patient with smallpox by drawing the excessively red blood outwards. In this particular case of Edward II's son it proved effective enough for John to record that "he was restored to health without a trace of the disease". The *Rosa* became very popular, and at different times editions were produced at Pavia, at Augsberg, at Venice, and in Ireland. Not a little of its success may have been due to the fact that an adequate sub-title for it would have been "How to Make Money in Medicine". John always prescribed twice as much of any drug for his rich patients as he did for the poor ones. He was also one of the first physicians to find a cosmetic gold-mine in the prescription of perfumes, hair-washes, dyes, and the like. Spikenard he used successfully in the treatment of dropsy, and laid it down quite definitely that this was a medicine to be paid for in advance. He was, too, courageous enough to label one section of his book "Disagreeable Diseases which the Doctor can Seldom Make Money By".

John subscribed to the belief that the Royal touch would cure the King's evil—tuberculosis of the skin and lymph glands—and if his own favourite applications, the droppings of a dove or the blood of a weasel, failed to cure this condition he always referred his patients to the reigning monarch. One of his innovations in the treatment of epilepsy was the addition of an extract of cuckoo—which bird he believed to have epilepsy once a month—to the mess of boar's bladder and mistletoe which was usually prescribed. John of Gaddesden must have been a likeable character. His *Rosa* is amusingly written and full of more or less apt verses and quotations, and quite apart from his versatile practice of physic, his surgery, and his dentistry, he was a grammarian and poet, and essentially a good business man. One other claim to fame he has in that he advised for the treatment of colic the constant wearing of a seal-skin girdle with a whalebone buckle. From this the well-known cholera belt is said to have been evolved.

John of Arderne was the first English surgeon worthy to be classed with the men who were recreating surgery in Europe. He was born in A.D. 1307, while Lanfrank, the most distinguished pupil of William de Salicet, had died only in A.D. 1306. Henri de Mondeville had gained notoriety by his refutal of the doctrine of healing by second intention, and Guy de Chauliac had yet to achieve his title of Prince of Surgeons. Like his distinguished European contemporaries, John of Arderne was trained in the wars. He seems to have served under two Dukes of Lancaster in succession, at Algeciras, at Antwerp, and later in Aquitaine. After a long apprenticeship to military surgery in the Hundred Years' War, he went to Newark, then a great centre of trade and an occasional meeting-place for the English Parliament. There he practised surgery from A.D. 1349 to 1370, devoting much of his attention to the surgical cure of fistulæ—openings through the skin made by accident or disease and forming abnormal communications with some internal organ. At the age of sixty-seven, when his practice was large and his reputation great, he came to London and joined the Guild of Military Surgeons. He knew well many of the noble and princely families of his time, and some of them he mentions by name as his patients. He is the only contemporary authority for the story of how the Prince of Wales obtained his ostrich-feather crest, which had formerly been part of the arms of the King of Bohemia. He seems to have been on terms of equality with the physicians of his day—an almost unheard-of thing for a surgeon of those times—and actually refers to himself as a surgeon among physicians, *chirurgus inter medicos*. He employed apothecaries to make up his prescriptions, and looked down upon barbers who practised surgery. John of Arderne was a little in advance of his English contemporaries in that he had more or less abandoned, for example, astrological methods, but he was skilled in leechcraft and still placed some reliance upon charms and spells. An instance of this is in his discussion of epilepsy. He recommends that the words Jasper, Melchior, and Balthazar be written on parchment with blood drawn from the patient's little finger. This parchment should be worn constantly by the patient, who was also instructed to say daily for a month three Pater Nosters and three Ave Marias for the souls of the fathers and mothers of these three Biblical Kings. Despite this and other charms, John of Arderne was a skilled and original surgeon. He was well-bred and was in many ways a follower of the teachings of Lanfrank, but always his own experience and judgment carried more weight with him than the rulings of any of the surgical authorities. He was a bold surgeon, and in his writings had two great merits. He describes in detail every step of the operations he practised, and in considering the results of his treatment he records his failures as carefully as he did his successes. The books he wrote, or rather the rolls of vellum that he illuminated (*see plate facing* p. 128), included works on the care of the eyes, on bleeding, on sinuses and fistulæ of the anus, on plants and their uses, and on clysters or enemata. In this last work on the use of rectal injections, he described and advocated the use of an instrument which he had designed himself for injecting medicinal solutions into the rectum.

His exact clinical observation and the way in which he advised against surgical meddling which would do the patient no good and might do great harm are well shown by his story of "a priest of Colstone" to whom "there fell a sore in the right pap within the skin". This was a case of cancer of the breast in the male, a condition rarely met with at any time. Gradually, over a period of two years, the cancer extended and the skin over it became livid. The priest had tried various medicines without avail, so at last he consulted a barber, to whom he had gone to be bled. The barber said he could promise a cure for the condition, but, before submitting himself to any treatment the barber might have undertaken, the priest consulted John of Arderne. He asked "if that he were curable or if that he might suffer any cutting or corrosive or any such other medicines?" John's advice, with a plurality of negatives, was "that he should in no mannerwise put no corrosive nor none other violent medicines, nor let no cuttings come therenigh. . . ." If the priest did permit any of these suggested treatments, John warned him quite clearly, and correctly, "that it would bring him to the death without any recovery".

John of Arderne's most important contribution to surgery was the operation he devised for the cure of anal fistula, a condition that most of his predecessors regarded as incurable. The first man he treated for fistula-in-ano was Sir Adam Everyngham, who had been in the service of the Earl of Derby, at that time warring in Lancaster. The operation, like most good operations, was well thought out, yet quite simple. John placed his patient in the lithotomy position—that is, with the knees drawn up and the operative area well exposed. A probe threaded with a fourfold ligature was pushed through the sinus, or fistula, into the rectum. One end of each ligature was brought down through the anus, and tied to the other end, which emerged from the fistula. A slim metal shield was then inserted into the rectum, and a similar grooved instrument into the fistula. Along this groove a scalpel was passed till its point just emerged against the rectal shield. With one swift movement all three instruments were withdrawn, so that the scalpel cut cleanly through the flesh between the tightly tied ligatures. The bleeding was stopped by pressure with sponges wrung out in warm water. The wound was powdered, and covered with clean, dry pads held in position by a T-bandage. No irritating salves were applied at all, and daily clysters or enemata of oil were given. The widely opened wound healed from its deepest part upwards and the fistula disappeared. The instruments he used for this operation John of Arderne described in detail. What we call a probe John referred to as *sequere me,* or "follow me", since by following it the surgeon would find "the way of the fistule Whider it goeth". Then there was the "*Acus Rostrata,* a snowted nedle". This was a long silver needle, "snouted" so that its eye would be large enough to contain the fourfold ligature. The *tendicula,* the *siringa,* and a scalpel, completed the armoury.

In this, as in other operations, John of Arderne relied upon non-irritating powders and clean dressings for rapid healing, a practice which reflects his training in France, where he must have met surgeons acquainted with the work and the methods of Henri de Mondeville. John was also in advance of at least his English contemporaries in his treatment of cases of stone impacted in the urethra. In one such case in which a stone "as big as a bean" had been formed in the bladder but passed onwards to become impacted in the urinary channel, he was able to record complete cure in a fortnight. He tied ligatures above and below the stone to prevent it slipping, made a small incision over the stone, and squeezed it out. He then sutured the wound and applied a favourite dressing of his—white of egg and finely ground flour. This simple dressing was left severely alone for three days, at the end of which time the stitches were removed. Most surgeons of that day and age believed that any wound through which urine escaped rarely healed. John deals with this question briefly: "There is no need for alarm in these cases, even though the urine escapes from the wound for three or four days after such an operation, for the patient will certainly be cured." His patients were cured, but those who fell into the hands of less well-trained surgeons may not have been so fortunate. The operation may have been performed well, but the wounds were slow to heal because they were irritated by complicated salves applied frequently, instead of being soothed, as by the simple dressings John used, and left untouched for the first forty-eight hours or so. Guy de Chauliac, the Prince of Surgeons, and many other authorities had given their blessing to these pus-promoting ointments, and so the delay in, or failure of, healing was attributed not to them—which would have been near blasphemy—but to the inevitable leakage of urine. That John of Arderne's patients should also have had urine escaping from urethral incisions for three or four days and yet have recovered was probably regarded as just another of the vagaries of human flesh. Incidentally, John's fee for his operation for anal fistula was "an hundred marke or fourty pounde, with robez and feez of an hundred shillyns, terme of life, by zere" from the rich, and from the poor never less than "an hundred shillyns". Even the very rich must have felt that a fee of about £70, at a time when the purchasing power of money was about eight times what it is now, was rather high, but according to John they paid him cheerfully.

John of Arderne was a shrewd diagnostician as well as a capable surgeon. Time after time he warns his readers of the dangers of mistaking for simple ulceration what is really a cancer of the rectum. He called this condition a bubo, and wrote that it "is called bubo from an owl, because that bird lurks in darkness". It was to be diagnosed by inserting a finger into the patient's rectum and exploring carefully. The cancer was painless at first, and of a "stony hardness", tending to hinder the passage of fæces. After a time it would ulcerate and cause pain, and soon the patient would be driven to stool two or three times an hour, and his motions would be "ill-smelling and streaked with watery blood". He warned against confusing this with dysentery, and enumerated the signs and symptoms by which the two conditions might be distinguished.

When a cancer of the rectum was once diagnosed, the surgeon was to give only simple enemata of bran water, and above all things ". . . do not be led away and offer to operate. It will only be a disgrace to you. Warn the friends of the certain ending. . . . I have never seen nor heard of any man who recovered from cancer, but I have known many who died of it."

John of Arderne was in distinguished company when he wrote "Of ye manere of ye Leche" in one of his works. Since the days of Hippocrates surgeons—and physicians—had been writing on this theme, but John amplified their exhortations. He advised his fellows to cultivate modesty, charity, and a studious and chaste mode of life, just as his predecessors had done, but he gave much more detailed instructions to this effect than did the earlier writers. Charity was to be displayed by visiting "poure men", the benefit to the leech being "that thai by their prayers may gete him grace of the holy goste". In visiting the "poure men", however, the leech was not to let his high-mindedness obscure the realities, if we may judge from a general medical treatise of John's. In this he recommended for the treatment of constipation a brew which was really the equivalent of beef-tea, "if he be rich". Then he goes on and adds, "but if he is a pauper he may just drink his own urine". Chastity was enjoined most sternly. The leech was advised to abstain from all harlotry, and he was to be particularly careful in his conduct towards the wives, daughters, and other women in the households of his patients. "Consider not over openly the lady or the daughters or other fair women in great men's houses, nor proffer to kiss them, nor touch their breasts privately or openly . . ." and more to the same effect. Like everyone else, John advised that the estimated time of cure for any condition should always be increased for the benefit of the patient and his friends, even going so far as to advise doubling it. Then if the patient should marvel at being healed much more quickly than he had thought possible, the leech was to tell him that it was all due to the fact that he "was strong hearted, suffered well, was of good complexion" and so forth, for such words make the patient "proude and delited". Sir D'Arcy Power describes John of Arderne as "a scholar and a gentleman, a man of good education, wide experience, and sound judgement". John of Arderne was all these things, and he was, too, the first English surgeon worthy of the name.

John of Mirfield, the third member of this fourteenth-century trio of Englishmen, was a priestly scholastic keenly interested in medicine and to a less extent in surgery. The date of his birth is not known, nor is it certain whether he ever received any regular medical education, either at the University of Oxford with which his name has been associated, probably mistakenly, or through some form of apprenticeship. He was closely connected with the priory and Hospital of St. Bartholomew, which Rahere had founded. He was perhaps a chaplain to the hospital and something of an amateur physician. He seems to have been a kindly man and of great integrity, and he wrote two treatises which he thought would benefit his fellows. The *Breviarium Bartholomei* is a purely medical work, probably composed between A.D. 1380 and 1395. The *Florarium Bartholomei* is a theological work with one medical section. The *Breviarium* contains nothing that is original. It is based on the manuscripts of classical and mediæval authorities, quoted at length and often verbatim. Thus there are sections which might have been written by Galen, others quoted direct from Bernard de Gordon, others which might have been composed by Guy de Chauliac. Mingled with all this are many charms, reminiscent of those in the *Leech-book of Bald,* and much magic.

John of Mirfield added to these quotations little or nothing that was original. He simply tried to present what he had thought good and worthy of quotation from the works of many well-known medical and surgical authorities. His *Breviarium* is probably a faithful picture of general medical and surgical treatment of that period, a picture which men like John of Arderne were beginning to re-touch. It was in treatment to the exclusion of all else that John of Mirfield was interested, and this accounts for some apparent deficiencies in his books. There is no anatomy, for example, and, what is more surprising, little or none of the discursive theoretical quibbling beloved of mediæval writers. John of Mirfield contented himself with giving a sufficient list of symptoms for some sort of a diagnosis to be made, and then listed beneath this diagnosis remedies of all kinds, good, bad, or incredible. It is only very occasionally that he comments on the recipes he gives. For example, he gives the wording of a charm to be written out on parchment and worn by a pregnant woman to assist in her delivery. His comments on this are to the effect that some men believe in such things, but he himself has little faith in them. This disbelief,

together with his temerity in describing contraceptive recipes—
even though in cypher—may have been responsible for his
rejection by his ecclesiastical superiors when he first applied for
ordination. The *Breviarium* he divided into fifteen parts, each
of which is further divided into "distinctions", and then into
chapters. The first two parts are concerned with fevers and
general diseases. The third, fourth, fifth, sixth, and seventh
parts are arranged regionally, starting with conditions affecting
the head and working down to the toes. The eighth part deals
with abscesses, the ninth with wounds, the tenth with fractures,
and the eleventh with dislocations. The twelfth, thirteenth,
and fourteenth parts deal with simple and compound medicines
and purgatives. The fifteenth and last part is devoted to advice
on bleeding and general hygiene.

In the nineteenth chapter of the sixth distinction of the first
part of the *Breviarium*—thus extensively are these fifteen parts
subdivided—John of Mirfield discusses the "Signs of Evil
Portent appearing in Feverish and Other Types of Patient".
This section is typical of the whole compilation, a bewildering
welter of classical, Arabian, scholastic, and magical ideas. There
are direct quotations from Hippocrates and Galen, from Rhazes
and Avicenna, and much that must have been taken unques-
tioningly from the Saxon leech-books. Typical of these latter
are some clinical tests of prognostic significance. If the right
eye of a sick man sheds tears, he will die; in the case of a woman,
this applies to the left eye. The sole of a patient's right foot
should be anointed with lard, which lard is then thrown to any
given dog; if the dog eats it without vomiting, the patient
will live, but if the dog returns it or makes no attempt to eat
it, the patient will die. Mixed up with these mystic and messy
investigations is much sound medicine, and even more common
sense. For example, if there is any doubt as to whether a person
is or is not dead ". . . apply lightly roasted onion to his nostrils.
If he be alive, he will immediately scratch his nose". Thrown
in presumably as a makeweight in part thirteen—on compound
medicines—John of Mirfield gives a prescription for the making
of "Powder for that devilish instrument of war colloquially
termed gunne", which seems to imply a regretful acceptance of
the unhappy fact that science is ever a handmaid of war.

In the theological *Florarium Bartholomei*, the eighty-eighth
chapter is devoted to physicians and their medicines. Much
of it follows the general lines laid down by John of Arderne

and by older authorities, but John of Mirfield takes the opportunity of expressing some criticisms, which seem to show that all was no more well with medicine and surgery then than it is to-day. He indicts first the quacks, and also ". . . what is worse, and is considered by me more horrible—worthless and presumptuous women, usurp this profession to themselves and abuse it". Writing on the attitude to be adopted towards the women of a patient's household, John of Mirfield, the cleric, is not unnaturally less blunt than John of Arderne, the surgeon. He simply suggests that it is not consistent with professional dignity to "speak shamefully to them, or turn bold glances upon them". The whole of this chapter is enlivened by rhyming couplets and quotations, many of them taken from the *Regimen Sanitatis Salerni*. One example which betrays the immutability of human nature is:

> When Physick's dearly bought, it doth much healing bring,
> But when 'tis freely given, 'tis ne'er a useful thing.

There is a clerical ring about much of the advice given. Thus, John explains that a physician or surgeon "incurs an irregularity" if by his negligence the sick man dies or suffers the mutilation of a limb. The surgeon is advised to leave his patient severely alone if he is in any doubt about the upshot of the operation. "For it is safer to leave a man in the hands of his Creator, than to put trust in surgery or medicine concerning which there is any manner of doubt." The surgeon may be forgiven even the death of a patient, however, "if death should supervene owing, perchance, to the fact that the patient has not the normal arrangement of limbs or of veins". Physicians receive even shorter shrift than surgeons in some sections of this chapter, for according to John of Mirfield "modern physicians" possess three special qualifications, and these are: "to be able to lie in a subtle manner, to show an outward honesty, and to kill with audacity". Perhaps even more crushing is: ". . . the physician if he should happen to be a Good Christian, which rarely chances. . . ."

There is one assertion of John of Mirfield's which John of Gaddesden and John of Arderne would both have supported wholeheartedly, and which their successors might well have heeded:

> Long ago, unless I mistake, physicians used to practise surgery, but nowadays there is a great distinction between surgery and medicine,

and this, I fear, arises from pride, because physicians disdain to work with their hands, though, indeed, I myself have a suspicion that it is because they do not know how to perform particular operations; and this unfortunate usage has led the public to believe that a man cannot know both subjects, but the well informed are aware that he cannot be a good physician who neglects every part of surgery, and, on the other hand, a surgeon is good for nothing who is without knowledge of medicine.

These three men, of Gaddesden, of Arderne, and of Mirfield, different though they were in their outlook on life and in their practice, had one quality in common. Each in his own way helped to make the fourteenth century a starting-point from which surgery in England was to arise and flourish. The start was a late one, but from that century onwards England was to advance the art and science of surgery as much as, if not more than, the many older empires had done.

IX. Barbers and Chirurgeons

DESPITE THE PLEAS OF JOHN OF MIRFIELD AND MANY OTHERS more eminent than he, surgery was becoming more and more widely separated from medicine, and the belief that it was an inferior art was held almost everywhere. Great universities had been coming into existence in every European country from the twelfth century onwards. By the beginning of the fifteenth century most of them had well-established faculties of medicine, but from none of the reputable faculties could a special degree in surgery be obtained. Licences to practise surgery were granted very occasionally by the universities, and quite commonly with the grudging proviso "so long as he does not practise medicine". Debarred from university education and with their art regarded generally as more of a trade than a profession, surgeons in London, in Paris, and in a few other great centres banded together to protect themselves and their profession, and evolved an educational system of their own.

The College of Saint Côme in Paris came into being as a loosely constituted guild early in the thirteenth century, taking its name from St. Cosmus, one of the two patron saints of medicine. Lanfrank, the virtual father of French surgery, joined the College in A.D. 1295, and by his lectures and his bedside teaching attracted as much notice to the College as to himself. The early objects of this French confraternity of surgeons were simple. They wanted to promote good fellowship and to help distressed brethren, even arranging for their decent burial if they died in poor circumstances. Lanfrank died in A.D. 1315, but his work went on, and the College was organized under the leadership of a duly appointed provost. A young would-be surgeon was first of all an apprentice attached to a Master of the College. In due course he became a Bachelor, at which stage the payment of a fee of one franc admitted him to membership of the College. After a period of study the Bachelor paid a fee of twelve gold crowns, took the Hippocratic oath, and became a Licentiate. He could then practise surgery anywhere in Paris or its environs. Four years later, if deemed competent, the Licentiate might become a Master and himself take apprentices. Members of the College were permitted to wear a long gown, by reason of which they became known as "gentlemen of the long robe", while the barbers practising surgery were "gentlemen of the short robe". Very occasionally the former gentlemen lectured to the latter, in which case they addressed their audience first in Latin, and then condescendingly translated their discourse into colloquial French. No fewer than three royal decrees laid it down at different times up to A.D. 1364 that the barbers should not be allowed to practise surgery without first being examined by the gentlemen of the long robe. The last of these three decrees was not in force for very long, for in A.D. 1372 Charles V decreed that the barbers should be allowed to treat wounds and not be interfered with by their long-robed superiors.

In London the small and exclusive Guild of Surgeons who had seen service in the Hundred Years' War developed in much the same way as did the formerly very humble College of St. Côme. It came into existence some time about the middle of the four-teenth century, and had no settled constitution, but seems to have co-opted members from time to time. John of Arderne was one of the most famous members of this Guild, which he joined when he moved from Newark to London. Another distinguished member was Thomas Morstede, who was surgeon-in-chief to the army which Henry V led to France in the Spring of A.D. 1415. The army, which was to win the Battle of Agin-court on October 25 of that year, consisted of six thousand men-at-arms and twenty-four thousand foot, mostly archers. Morstede was paid twelvepence a day in addition to the usual allowance of one hundred marks a quarter for supervising the surgical care of the whole army. This scale of payment was fairly liberal and its equivalent to-day would be a retainer of about £250 a year, and remuneration while on active service at about thirty-six shillings a day. His second-in-command was William Bradwardyne, and he had twelve assistant surgeons—all paid sixpence a day—and a bodyguard of three archers, paid at the same rate as the junior surgeons. He was also allowed the use of one chariot and two waggons. Morstede was per-mitted to impress into his service any assistants he wanted who would not come willingly, and as a pledge for the punctual payment of himself and his staff he took certain jewels belonging to the King—a necessary precaution at a time when Kings' purses were as short as their memories.

The Treaty of Troyes which Henry V concluded in A.D. 1420 seemed to have ended the French wars, and the King and his counsellors had rather more time than usual to devote to domestic

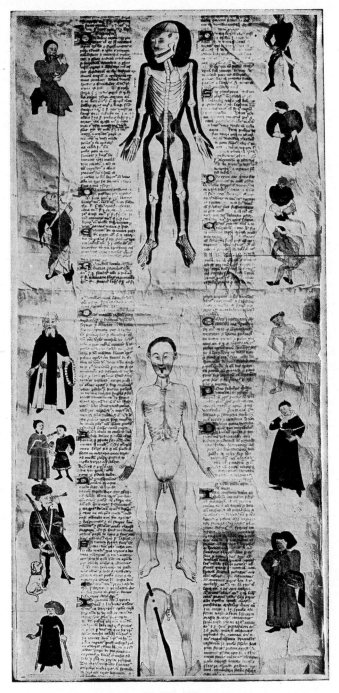

PLATE VII

From the manuscript of *De Arte Phisicali et de Cirurgia*
by John of Arderne (A.D. *1412*).

PLATE VIII

Henry VIII granting an Act of Union to the Barbers and Chirurgeons. This is a copy of Holbein's original painting, and is believed to be the one that James I ordered to be made in 1618.

legislation. So it was that the first Act regulating the practice of surgery in England was passed in A.D. 1421. For some time before this the physicians had been clamouring for the recognition of their social position, and for legislation directed against the hosts of quacks and impostors who overran the country. They presented a petition asking that no one should be allowed to practise physic unless they had graduated from the recognized "scoles of Fisyk withynne som Universitie". No woman was to practise, and the fine suggested for any breach of these conditions was £40. As a result of this effort on the part of the physicians, Parliament enacted that the King's Council should have the authority to legislate by ordinance against unqualified practitioners of either medicine or surgery, so the surgeons benefited as much as the physicians who had initiated the demand for legislation. The enactment was duly recorded, but it seems that little or nothing was done to enforce it. The physicians took matters into their own hands and formed a society which in A.D. 1423 entered into an alliance with the fellowship of surgeons, with the idea of establishing a college of medicine and surgery and so restoring the old unity. The death of Henry V plunged the country into political difficulties at this time, and the physicians and surgeons, knowing that Parliament would have little time for their scheme, made the astute move of approaching for support the Lord Mayor and Aldermen of the City of London. An exact and detailed constitution for the joint college was drawn up, and was approved by the Mayor and Aldermen on May 15, A.D. 1423. The college had a Rector with two Supervisors of Physic and two Supervisors of Surgery, one of whom was Thomas Morstede.

Unfortunately it must have been found in practice that old enmities and jealousies between physicians and surgeons did not make for easy administration. There was no violent rupture of relations, the physicians and surgeons must simply have drifted apart again. The college ceased to exist after two or three years, but it did show that physicians and surgeons could co-operate—if only for a short time—and, by exercising the powers it had been granted for dealing with "ignorant and unauthorized practitioners", it so upset the barbers who practised surgery that within eighteen months of the joint college being established they sought a fresh confirmation of the power to practise surgery unmolested which had first been granted them in A.D. 1415.

After the gradual dissolution of the joint college the physicians took no further action to re-establish the society they had formed. The surgeons, on the other hand, went on organizing their craft till in A.D. 1435 the Guild of Surgeons revised its rules. It had then seventeen members, including Morstede and Bradwardyne, not a large number, but large enough by the standards and conditions of life at that time. The craft was to meet each year on September 27, or more precisely the day of St. Cosmus and St. Damien. Damien and Cosmus were two brothers who practised in Silicia and were martyred in the early part of the fourth century. They were said to have been the first practitioners to refuse fees, and this may have been the reason for their selection as patron saints of the Guild, and for the naming of the College of St. Côme in Paris—by a process of inverse association.

At this meeting on the Saints' day four Masters were to be elected to rule and govern the craft, and to hold their treasure and common goods. Every surgeon of the fellowship was to pay twopence a quarter to a common fund held by the Masters. There were also quarterly and other meetings, and a system of fines for members who did not attend them and had no reasonable excuse for failing to do so. Members of the craft could accept apprentices who had to be examined by the Masters, within the first month of taking up their duties, before they could finally sign a three-year agreement with their employer. Any member of the craft attending a case "likely to result in death or maiming or which to him may be unknown" had to consult with a Master, or be fined thirteen shillings and fourpence. If on consultation the Master did not attend the case, he was fined six shillings and eightpence. On the other hand, if "profit or advantage of gift" accrued to any one of the Masters as a result of such consultation, he had to share the spoils with his three Master colleagues. Altogether the new constitution of A.D. 1435 was a most comprehensive document, providing even for an annual dinner to be held on St. Luke's day, and detailing a series of fines in arithmetical progression for those rowdies who did not hold their peace at any meeting of the craft when ordered to do so by the Masters. For the first offence a reprimand was sufficient, for the second a fine of twelvepence was to be paid, for the third two shillings, for the fourth a noble, which was about six shillings and eightpence, and if at the fifth time of asking the recalcitrant member still refused to keep the peace, he was "to be taken for a rebel"! Thomas Morstede, who probably had much to do with the passing of this revised constitution, had been in turn surgeon to three successive Kings of England. He died in A.D. 1450, just two years before the barbers, with whom the surgeons seemed to have called some sort of truce, obtained a grant of arms.

The barbers had been growing into an increasingly important civic body. A grant of arms in A.D. 1452 merely crowned their achievement of A.D. 1450, when the Mayor and Aldermen of London sanctioned a code of laws they had drawn up for the protection and government of their craft. In it they again insisted on their right to practise surgery. Then in A.D. 1462 Edward IV granted them a charter of incorporation, which marked by its omissions another step forward. In theory the charter was granted to the barbers as a class, but actually the charter refers specifically to ". . . free men of the Mystery of Barbers of our City of London exercising the Mystery or Art of Surgery . . .", and goes on to describe their diligent and laborious occupation in tending to wounds, bruises, hurts, and other ailments, and in bleeding and drawing teeth. This charter staked out a wide field in minor surgery for the barbers, and mentioned not at all the less dignified but none the less necessary activities which for so long had been their province. Shaving, bathing, trimming beards, cutting hair, and delousing are forgotten, and not even a footnote is devoted to the brothel-keeping branches of the older barbers' businesses. Furthermore, the barbers were to be exempted from serving on juries.

The surgeons proper had previously secured the same privilege, and they, too, in the latter half of the fifteenth century began to consolidate their position. To do so involved a long struggle with the authorities, but in A.D. 1491 they were at last exempted from "keeping watch and bearing arms"—two duties which bore heavily and expensively upon such a relatively small company. In the following year arms were granted to the Guild of Surgeons. Unfortunately, despite the grant of arms their hard-won exemptions from keeping watch were so far forgotten that in A.D. 1513 they had to appeal to Parliament for the privilege already granted them once. From the point of view of numbers and in the superiority of their position and power, thanks to Edward IV's charter, the barbers had the advantage of the surgeons. But on the other hand the surgeons had a better social standing and much higher professional attainments. As a result each body was able complacently to point to certain advantages it had over the other, and they lived in comparative amity from that point onwards. So much improved were the relations of the two bodies that in A.D. 1493 they entered into an agreement whereby all the chartered privileges of the barbers were conceded also to the surgeons, with the sole exception of admission to the freedom of the Barbers' Company.

In A.D. 1511, the third year of the reign of Henry VIII, an Act was passed which forbade any person in the City of London or within a radius of seven miles to practise as either a physician or surgeon unless he had first been licensed to do so by the Bishop of London or the Dean of St. Paul's. These ecclesiastical dignitaries were assisted by expert physicians and surgeons, and in other parts of the country similar licences were granted by the bishop of the diocese or by his vicar-general. The passing of this Act, which would undoubtedly have improved the standards of practice of both medicine and surgery, raised a storm of protest. The herbalists in particular saw their livelihood being taken away from them, and to defend themselves they attacked the surgeons. In a petition they got up they described at length how good herbalists were saving, free, gratis, and for nothing, the lives of poor people whom the surgeons neglected because they could not pay their fees. So powerful was the agitation that Parliament hastily enacted that it was lawful for any of the King's subjects to practise as herbalists. This amounted to a virtual repealing of the previous Act and did the herbalists a great deal of good and the surgeons not a little harm. The licensing system which would have increased their prestige being thus set aside, the surgeons fell very low in the popular esteem, and in A.D. 1530 they were subjected to the indignity of having directed at them an Act which was entitled "An Acte concrnying Bakers, Bruers, Surgeons, and Scryveners". The Act stressed even further the distinction between physicians and surgeons, especially so because in A.D. 1518 the physicians had formally created the powerful College, which in 1851 was to become the Royal College of Physicians. This disrepute into which surgery had fallen had one good effect. It caused the surgeons to lean upon and associate themselves more and more closely with the Barbers' Company, which, unlike the Surgeons' Guild, had gone on from strength to strength. This union in practice was recognized statutorily by the passing of a formal Act of Parliament on July 12, 1540, incorporating the two companies.

The Act of Incorporation consolidated the position of the increasing numbers of barbers devoting themselves to surgery, and gave the Guild of Surgeons the advantage of sharing in all the privileges of the barbers, privileges which had previously been the surgeons' only in part and on sufferance. The United Company was to have four Masters, two expert in surgery and two in barbery, to control the two professions which were still to remain distinct though within the same Company. A further privilege granted to the Company was the right to take each year the bodies of four executed felons for the purposes of dissection. The first surgical Master of the Company was Thomas Vicary, "Sergeant-Chyrurgeon to King Henry VIII".

Holbein, in what is perhaps the best of his English works, commemorated this incorporation of the two companies. In his picture Henry VIII is depicted, sumptuously apparelled and with the sword of state in his right hand, presenting the statute of A.D. 1540 to Thomas Vicary, who is kneeling. On the King's right are two of the Royal Physicians, Dr. John Chambre and Dr. William Butts, with the Royal Apothecary, Thomas Alsop. Chambre stood high in the King's favour, and was one of the physicians in attendance on Queen Jane at the birth of Edward VI. He also attended Anne Boleyn on a similar occasion. Butts also was a close personal friend of the King's, so much so that on one occasion he was able to intervene success-fully on behalf of Archbishop Cranmer, whom the Roman Catholic party in the Council wanted to commit to the Tower. On the King's left are fifteen liege subjects, all on their knees. Behind Thomas Vicary, the Sergeant-Surgeon to His Majesty, is Sir John Ayleff, Surgeon to the King, who was granted a large estate in Wiltshire, token of the King's undoubted gratitude for having been cured of a fistula. Next come two of the King's Barbers, another of the King's Surgeons, a third King's Barber, and several others whose names and offices are unknown. In-cidentally, the chief of the King's Barbers was bidden to attend the palace every Saturday night, Saturday night being the Royal bath night, but a phrase in the standing orders—"if it please the King to cleanse his head, legs, or feet"—suggests that the Royal prerogative could be exercised to prevent any danger of habitual bathing. The likeness of King Henry VIII in this picture is said to be the most perfect in existence. King James I desired to have a copy made of this work (*see plate facing* p. 145). He asked the Company to loan the picture to him. The Company, acting apparently on the precedent set by Thomas Morstede in dealing with crowned heads, did lend him the picture, but only after they had received from their monarch a pledge approaching the value of the painting. Samuel Pepys wanted to buy the picture at one time, and recorded in his diary "I did think to give £200 for it, it being said to be worth £1,000".

The men who had achieved the formation of the Barber-Surgeons' Company did not imagine that a statutory union of the two companies would immediately give reality to the ideals for which they had striven. They wanted to raise the status of the profession, and so they proceeded to organize a course of systematic teaching for all who practised surgery. Young and well-educated physicians were engaged to teach the anatomy of the normal and of the diseased body. Surgery was taught systematically by Thomas Vicary and William Clowes and others. Regulations were drawn up with regard to the supervision and examination of the apprentices. At the same time an effort was made to diminish the number of quacks. This failed signally except in the few districts where surgeons were also justices of the peace. One such surgeon was John Halle of Maidstone, who made that district quite uninhabitable so far as quacks were concerned. Anyone professing to practise medicine or surgery was examined by him, and Halle himself records how an old man who said he was a physician was brought up before him.

"What authors have you read?" asked the surgeon.

"Eliot and others," said the old man brightly.

"What others?"

He had forgotten what others, so he was asked to recite the names of Eliot's books. These he had not forgotten, but he could not remember them. John Halle gave him a book and asked him to read it. Indignantly, the old man refused to do so. His memory might be failing, but that was no reason for suggesting that he could not read. Unfortunately, Halle insisted on this reading test, and at length the examinee broke down and explained that he could not read, that he was a poor old man, and that he had not intended to stay for long in Maidstone, anyway. He was instructed to leave the district tthe next day, and otherwise left unpunished apart from "being warned with exhortations to leave such false and naughty deceits".

Another ideal of this small body of far-seeing surgeons had been to ally surgery with medicine. The ill-fated joint college which they created was as far as they got in this direction. The efforts of such men as John Halle freed a few isolated districts from their many quacks, but these gentlemen simply moved out of the jurisdiction of one court into that of a less surgically inclined magistrate. Vicary and his friends were more successful in raising the standards of education of surgeons and their apprentices. Their regulations laid it down that the apprentices should be able to read and write and should know a little Latin before they were admitted. Then before an apprentice became a member of the Company and was given a licence to practise surgery he had to pass a very thorough examination in all the subjects on which lectures had been given. These public lectures had to be attended by every member of the Company from the Master downwards, and non-attendance except in case of illness involved the payment of a fine. Thomas Vicary, who apart from being surgeon to the King and the first Master of the new Company was also "overseer of all the offices" of the newly restored hospital of St. Bartholomew, was particularly interested in the teaching of anatomy. He wrote for the benefit of the apprentice-students *A Profitable Treatise of the Anatomie of Man's Body*. This was an elementary text-book, in the preface to which the author outlined the qualities with which he thought "A Surgion should be indued". These were that he should be learned, expert, ingenious, and well-mannered. The anatomy itself in this book of Vicary's is arranged regionally, starting at "The Bone of the Pot of the Head" and working downwards. The book is not a good anatomy, but is no worse than many that preceded and succeeded it. It might have been better than it is, however, for it is based upon the old treatises of Galen and his fellows, when it might have followed the teachings of Vesalius.

Vesalius was born in A.D. 1514, just five years before the death of Leonardo da Vinci, the greatest artist and scientist of the Italian Renaissance, who had had the courage to draw anatomical dissections and preparations as he saw them and not as Galen's copyists imagined them. This was simply part of the insistent artistic demand of the time for realism. Many Italian artists assisted at the private dissections of surgeon friends of theirs, or even, in some cases, took up grave-robbing and body-snatching on their own account, simply because they believed that a knowledge of anatomy was even more important than that study of the nude figure, in action and repose, which Greek sculptors and artists had made so peculiarly their own. Leonardo da Vinci made over seven hundred drawings of anatomical preparations, and this it was that prompted Ruskin's sneer that he polluted his work with "the science of the sepulchre". Andreas Vesalius was the natural successor of Leonardo da Vinci. From the death of Galen to the birth of Harvey, Vesalius was the most outstanding figure in European medicine and surgery. After five years' experience as a public dissector, teaching anatomy to students at Padua, he wrote at the age of twenty-eight *De Fabrica Humani Corporis*. This folio of over seven hundred pages, profusely and accurately illustrated, threw overboard the tradition of reliance on authority and substituted for it a science of exactly observing and recording. The bone of Luz and Adam's missing rib joined all the over-neat and tidy descriptions of blood-vessels as they might be, in being displaced by an account of anatomical relations as they were. A pet theory of Galen's was that the blood in the right side of the head and chest passed through hypothetical pores in the strong muscular septum which divides the heart into chambers to reach the left side of the heart. Vesalius commented on this theory: "We are driven to wonder at the handiwork of the Almighty, by means of which the blood sweats from the right into the left ventricle through passages which escape the human vision."

Vesalius founded modern anatomy. He said in as many words that whatever the older authors had written about the skeletons and internal organs of pigs or monkeys or horses, while true enough so far as horses or monkeys or pigs were concerned, was not necessarily true of the human organism. This rudely shattered the traditional calm in which his surgical and anatomical colleagues had been quietly stagnating. Their first thought was that the man who challenged the thousand-year-old teaching of Galen must be mad. That the challenge might be directed at Galen's misinterpreters rather than at Galen himself never occurred to them. On second thoughts, when it was learnt that he had actually dissected human bodies, his morality was as much in doubt as his sanity. Later still, when Vesalius, despite open derision on the part of his colleagues and continuous religious persecution, did not retreat from his heretic immoralities, it was generally agreed that mankind must have deteriorated sadly. Galen who could not be doubted—even in a translation of a translation of a translation—had described an easily memorized and extremely symmetrical system of anatomy. Vesalius, who had bony proof of it, described a much less tidy framework with many more bits and pieces than Galen had recognized. This progressive breaking up of Eve's one-piece skeleton was almost certainly attributed to the rush and bustle of an over-organized civilization. There remained the moral problem, and this was referred to the University of Salamanca. The University, with shrewd foresight, decided that dissection of the human body was both lawful and moral, and slowly the truth of Vesalius's observations was established. Thomas Vicary, however, either did not know of, or still refused to recognize, the work of Vesalius, but even so his *Profitable Treatise* won a reputation for him and saw many editions.

Vicary believed that a surgeon should know the principles of medicine as well as those of surgery, and also that he should know "the Anatomie"—presumably according to Vicary rather than Vesalius—and be reasonably well versed in Philosophy, Grammar, Logic, and Rhetoric. This standard of education was not to be achieved within the lifetime of Vicary—and in fact it is doubtful whether it has been achieved to this day. At the same time Vicary and his colleagues achieved a great deal, particularly when it is remembered that every advance had to be made through the cumbrous machinery of a Livery Company. As a Livery Company the Barber-Surgeons were bound on certain feast-days and other occasions to attire themselves in full livery. A gown made of "four-yards of broad cloth, striped athwart" was the first uniform worn, but this was modified later. The result of this and other changes was that the minutes of the meetings of the Barber-Surgeons show evidence of having been compiled around what must have been most varied agendas. A discussion of the way in which the bodies of four felons were to be collected may easily have been followed by prolonged debate on the thorny question of whether the new livery of doublets made from three yards of satin was quite as consonant with the dignity of the profession as had been the broad-cloth gown. The same meeting may have elected a Master, by ballot, and proceeded to admit the first dentist to the ranks of the company—namely, "John Brysket, toothe drawer".

In the session A.D. 1555 to 1556 new ordinances were drawn up, one of which forbade the members of the Company to "shave, wasshe a Beard, or tryme any man with any Instrument, or to make cleane teethe, upon the Sondays". At the same time thirteen examiners were appointed, a number which may have been unlucky for some of the apprentices, and it was decided that a book should be kept in which were to be recorded the names of all those licensed to practise surgery. Other rulings detailed more exactly the methods of examination, and laid it down that no apprentice should wear a beard, a beard being exactly defined as anything more than "a fifteen days' growth".

Thomas Vicary did much for the Barber-Surgeons, and on August 26, 1557, the Company placed itself more literally in his debt when it asked him to "paye and dyscharge the debts of the house . . . and shall have the plate of the crafte in pawne or pledge, untyll such tyme as the sayde sumes of money be unto hym payde agayne". Vicary died in 1562, but there lived after him many surgeons who had been contemporary with him and had assisted him in all his works. Notable among them were Thomas Gale and William Clowes, who were surgeons in London, and John Woodall, Surgeon-General to the East India Company.

X.   A Surgeon of France

WHILE IN ENGLAND THE BARBER-SURGEONS' COMPANY WAS IN process of creation and corporate surgery was coming into existence, and in Italy Vesalius was founding a true anatomy, France was advancing pure surgery.   Right up to the middle of the fifteenth century the operation of lithotomy—the removal of a stone from the urinary bladder—had been almost a monopoly of itinerant specialists.   The technique of operation was exactly the same all over the world, and had been so for nearly a thousand years.   The patient was placed flat on his back with his buttocks at the edge of a table and a strong man held his knees high up.   The operator placed one finger in the rectum, or the vagina in the case of female patients, and hooked down the stone which could be felt in the bladder, so that the taut skin between the buttocks was lifted up by it.   A quick incision was made over the protuberant stone, it was hooked out, and the operation was over.   The operator received his fee and went on to the next village.   If the wound healed, all was well; if not, then the patient might die—which was unfortunate—or live a leaky and miserable life, in which case that particular operator would not come near the village again for some years.   Most expert of all lithotomists were certain wandering Italians, and it was their method which Germain Colot, a Frenchman, studied.   He won their confidence, and was allowed to be present, and even to assist, at certain operations.   He then betook himself to a dissecting-room, performed the operation on cadavers, and studied carefully the structures through which his knife passed.

The results of these investigations he communicated to the medical faculty of Paris and to the physicians at the Court of Louis XI, in whose favour he stood high.   The King was interested in Colot's contention that the operation was so important that it ought not to be allowed to remain in the hands of the ignorant wandering stone-cutters.   Other surgeons before Colot had expressed the same belief, but had not been blessed as he was with the royal approbation.   Colot, having gained the King's interest, waited until an opportunity arose to put his theory of the operation into practice.   Soon he learnt of a malefactor who was sentenced to death and who had long suffered from stone in the bladder.   With the royal assent this man's sentence was commuted from death to lithotomy, and the next

morning the King and interested members of his Court assembled
in the churchyard of St. Severins to watch Colot operate.   The
operation was successful, the cured patient was freed, and Colot
received a liberal pension and considerable acclamation.   Colot
kept his method secret for many years, and used to travel far
and wide to operate upon distinguished sufferers from stone in
the bladder.   On one occasion he was assisted by a barber-
surgeon's young apprentice.   This young man had been born
about 1509.   His parents were poor and his early education was
practically nil.   Then a kindly parish priest undertook to cultivate his mind, while the young man cultivated the priest's garden
and groomed his horses.   Later he was apprenticed to barber-
surgeon Vialot, and it was during his apprenticeship that he was
privileged to hold the kicking legs of one of Colot's patients.
The skill and dexterity of the great master so impressed the
young apprentice that, once his term of service with Vialot had
ended, he went off to Paris to try to perfect himself in the art of
surgery.   For three years he worked as a sort of house-surgeon
in the Hôtel Dieu, the largest hospital in Paris.   Then, at the
age of twenty-seven, young Ambroise Paré became a military
surgeon.   He had no rank and no recognized position in the army,
and he was paid by his patients whatever they thought he deserved.

He travelled far and wide with the French armies, and wrote
several books in a garrulous and pleasantly gossipy style, one of
the best known being *Journeys in Divers Places*.   The first of
these divers places was Turin, which he visited in 1536, when
France sent a large army there.   The enemy occupied the Pass
de Suze, but they were forced to retreat, notably by the efforts of
Captain Le Rat, who was unfortunate enough to receive an
arquebus shot in his right ankle.   Paré's description of the
incident and of his treatment of the injured ankle is a classic of
brevity and humility.   The captain

> . . . fell to ground at once, and then said, "Now they have got the
> Rat."   I dressed him and God healed him.

In these seven words Paré expressed a philosophy of life and
a practice of surgery, and typically, without even pausing to
elaborate either theme, spurred his horse pell-mell into the
captured city.   He rode over heaped bodies, many dead, some
not yet dead.   He found a stable, and in it were four dead
soldiers and three just alive.   They were propped against the
wall and their clothes were still smouldering from the burning of

gunpowder. They could not move, nor see, nor hear, nor speak. An old soldier of the French army joined the young surgeon. He asked if there was any hope for them, any possibility of cure? Paré shook his head. The soldier went up to them and cut their throats—gently and without ill will towards them. Appalled at this cruelty, the surgeon called him a villain. Probably because Paré was young and unaccustomed to the art of war, the old soldier did not abuse him. He told Paré, simply, that if ever he should be in such a plight he prayed that some comrade, either friend or foe, would do as much for him.

That was Paré's first taste of war. He watched next the retreat from Turin to the Château de Villane. This castle was attacked on the following day. A breach was made in the walls and all who manned them were cut to pieces ". . . save one very fair young girl of Piedmont. . . ." Her fate was to be something other than death, thanks to the discerning eye of a "great seigneur." The garrison left within the castle must have been able to estimate from the fate of their comrades on the walls exactly how much mercy they were likely to receive. They died to a man, but not before they had left Paré and his brother-surgeons with more work than they could handle. Paré was inexperienced, but he had been taught that wounds made by fire-arms were envenomed and poisoned by gunpowder. It was therefore necessary that they should be cauterized. This was done simply by holding the edges of the wound widely apart, and pouring into it a grumous mixture of oil of elders and treacle, scalding hot. Paré, anxious to make no mistake, consulted the more experienced army surgeons and learnt that they all practised the treatment he had been taught. Great cauldrons of oil and treacle were already boiling fiercely over wood fires. Each surgeon had to hand irons for cauterizing severed blood-vessels, tents or wedges of wood with which to keep the wound open, metal spoons for ladling the boiling oil, and rough dressings. Paré worked as hard as any of them. Soldiers were brought to him by the men-at-arms and their wounds were lavishly and correctly treated with the boiling oil.

At last the precious oil was finished. Some sort of dressing had to be applied to the many wounded who remained. A simple mixture of yolk of eggs and oil of roses in turpentine was a poor substitute for boiling oil of elders and treacle, but there was no other. Doubtfully, the young surgeon applied this cool paste to shattered arms and legs, to broken heads, and to mangled limbs. When the last of the procession of wounded had been dressed, Paré went wearily to his tent. He lay there, wakeful, wondering how long it would take for the poison from gunshot wounds which had not been cauterized by boiling oil to kill those who had come too late to be properly treated. He was up early to see how his patients were faring. He glimpsed first the men who had had the benefit of boiling oil. They were feverish and sleepless, tossing and turning, moaning of the pain in wounds which were swollen and reddened. That was as it should be. The boiling oil had counteracted the deadly poisons of burnt gunpowder, but had inevitably damaged the patients' wounded flesh.

He went on to the unfortunates, to see how many remained alive. Most of them were asleep, but those who were awake were quiet and cheerful. Paré took off their dressings and looked at their wounds. They had no pain and their wounds were neither reddened, nor swollen, nor inflamed in any way. The inference was obvious, and from that moment onwards Paré discarded boiling oil and any other form of cautery in the treatment of gunshot wounds, insisted on the good results which could be achieved with "digestives" or "balms" or "salves", and threw himself wholeheartedly into the controversy on gunshot wounds. It had long been taught by many authorities that such wounds were poisoned. His early experience convinced Paré that this was not the case, and he devoted much time and much ink to informing the less discerning that they were mistaken in their beliefs.

For all his perspicacity, Paré did not realize that any wound would heal well in the absence of infection provided it was treated gently and dressed with some simple mixture, whatever the nature of that mixture. He still believed that the ingredients of the salve were all-important, and so he cast round to try and improve upon his mixture of yolk of eggs, oil of roses, and turpentine. There was a surgeon of Turin who was famed far and wide for his successful treatment of gunshot wounds. Determined to know his secret, Paré courted this man's favour for two years. At last the assiduous homage he paid and the gifts and presents he brought had their effect. The Turin surgeon gave Paré his secret recipe for a salve which cured all wounds. Paré was overjoyed at having won this secret, and especially delighted to find that the mixture was not nearly so plebeian as the one he had used. The surgeon of Turin used oil of lilies, which he boiled, then while the oil was boiling he plunged into it earthworms which had been steeped in Venetian turpentine and young whelps "just pupp'd".

Paré quickly rose to fame in the army, and though the pups just whelp'd may have had something to do with it, much more of his reputation was solidly founded on his own courage, ability, and common sense. The fees he was paid at different times speak eloquently enough of the circumstances in which he rendered service to his patients and of the way in which they appreciated him. A cask of wine was his fee on one occasion, on another a diamond; a collection of half-crowns and crowns was presented to him by the soldiers of the French army; a nobleman gave him a horse and fifty double ducats; another diamond was from the finger of a duchess. The King himself gave Paré three hundred crowns, and promised that he would never let him want. Four successive monarchs of France, Henry II, Francis II, Charles IX, and Henry III, appointed him surgeon-in-chief to the Royal household, and, thanks to the royal favour, Paré was the only Protestant spared in the massacre of St. Bartholomew's Eve. The King made Paré stay in the royal apartment that night.

Ambroise Paré became one of the leaders of the College of St. Côme, though at first his admission to the College had been strongly opposed—because he could not write a thesis in Latin. Paré knew enough Latin, however, to epitomize in vernacular French, and so make accessible and popular, the book which more than any other influenced his work as a surgeon, the *De Fabrica Humani Corporis* of Vesalius. Vesalius and he had met in consultation at the death-bed of Henry II, who was mortally wounded while jousting with the Comte de Montgomery. This and other vernacular sins were perforce overlooked by the College of St. Côme. No college could deny admittance to a man who was not only surgeon to the King but so popular that when one night he went to Metz incognito he was sought out by his comrades and carried through the town in triumph.

Paré was a practical and observant surgeon. His abandonment of boiling oil, even though he did substitute a concoction of puppies and worms for it, was an original contribution, and a great one, to the surgery of his time. He was responsible, too, for many other advances. Trusses for the support of ruptures had long been known, but Paré improved and popularized them. He introduced a form of massage, he linked up the symptom of pain in passing water with the enlargement of the prostate gland which may cause it, and he was the first to suggest that syphilis might affect the walls of arteries and allow them to swell and dilate into aneurysms. In midwifery, in cases in which the child presented by the breech, it was his revival of podalic version, or "turning" the child so that it arrived head first, as described by Soranus of Ephesus, that made the procedure popular again. He also had the courage in cases of severe bleeding from the womb to take the obvious course and stop the hæmorrhage by artificially inducing labour to start.

Paré had to work hard for two years to win his puppy-dog recipe, and should be forgiven for clinging to a treatment so hardly gained, particularly when there is balanced against this his onslaughts on the bogus but much-boosted virtues of other less admirable mixtures. Mummy, or rather a small portion of a mummy, was supposed to be invaluable for staunching bleeding. Paré's colleagues were gently critical because he did not use this particular ingredient in his mixtures. Criticism of any sort, and particularly gentle criticism from the Latin-conscious gentlemen of the long robe, always stimulated Paré. The discourse he wrote on mummy was a virulent one, and for full measure he threw in unicorn horn and pointed out, in terms far from measured, exactly how little he thought of these symbolic medicaments. This silenced his critics, and probably upset badly the then King, who had just refused a firm offer of 100,000 crowns for a unicorn horn which was in his possession.

Another much valued cure-all with which Paré dealt faithfully was bezoar stone. These stones were concretions found in the bodies of certain animals, notably as gallstones in goats, and were supposed to prevent melancholia and all kinds of poisoning. Charles IX was presented with a bezoar stone of which he was very proud, so much so that when Paré, as his surgeon-in-chief, told him that it was valueless King Charles was indignant. However, he agreed to experiment with it. He sent for a condemned prisoner, a cook who was to be strangled for having stolen two silver plates from his master. The cook quickly decided to take a poison and the famous antidote rather than be publicly strangled. Accordingly he was given corrosive sublimate and immediately afterwards the bezoar stone to swallow. Paré saw him an hour later. He was on all-fours in his cell, retching and vomiting and purging, bleeding from his ears, nose, and mouth. Paré gave him oil to drink, hoping to help him, but it was too late. The man took seven hours to die. King Charles IX was convinced—that the bezoar stone was a counterfeit pebble and a real bezoar stone would have saved the unfortunate cook.

Paré lived to the ripe age of eighty and, apart from the many minor contributions of his original inventive genius and his independent frame of mind, was personally responsible for two most important advances. The first was his abandonment of boiling oil and of the cautery except in cases where it was specially called for, the second was the way in which he made safe and practicable again the amputation of limbs. This he did by re-introducing the use of the ligature to tie bleeding blood-vessels and so stop hæmorrhage. Paré did not discover the ligature. Galen and Celsus described the use of the ligature as if it were an ordinary and well-known method of stopping bleeding, as did other Roman authors and the Greeks before them and the Arabians after them. In the Middle Ages Roger and Roland and Jehan Yperman used ligatures, and so did many lesser surgeons. But despite the fact that ligatures were known, surgeons were never enthusiastic about undertaking the larger amputations. They had good reason for avoiding these operations. Whether ligatures were used or forgotten, the results of amputation were uniformly disastrous. This was simply because the battered stump of the limb was always smothered in scalding oil or roasted with a red-hot iron, or else favourite styptics of rabbit's fur and aloes and the like were applied. Paré realized that it was these things which injured the flesh, fouled the wound, and set up a high and possibly fatal fever in the patient, and not the operation itself which was at fault. He realized, too, that because of these after-effects and the consequent high death-rate, his colleagues, excepting perhaps the redoubtable Gerssdorff, were so loath to amputate that they shelved the question till the patient was almost dead or the whole limb gangrenous. So he experimented with the forgotten ligatures, and, after tying the vessels at the point of amputation, he applied one of his simple digestives. His patients did well and so did the patients of other younger surgeons who were wise enough to listen to his counsel: ligature blood-vessels, apply simply digestives instead of rabbit's fur, and "abandon this miserable way of burning and roasting".

Each advance that Paré made was in the direction of a rational simplicity and a reasonable cleanliness. When there was a bullet in a wound there was much probing and hacking to find it, till, in many cases, the surgeons did more damage than the harquebus had done.   It was Paré who pointed out that if the patient was restored to the approximate position he was in when struck, then the ball would be found somewhere along a straight line drawn more or less horizontally from the point at which it had entered.   Paulus of Ægina had described the same manœuvre nine centuries previously in connexion with the treatment of buried arrow-heads.   Paré revived it and popularized it, just as he had revived and popularized the use of the ligature and the "turning" of unborn children within their mothers' wombs. It was Paré who explained that a deep-seated abscess need not be opened every day; if it was opened once and a drainage tube inserted, it would remain open till all the pus was evacuated and healing began.   Patients whose limbs he had amputated he fitted with serviceable artificial ones, and for patients who were convalescent he ordered good food, good drink, and even good music.   His insistence on cleanliness was shown by the way he ordered new, or at least freshly-washed, bandages to cover the original dressing every day.   At the siege of Metz bandages were scarce, and the washing of them became a spare-time duty for four fat prostitutes.   The end results of their activities distressed Paré, but he admitted that the poor laundering might have been due to the fact that the four ladies "had no water at their command and less soap".

Paré wrote at one time, "You will have to render account not to the ancients but to God for your humanity and your skill". Humanity came first and skill second with Paré, and soon it was so with the men who followed him, for the humanity which Paré typified was the greatest of the changes brought about by the Renaissance in all the arts and all the sciences.

It might have been thought at Paré's death in 1590 that his carefully recorded experiences and his undoubted authority would have ended for ever the controversy as to whether gunshot wounds were or were not poisoned.   Actually, the debate continued.   It had been started by Jerome of Brunswick and by John of Vigo, who was born in 1460 and became surgeon to the fighting Pope, Julius II.   His text-book, the *Practica Copiosa*, which appeared in 1514, succeeded in popularity the works of Guy de Chauliac, not because the *Practica* was a very good text-book but because it was the first book to deal at any length with two great problems only newly arisen: epidemic syphilis and gunshot wounds. Both John and Jerome taught that the wounds made by firearms were scorched and envenomed and poisoned, and that it was therefore necessary to purify them by applying the actual red-hot cautery and boiling oil. It was a French translation of John of Vigo's book from which Paré had learnt the accepted method of treating gunshot wounds, and the accepted theory that they were poisoned. Chance gave him the opportunity of comparing wounds treated by the cautery and boiling oil and similar wounds treated with his digestive of oil of roses and yolk of egg. This comparison convinced him that the boiling-oil method was wrong, and therefore that the theory on which it was based was wrong. So the weight of his authority was thrown into the scale against the teachings of Jerome of Brunswick, John of Vigo, Gerssdorff the German, and others.

Hans von Gerssdorff had a considerable claim to authority at this time. His *Field Book of the Treatment of Wounds* announced the fact that he had done between one and two hundred amputations—a far greater number than had been performed by any of his contemporaries. He gave his patients opium before operating, used the cautery to check bleeding, and enclosed each amputation stump in the bladder of a bull, put on wet so that in drying it would contract and apply an even pressure, which would tend to check any bleeding. Gerssdorff's opinion of his own importance in the surgical scheme of things is immodestly conveyed in the doggerel quatrains which formed the legends for the illustrations to his book. Two of them have been freely rendered from the German:

> To cure St. Anthony's fiery smart
> Removing arms has certain art
> Which is not in all men 'tis true
> So send your case to me to do.
>
> When I am stricken hip and thigh
> Or wounded grievously do lie
> I hope that God will bring to me
> Gerssdorff's artistic surgery.

On the vital question as to whether gunshot wounds were or were not poisoned his views were those of Jerome of Brunswick and John of Vigo. On the other hand, Paré was supported by Bartholomew Maggi, a surgeon of Bologna. While Paré was investigating the problem clinically, on the field of battle, Maggi was approaching the same question experimentally. His experiments were simple if hazardous. To prove that bullets did not "scorch and envenom" the flesh, he fired from a harquebus arrows tipped with wax. The wax did not melt, so it could not have been heated overmuch. Other arrows tipped with sulphur were not ignited, so the sulphur could not have been warmed unduly. The scorching theory seemed to be disposed of, but Maggi insisted on exploding it completely. To the dismay of his friends and neighbours, he suspended from a beam in the roof of his house a large bag full of gunpowder. Then he took up a harquebus, watched the friends and neighbours scuttling for cover, and fired a ball through the bulging bag. Nothing happened, and so Maggi dealt with Jerome's theory as effectively experimentally as Paré had done clinically. Even this did not convince many of the devotees of John of Vigo, and the cudgels had to be taken up again, this time in England. The two men who were next to be involved in this long-drawn-out battle of words were Thomas Gale and William Clowes. These English surgeons were the natural successors of John of Arderne in that they did much to advance surgery in England, and of Thomas Vicary in that both were prominently associated with the Worshipful Company of Barber-Surgeons.

Thomas Gale was a contemporary of Paré's, born in 1507, and, like Paré, he served as an army surgeon, being with the troops of Henry VIII at Montreuil. The pay of army surgeons was sufficiently high to attract all sorts of quacks. So at Montreuil there was a gang of "sow-gelders and some horse-gelders, with tinklers and cobblers". They were collectively referred to as the dog-leechers, and the man who fell into their hands and did not die counted himself fortunate. At this particular camp their stay was brief, for the Duke of Norfolk, who was in command of the army, asked Gale and some others to find out whether his regiments were being decimated by the enemy or the so-called surgeons. Gale found that the cobblers and tinkers had a combined salve made of the shoemaker's wax and the rust of old pans, while the horse-gelders and their porcine colleagues were busy applying to wounds the grease which was normally applied to horses' hooves. A well-phrased report by Gale and the threat of hanging soon restored these gentlemen to those sections of the commissariat to which they belonged.

Gale settled in London in later life, and in 1561 became Master of the Barber-Surgeons. Two years later he published his *Certaine Works of Chirurgerie*. This was in four parts, of which the third was entitled, in a manner that admitted of no mis-interpretation, "An excellent treatise of wounds made with gonneshot, in which is confuted both the grosse errour of Jerome Brunswicke, John Wiga, Alfonse Ferrius, and others. . . ." "Both" three of these surgeons, as Gale would have it, were protagonists of the "envenomed" theory of gunshot wounds. Alfonse or Alfonso Ferri, Ferrus, or Ferrius, incidentally, was a native of Naples who won fame by his invention of the "Alfonsi-num", for then, as now, the surgeon who could not devise a new operation and attach his name to it satisfied himself with inventing a new instrument for an old operation and attaching his name to that. The "Alfonsinum" consisted of three steel prongs, ending in sharp teeth and so curved that they would spring apart when an encircling steel band was pushed upwards towards the wooden handle of the instrument. This was inserted, closed, along the track of a bullet. Once the end of it grated on the deeply buried ball, the steel ring was pulled up-wards and the three prongs opened widely. The instrument was pushed in a little further and the teeth surrounded the ball; then the ring was pushed down again till the sharp teeth held the ball tightly so that it could be withdrawn from the wound.

Gale was wiser than Jerome and John of Vigo and Ferrius in that he refuted this wrong theory of the effect of gunshot wounds, but his treatment was not much better than theirs, for he was very keen on applying to wounds messy and complicated unguents and styptics and the like, which must have done much more harm than good. He was not as meddlesome as many of his contemporaries, for if a ball entered the body in such a way that there was great difficulty in extracting it, he advised leaving it alone. He described the cases of eleven soldiers who had been shot in the body and whom he had treated in this wisely conserva-tive way. All did well.

The first part of his book contained "the sure grounds and principles of chirurgerie", and the enunciation of these principles gave Gale the opportunity of dealing with the state of civil surgery, which seemed to be no less degraded than was military surgery. He wrote bitterly of men who called themselves surgeons yet were "rude and unskilful . . . in an arte . . . accounted so beggerly and vile"; and of carpenters, weavers, tinkers, cobblers, and women, who were said to cure more patients than did the men engaged in surgery at the Royal Hospitals of St. Bartholomew and St. Thomas. At these two hospitals Gale saw over three hundred patients, and estimated that at least one hundred and twenty of them would not recover without the loss of a limb or other gross deformity, if indeed they were fortunate enough to recover at all. The principles themselves were simple and direct. The surgeon was to be courteous and gentle and cause as little pain as possible; cure was to be effected as soon as might be, and treatment was never to be undertaken "for lucre or gayne's sake" only, though an "honest and competent rewarde" could be rightly and properly claimed. Lastly, the surgeon was never to promise a cure in cases of cancer or in cases of elephantiasis, a disease which causes enormous swelling of the affected parts and especially the lower limbs. The "sure grounds" on which surgery was to be based were that the student should be "lettered", "expert", "ingenious", "vertuous", and "well-maneryd". Though not essential, "it ware very commendable" if he knew also enough geometry to plan incisions so that the cut edges about an ulcer which was to be surgically removed could be accurately apposed. This book is arranged in the form of a conversation between two surgeons, and includes the first mention in the English literature of syphilis. It is referred to as the *morbus Gallici* or the French pox, a typically insular English christening—which was reflected in every other country in the world, for the French called it the Italian disease, the Russians the Polish disease, the Japanese the Portuguese disease, and so on.

Thomas Gale made no appreciable contribution to the advancement of pure surgery, but he did help in his own country in raising the standards of surgical practice and improving the education and character of the barber-surgeons' apprentices. This he achieved as much by his lectures to the apprentices as by the diatribes he directed against quacks and pseudo-surgeons.

One of William Clowes' lectures on this same subject indicted comprehensively all the quacks that ever were:

And some of them be Painters, some Glaziers, some Tailors, some Weavers, some Joiners, some Cutlers, some Cooks, some Bakers and some Chandlers. Yea now-a-days it is apparent to see how Tinkers, Tooth-drawers, Pedlars, Ostlers, Carters, Porters, Horse-gelders and Horse-leeches, Idiots, Apple-squires, Broom-men, Bawds, Witches, Conjurors, Soothsayers, and Sow-gelders, Rogues, Rat-catchers, Runagates and Proctors of Spittle houses with such other like rotten and stinking weeds which do in Town and country, without order, honesty or skill, daily abuse both physic and surgery, having no more perseverance, reason or knowledge in this art than hath a goose, and most commonly useth one remedy for all diseases and one way of curing to all persons both old and young, men, women and children which is as possible to be performed or to be true as for a shoe-maker with one last to make a shoe to fit for every man's foot and this is one principal cause that so many perish.

As an example of well-directed invective this would seem to rank equal with the work of the Puritan John Halle, the man who made Maidstone too hot to hold its many quacks, entitled, *Historical Expostulation against the Beastlie Abusers of Chirurgery and Physick in our Time.*

William Clowes was born about 1540, and was probably the greatest of the Elizabethan surgeons. Early in life he served in the Earl of Warwick's army at Le Havre, and later, as a naval surgeon, he saw the defeat of the Armada. After long military and naval experience he was appointed surgeon to the Queen, and was on the staff of St. Bartholomew's hospital. Clowes, like Gale, was soon involved in the gunshot-wound controversy. He had been taught that these wounds were not poisoned, and firmly believed it till he came across the case of a young lieutenant who had been shot in the buttock. Clowes was unable to reach the bullet at his first probing, so he simply dressed the wound and left the young man to get a night's sleep. The next morning the wound was badly swollen and discoloured, and the patient was extremely ill. An experienced physician was brought into consultation, and insisted that since the man was obviously being poisoned by the bullet, the wound should be freely opened and the bullet extracted. Clowes said that he had never seen a wound due to a poisoned bullet, and argued that even if the bullet had been poisoned in some way, the heat of the explosion in the harquebus would destroy the poison. At the same time he admitted that the flesh around a bullet wound was so bruised that it might easily become infected. Finally, he operated and succeeded in extracting the bullet, which was flattened on one side and of a curious greenish colour. In this instance the theory that the bullet had poisoned the wound seemed so rational that Clowes' early faith in the non-poisonous character of gunshot wounds was rather disturbed. So, some time later, when the Earl of Sussex had him brought down to Portsmouth to attend a patient, he asked a master gunner to let him see an arrow shot out of a musket. The arrow was fired at a gate-post about two hundred paces away. Clowes examined the arrow carefully, and found the feathers at the end of it quite unburnt. The same thing happened with a sheaf of arrows fired from a caliver. This satisfied Clowes that the old idea of the heat of explosion being sufficient to cause poisoning was wrong, but it was clear that his own suggestion that the heat generated at the moment of firing would be sufficient to render harmless a bullet treated with some poison was also wrong.

He discussed the whole problem with some of his military friends, and came to the conclusion that an ordinary bullet could not possibly poison a wound, but on the other hand a bullet could be smeared with some poisonous liquid, and there was no reason why a poison introduced thus violently into someone's body should not prove as effective as if the poison had been swallowed. This conviction was supported by several eminent naval and military authorities, who assured Clowes that bullets could be—and were—intentionally poisoned, though under the Law of Arms this practice was punishable with death, and in fact men had been executed for it.

Clowes wrote several treatises in English, and in one of them quoted Sir Thomas Elyot to defend his use of the "vulgar tongue". The Greeks wrote in Greek, the Romans in Latin, and the great Arabians in Arabic, "their own propre and maternal tongues". "Paynymes and Jews" though they were, they had more charity than Christian physicians, for they wrote in a language which could be understood. Clowes saw no reason why he should not follow their excellent example, and he too wrote in his native tongue. His first book was *De Morbo Gallico,* which was published in 1579, and only the title of which lapsed from the vernacular. Six years later he wrote another treatise on the same condition, and expressed his belief that the disease was never more rife in France or Italy or Spain than it was in England at that time. The spread of syphilis he rightly attributed to "the licentious and beastlie disorder of a great number of rogues and vagabonds, the filthy life of many lewde and idle persons, men and women, about the citie of London . . .". St. Bartholomew's alone had treated more than a thousand cases in five years, chiefly by rubbing in mercurial ointments. Another essay was on tuberculous affections of the skin, and in this, as befitted a surgeon to the Virgin Queen, Clowes affirms his belief in the efficacy of the royal touch in those cases in which more pedestrian treatments had proved unsuccessful.

His best book is his *Proved Practice for all Young Chirurgians,* which records in detail many of his own cases and represents the collected wisdom of his long experience in surgery. One case was that of a naval gunner with a great wound of the belly. Projecting from the wound were his intestines and the omentum, an apron-like mass of fat which normally covers all the coiled gut. Not many years previously a man in this condition would have had his throat cut or been dropped quietly overboard. Clowes had the man laid on his back and made certain that the gut was uninjured. Then with a strong double thread he ligatured the whole omental mass of fat as high up as possible, and cut it off about a finger's breadth below the tight ligature. A red-hot iron was applied to cauterize the stump of omentum and stop any bleeding. Then the gut and the omental stump were pushed back into the abdomen, only the end of the double thread being left outside, so that in course of time it would be discharged naturally. A large needle with a double thread of strong silk was used to stitch the abdominal wall, the sutured wound was dressed, and the patient left alone. An ague developed, and this fever was relieved by bleeding and by clysters or enemata. The patient recovered, and save for a wide abdominal scar was completely whole. A similar case was that of a girl, aged ten or twelve years, who fell while holding a sharp knife in her hand. In this instance the child's relatives refused to let Clowes apply the red-hot irons, so Clowes did without them and did not find "any discommodity from not using them".

Another wound which might have been mortal was in a man who received a sword-thrust through the breast-bone or sternum, the point of the sword coming out at his back. Clowes felt so sure that the man would die that at first he refused to treat him, but the wounded man pleaded with him: "My heart is good, though my wound be great". Clowes cured him, and saw him again five years later, still in good health and very proud of the two scars showing where the sword entered and emerged from his body.

There was a soldier named Giles, who, three years before coming under the care of William Clowes, had been wounded by a bullet which had entered the left lower abdomen and had never been recovered. A deep sinus near his left hip the surgeon explored and even enlarged surgically without being able to find the missing bullet. All ordinary methods of determining the

[*153*]

whereabouts of this elusive ball having failed, Clowes tried a most ingenious method, apparently first described by a Belgian surgeon, Jean Tagaut, in 1543. Through a long tube he injected into the sinus a solution of alum and silver. Twenty-four hours later the soldier complained of pain in the right buttock, which was found to be swollen. Clowes cut down upon the swelling and recovered the bullet, and then the whole condition quickly cleared up after treatment by different dressings. In this case Clowes seems to have anticipated by nearly four hundred years a modern method of injecting an opaque substance into a sinus and taking an X-ray photograph in order to determine exactly where the sinus ends. Clowes' method was simpler. His solution of alum and silver was a known irritant which would cause inflammation to be set up at the end of the sinus.

Other patients of his were a lieutenant of Sir Philip Sidney's and a sailor who accompanied Sir Francis Drake on his last voyage. There were, too, a Captain Flemming who was wounded by a poisoned arrow in an encounter with a native tribe off the coast of Brazil, the servant of a barber-surgeon who—"by the intisement of the devill"—cut his throat, a sailor wounded while boarding a pirate off the mouth of the Thames, and a gentleman, "who had already given evidence of a violent disposition by shearing off his physician's beard and hair with a pair of tailor's shears". Of this last unruly patient Clowes records with some satisfaction that not long afterwards he broke his neck while out riding. Other cases illustrated the treatment for wounds of the head, gangrene of the limbs, wounds made by pikes, halberds, lances, and so on.

William Clowes, like Paré, was an eminently practical surgeon. He was fond of using the actual cautery and wrote that: "The yron is most excellent, but that it is offensive to the eye and bringeth the patient to great sorowe and dread of the burning and the smart". He had great faith in his salves and styptics, some of which had as many as forty-odd ingredients, but, despite these things and largely because of his fundamental common sense, his results were good. For instance, while campaigning with the Earl of Leicester in Flanders he and another surgeon were able to record cures in all cases of gunshot wounds other than those which were so nearly mortal that the patients died within a short time of being wounded. Yet with the same army there were so many quacks calling themselves surgeons that they "slew more than the enemy".

Clowes had fairly good results, too, in the treatment of fractures. In cases of fracture of the thigh he would have two towels tied above and below the fracture so that his assistants by pulling upward and downwards separated the fractured ends of the bone. He himself then manipulated the bones into correct position, and applied splints of willow and bandages soaked in egg-white and vinegar. Finally, the injured leg was laid in a bed of rushes. If, as sometimes happened in adults, the union was such that the affected leg was shorter than the uninjured one, then Clowes explained to the grumbling relatives that the results in adults were never quite as good as in children. In the treatment of syphilis, on one occasion at least, Clowes was not successful, for it is recorded in the annals of the Barber-Surgeons that one William Goodnep complained before the Masters of the Company that Clowes had failed to cure his wife of this condition. The Company was no respecter of persons, and Clowes, sergeant-surgeon to the Queen though he was at the time, was ordered to either cure the woman or pay a fine of twenty shillings. Wisely, Clowes paid the fine. Clowes had a rough tongue and a ready fist. On one occasion, in 1577, the Court of Barber-Surgeons pardoned his great offence in fighting in the fields with one George Baker, who was also a surgeon to the Queen. Exactly what quarrel prompted this bout of fisticuffs between the two Royal surgeons is unfortunately not known. Clowes' works have been described as "the very best surgical writings of the Elizabethan age". There is no doubt that the Company of Barber-Surgeons were indebted to him, as they were to Thomas Gale, for much sound teaching. Neither Gale nor Clowes ever achieved the eminence of Ambroise Paré, but, like him, they helped to make their colleagues and their successors realize that surgery was essentially a simple art, which would not be advanced by confining it to the Latin tongue or by regarding it as a mystery and shrouding it in secrecy.

XI.   Corpses, Curiosities, and Quacks

A HUMAN BODY WAS PUBLICLY DISSECTED FOR THE FIRST TIME
in many hundreds of years in Venice in 1308.   At first there was
an outcry against the sacrilegious immorality of such a proceeding.   In the course of years, however, the practice became
accepted and remarkably elaborated.   Two ecclesiastical dignitaries and two distinguished surgeons would select carefully a
young and healthy criminal.   Early on a fine morning he was
brought by his warders, who were very proud of him, to the
hall of the university.   There was gathered a great concourse
of people.   All the dignitaries of Church and State were
assembled, with professors of the university and physicians and
surgeons in their long robes.   Great merchants and their wives
were there with their pretty daughters, the merchants very
conscious of the fact that they had been singled out for invitation
to a most important social function, their wives just as conscious
of the fact that their pretty daughters were ogling apprentices
and students who needed no such encouragement.   There was a
buzz of conversation and all eyes turned to the high platform to
which the condemned criminal had been led.   The prolonged
rites proper to the occasion were begun.   They ended with the
certain promise of spiritual indulgence as some compensation
to the soul of the prisoner, whose bodily frame was to be subjected
to no little indignity.   The ecclesiastics stepped back and gave
place to the executioner.   The young man was efficiently
strangled, and thus transferred from the protection of the Church
to the care of the waiting stewards.   His body was extended,
face upwards, upon a low table.   The chief surgeon seated himself upon a chair raised high above the body.   A grey-bearded
colleague on his right began to read from a vellum roll.   He
described first the four abdominal muscles.   The steward's
knife opened widely the abdominal flesh, and the long ivory wand,
which the chief surgeon held, waved vaguely.   There was a
gratifying murmur of awed interest from the intent audience,
a murmur which reached its height a little later as the wand
waved even more vaguely about a multi-lobed liver and its double
bile-duct.   So it went on for the whole day, with frequent
pauses for rest and for food and drink.   By the time the white
wand was wandering about the segmented sternum and dipping
down regretfully to indicate just where a horned uterus might

have been found had the young male been a female, the ecclesiastics had disappeared and the merchants had stopped trying to
look interested. Their wives were too intent on anticipating
the dim prospect of a happy release from their tight stays to
bother about their missing daughters, which was perhaps just as
well. At length the wand was still, and the grey-bearded reader
reached the end of the last and the longest roll of vellum. The
public anatomy had been made. Tribute had been paid in full
to Galen and all his copyists. The mutilated corpse was borne
away to be restored as far as possible before being decently interred. The chief surgeon and his aged assistants were con-
gratulating each other upon the best-attended anatomy they had
ever conducted. Their apprentices and students were dis-
coursing learnedly, if a little drunkenly, on the bone of Luz and
Adam's missing rib, and delighting in the blushes of the merchants' daughters, who had accompanied them to the nearby
taverns.

Such were the pleasant social functions which the realist
Andreas Vesalius so disturbed when he restored to the animals
to which they correctly belonged the four abdominal muscles,
the segmented sternum, the multi-lobed liver, the double bile-
duct, the horned uterus, and so many other things which Galen
had described in animals and which tradition had ascribed to man.
He upset not only Venice and Padua, where he was public pro-
sector, but many other university towns, all of which had had
public dissections from the fourteenth, or early fifteenth, century
onwards. Among them were Montpellier, Florence, Lerida,
Vienna, Bologna, Prague, Paris, and London.

In London the practice of dissection and the study of anatomy
were encouraged by a clause in the Act of Incorporation of 1540
which gave the Masters of the Barber-Surgeons the right to take
each year for dissection, free, gratis, and for nothing, the bodies
of four felons immediately after their execution. Dissections
had been arranged at infrequent intervals before the passing of
the Act, bodies being obtained presumably by the kindness—or
more probably the bribery and corruption—of the public executioners. The Act of 1540 simply regularized an accepted but
irregular state of affairs. Edinburgh had advanced thus far
even as early as 1505, when the City Fathers granted the request
of the newly-formed corporation of Edinburgh surgeons and
barbers for "ane condampnit man after he be deid", at the same
time that they gave the guild the monopoly of distilling and

selling whisky. In London, Thomas Vicary, the first Master of
the United Company, was probably responsible also for lecturing
on anatomy while the corpses were being duly dissected by two
specially appointed stewards under the direction of two Masters.
Little progress was made in the science of anatomy because of the
scantiness of the material, and because private dissection of the
human body was forbidden. This regulation was strictly enforced, and at least one member of the Company was fined £10
"in that he had an anathomye in his house". The stewards
and the Masters acted on exactly prescribed rules and regulations
in everything that concerned the "making of anathomies",
but even they could not control the public taste for the morbid.
It had to be laid down as a special regulation that a fine of £5
would be the penalty for taking away any part of the skin of a
body in order to have it tanned. The tanning was done by
opportunist tanners, whose ritual, if fabulous, descendants
lived at Meudon during the French Revolution. It was
commonly believed that the bodies of guillotined aristocrats were
taken to Meudon for the skins to be flayed and tanned. The
end-product was an excellent soft leather used for making
breeches and belts. The skin of men was said to produce leather
superior in toughness and quality to chamois leather, that of
women to be too soft for any useful purpose.

Among other duties of the anatomy stewards at the Barber-
Surgeons' Hall was the provision, for whoever was Reader in
Anatomy, of a mat so that he should not "take colde upon his
feete", fine white rods for touching the body, and a wax candle
for looking into it, together with two aprons and two pairs of
sleeves, so that he should not have to wear the same apron on
successive days of the dissection, "which ys unseemlie". The
stewards and the Masters were also responsible for bringing the
bodies from the place of execution to the Company's Hall.
This was not always as easy as it might have been. Certain
Sheriffs of the City found that there was a good market for bodies,
despite the enactment of the Company forbidding private
dissections. So semi-public auctions were held at which the
freshly executed bodies were knocked down to the highest
bidder. The Sheriffs probably received most of the booty, but
the executioner and his assistants must have had some sort of a
rake-off, unless they were men of exemplary character—which
seems unlikely. This particular abuse was greatly diminished
by that doughty fighter, William Clowes. He complained so

effectively, in his usual unmeasured terms, that certain of the Sheriffs' servants who were involved in this posthumous racketeering were summarily dismissed. Another difficulty was due to inefficient executioners. Occasionally, apparent corpses would be conveyed at some expense to the Barber-Surgeons' Hall and then come to life again, to the great annoyance of the Masters and stewards.

The Barber-Surgeons' Company at this time had many individual members who did all they could to discourage quackery, but as a company the Barber-Surgeons found it politic to deal gently with charlatans. All who presented themselves to the Masters of the Company were examined, and even those with a minimum knowledge of the prescribed subjects were given some sort of temporary licence to practise. Only those who knew nothing at all were completely rejected. The licences were often limited ones, and would state that the reformed quack was to practise only couching for cataract, the operation in which a long needle was inserted into the eye to destroy the cataract which was interfering with the patient's sight, cutting for stone in the bladder, operating for rupture, or whatever the particular operation was that the man had previously practised outside the profession. Two other operations, belonging properly to plastic surgery, were practised almost exclusively by quacks within or without the shelter of the Barber-Surgeons' Company—namely, the operations for hare-lip and for wryneck. The latter condition was treated dramatically and usually successfully. Wryneck is due to the fixed contraction of a long muscle which arises behind the ear, sweeps down the neck, and is inserted into the inner end of the collar-bone; this contraction causes the head to be perpetually bent forwards and twisted to one side. The operation was simply the severing of the fixed and fibrous muscle so that the head could swing back to a more normal position. It was usually performed on the village green to the accompaniment of clapping cymbals, which served the dual function of advertising the presence of the itinerant operator and drowning the howls of his patients. A short, sharp knife was jabbed into the neck, just above the collar-bone and outside the fixed tendon of the affected muscle. It was swept quickly inwards, severing the contracted tendon, and then withdrawn. The twisted head was restored to a normal position with sensational suddenness, a dressing was applied, and the operation was over. Most of the operators were so expert in this simple proceeding that only occasionally did they injure the great blood-vessels immediately beneath the affected muscle. This was fortunate, since such an accident was almost invariably fatal.

Other branches of plastic and cosmetic surgery seem to have lapsed out of all knowledge, from the time when operations for the reconstruction of judically amputated ears and noses were practised by Sushruta and his pupils in ancient India up to the fifteenth century. Then a Sicilian family of itinerant surgeons, the Brancas, revived the operation of rhinoplasty or reconstruction of the nose and practised it as a speciality, in the same way that other families practised only cutting for stone or couching for cataract. Many of these wandering quacks did surgery good service in preserving a knowledge of different operations and in improving and perfecting them. Certainly, Gaspar Tagliacozzi, a surgeon of Bologna in the late sixteenth century, based his method of performing rhinoplasty on the operation that Brancas had used. There must have been plenty of scope for this work. Syphilis was rife at the time and gross disfigurement of the nose was not an uncommon result of this condition, and there were, too, the many noses injured in brawls or minor wars, or bearing mute witness to the active displeasure of some all-powerful noble. What Tagliacozzi did was to lift up a flap of flesh of suitable shape from the forearm and apply it to the injured or deformed nose, which had been previously scarified by criss-cross incisions. The raised arm was then bound tightly to the face, so that at the end of four or five days the flap of flesh and skin, still firmly attached to the forearm, would also be attached to the nose. The forearm end was then cut away, and the whole flap trimmed and moulded till it formed a new nose. The book Tagliacozzi published, *Concerning the Surgery of the Mutilated by Grafting,* established his reputation. His fame spread throughout Europe, where he was known sometimes as "Taliacotius". Butler knew of him under this name and in *Hudibras* commented in his usual vein on the work he had done:

> So learned Taliacotius, from
> The brawny Part of Porter's Bum,
> Cut supplemental noses, which
> Wou'd last as long as Parent Breech;
> But when the Date of Nock was out,
> Off dropt the sympathetick Snout.

This reconstruction of the human face, even though the contours

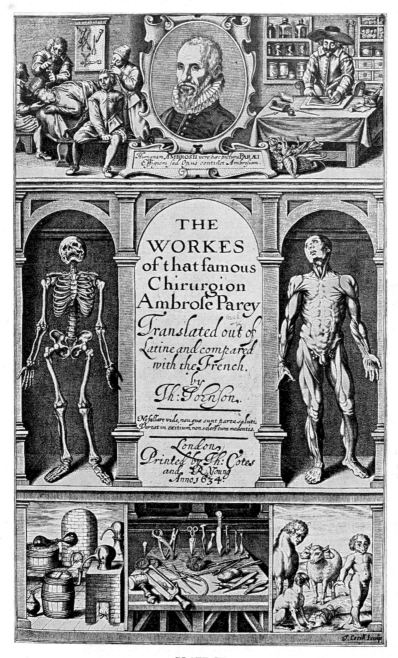

The following text appears within the engraving:

THE
WORKES
of that famous
Chirurgion
Ambrose Parey
Translated out of
Latine and compared
with the French.
by
Th: Johnson.

London,
Printed by Th: Cotes
and R. Young
Anno 1634.

PLATE IX

The title-page of the first English edition of the works
of Ambrose Paré (*London*, A.D. *1634*).

PLATE X

(a)   (b)

Illustrations from the Chirurgia of Vidius, showing the machines used for (a)
setting a fracture of the upper arm; and (b) treating a fractured or a dislocated
jaw (A.D. *1544*).

of that face had been ravaged by syphilis or materially disturbed by a well-directed weapon, was regarded as a blasphemous encroachment on the prerogatives of the Creator. Even Ambroise Paré held this view, and clerics who had persecuted Tagliacozzi during his lifetime felt so strongly about it that they did not even leave him in peace after his death. He was buried in the Convent of St. John the Baptist in Bologna, but so effective had been the curses showered upon him that his cries of everlasting torment drove the nuns in the convent frantic. Their sanity was saved, and the convent's sanctity restored, by exhuming the unhappy corpse and consigning it to the unconsecrated ground in which it rightly belonged.

In England no surgeon of that time ever received the abuse that was showered upon Tagliacozzi, but then none of the surgeons had ventured upon the speciality he had adopted. In France there was the same lack of interest until about 1742, when the activities of a few surgeons constrained the Paris Faculty sternly to forbid such creative endeavours. The Barber-Surgeons' Company of London was never called upon to intervene in this way, though the early seventeenth century did involve it in some curious problems.

There was, for example, the case of the monstrous child. One Humphrey Bromley, in 1627, wished to open a sideshow in London. He applied to the Master of the Revels for a licence, and, as was usual, was asked what he proposed to show. Humphrey replied that he had the body of the most monstrous child ever conceived by woman. Inquiring more closely, the Master of the Revels learnt that the child had two heads, three legs, and four arms. Since there was no precedent for showing any such monster, the Master of the Revels appealed to the Lord Mayor. The Lord Mayor considered the problem and instructed Humphrey to take his monstrous child to the Court of the Barber-Surgeons, and wrote privately himself asking the Court to advise him as to whether it really was a child or whether it was a fake. The Company inspected the horror and reported its findings back to the Lord Mayor. The Barber-Surgeons said, very wisely, that they could not positively affirm that the monster "proceeded not from a woman", but added, even more wisely, that the monster rather looked as if a few "untimely birthes", and possibly the offspring of occasional monkeys, had been hacked to pieces and then carefully put together again, a suggestion which could not be supported or rejected properly because it was a "Bodye of Antiquitie". Two further points were that Humphrey had omitted to collect testimonies from learned men and magistrates in the district where the remarkable infant was born; and that in his "printed demonstracion"— which nowadays would be his publicity agent's blurb—learned medical authors were quoted wrongly, and with "a great deale of addition and a manifest disagreement". As a result of this advice it is probable that the citizens of London were denied the pleasure of viewing the monstrous child.

Other difficulties were financial, and on one occasion the Company, on being asked by a royal commission set up by Queen Elizabeth for a true return of its total revenues, replied laconically that the revenue from its lands was only twenty-two marks, which was largely disbursed in the form of pensions, and it had "no goods". It also had trouble in enforcing strictly a new ordinance forbidding any member of the craft who practised bleeding from setting out vessels and measures filled with blood either in his shop window or outside the shop. The glass jar filled with rich red blood was a sign of good craftsmanship and a potent advertisement, which those members of the Company who practised barbery and bleeding almost exclusively were loath to forego. The chemists of to-day, if they were members of the Company, would find their large glass bottles filled with a watery red liquid an expensive adornment, for the fine for "everye suche Default" was three shillings and fourpence.

As for the apprentices to the Company, rarely a session of the Court of the Barber-Surgeons passed without some of them being reprimanded, or fined, or otherwise chastised. There was William Fish, who stole his master's surgical instruments and ran away with the intention of going to sea. William for his pains "and accordyinge to his desert had correction and punnyshement . . . with roddes". At a later date it was customary to pay the officer of the Company who wielded the "roddes" the sum of sixpence. Gyles Swalldell had to be similarly flogged for leaving his master's house at unlawful times, keeping evil company, and wasting "grocery wares". Another apprentice was forgiven, on making the appropriate apologies, "for evyll behavior commytted in his master's house with his master's mayde". Master Ralph Soda, a large-scale lady-killer, had his indentures delivered up to his father, for his master, Henry Lusshe, "witnessed how that his apprentice Rafe Soda ranne away from hym and contract hymself to three wemen . . . and also had delt unhonestly with his mayde servant". Thomas Hill was whipped for the more general offences of neglecting his work, playing at dice, and whoring.

The complaints of the apprentices against their masters were listened to just as patiently, and dealt with just as fairly. Noah Bayley was fined forty shillings for striking his apprentice. The apprenticeship of Robert Wallis was discharged because his master did not maintain him with sufficient "meate, drynck and apparrell". Nicholas Bray was informed that his apprentice would be taken from him and turned over to another freeman of the Company if he did not keep him better, for the Masters on examining the lad found him to be "lowsie"—in the Elizabethan sense of the word. An abuse which the Company frowned on was the practice of making apprentices do the menial work of their master's household. It was even found occasionally that the masters hired out their apprentices as valets and the like. It was generally the policy of the Masters of the Company, however, to reconcile freemen and their apprentices without punishing either of them, and to the credit of the whole Company it may be noted that promises of better behaviour on the part of either apprentices or freemen were more commonly elicited than were fines and whippings inflicted.

Despite all its troubles the Company was slowly developing both pure surgery and anatomy. Surgical lectures were delivered in the Barber-Surgeons' Hall every Tuesday. Thomas Vicary had been succeeded as lecturer by Thomas Gale. Gale gave way to William Clowes, in his turn Clowes was followed by Alexander Read. Read published his lectures and revealed himself as a clear, systematic, and learned writer. He detailed three methods of holding wounds together. Extensive wounds were to be stitched, using a continuous or an interrupted suture— that is, one long piece of silk for the whole length of the wound or a series of short pieces for several single sutures at half-inch intervals. The least serious wounds were treated simply by bandaging, but some wounds, the edges of which could not be apposed by bandages, might be effectively treated without recourse to suturing the skin. The method used was called "dry stitching". Strips of plaster or cloth were glued to the uninjured skin along either side of the wound; stitching the edges of these strips with an ordinary linen thread drew the wound edges

[*163*]

together, and probably gave a very good result. Read described, too, what was perhaps the first experimental excision of the spleen. Very little was known about this organ, which is situated on the left side of the abdomen in the angle between the liver and the left kidney. Absence of knowledge has always lent an added heat to academic discussions. Discussions centred chiefly round the question of whether the spleen was or was not necessary to life. Hippocrates, Galen, Celsus, and Avicenna, were quoted at length, and misinterpreted freely, in support of opposing schools of thought. It was generally held that the spleen was just as essential to life as were the heart and the lungs. Read brought to this problem the same inquiring spirit that had prompted the work of Vesalius and other pioneers. The ancients might or might not have had the right views on the subject, but there was no harm in verifying their conclusions. Verifying traditional conclusions at that time was usually effected by listing the authorities in favour of a particular theory, balancing against that list the authorities who advanced opposing theories, and doing some rather involved addition and subtraction.

This approach to a problem was a considerable advance on a previous line of thought which had been popular for centuries—if Galen said so it was so. But just as the staunch adherents of Galen were shocked when younger men probed the literature more deeply, and flew in the face of all tradition by daring to suggest that if Galen said one thing and Celsus another, then perhaps Hippocrates was right, so the young men who had grown old juggling with the respective merits of innumerable authorities were stunned when their grandsons suggested that their most sacred theories might be investigated experimentally. This was what Alexander Read did to the theory that the spleen was necessary to life. He tried it on a dog. He made a four-inch incision just below the left lower ribs of the dog, drew out the spleen, tied all the large blood-vessels entering into its centre, removed the entire organ, and then stitched the wound. The wound healed and the dog lived, convincing Read once and for all that the spleen was not necessary to life. As to the part it played in maintaining health he was not so certain, for six weeks after the operation "the cur was mangy", which condition Read thought might be due to "the spleen belike not drawing into it the feculent blood". This direct simplicity of thought, which prompted a simple experimental solution of a problem that had been the subject of academic controversy producing more heat than light for many scores of years, was also seen in his surgical practice.

Read was called by the grandfather of Lord Gerard to see his tailor, who had sustained a compound fracture of both bones of the leg, a little below the knee, ten weeks previously. The injury had not been treated properly, if at all, the bones were not united, and the knee was greatly swollen. Read gave it as his opinion that the unfortunate man would die slowly unless "he were out of hand dismembered above the knee". The old Earl and the injured tailor asked Read to perform the amputation. He was rather loath to attempt it, for he had none of his instruments with him. Finally, he consented to undertake the operation and completed it successfully. He employed a "joiner's tooth saw, newly toothed", and improvised a caustic mixture for use as a dressing. Fortunately, the house in which the operation was performed was being decorated at the time, so Read was able to obtain umber and unslaked lime, which he reduced to a liniment by adding the beaten white of several eggs. The hairs of a hare were added as being potent preventives of bleeding.

In this and in other operations Alexander Read revealed himself as a quick and skilful surgeon. Speed was all-important for effective surgery with a minimum of pain, and since pain is remembered in terms of the length of time for which it persisted, the surgeon who did his lancings quickly was always sought after. An ingenious instrument which appeared about this time and was of great assistance in this respect was the lancet-ring, a heavily ornamented affair in which a tiny but sharp lancet was so hinged that when not in use it was concealed in a deep groove in the ring. In incising an abscess the business end of the ring was turned towards the palm of the hand, and the blade opened without the patient's knowledge. The abscess would be stroked with the tips of the fingers, just often enough to win the patient's confidence—and to determine where best to open it. Then without warning the flat of the hand would be drawn sharply across the inflamed swelling. The patient would hardly have time to realize he was hurt, the abscess would be widely opened, and the surgeon would retire well satisfied.

Contemporary with Alexander Read was John Woodall, who was born in 1556 and started his career as a military surgeon in 1591. He was admitted to the Barber-Surgeons' Company eight years later, and became Master of the Company in 1633.

From 1612 onwards he was the first Surgeon-General to the East India Company, and some few years afterwards he was also appointed surgeon to St. Bartholomew's Hospital. It was as the East India Company's Surgeon-General that he wrote *The Surgeon's Mate,* the first book designed to instruct the ship's surgeon. In this book Woodall described most of the conditions which a ship's surgeon might be called upon to treat, mentioning scurvy in particular. Scurvy is a deficiency disease, the deficiency being one which can be remedied by giving the juice of lime or lemons. Woodall has been credited with the discovery of this simple method of treatment and prevention, but he refers to it as if it were an established practice, and it was certainly known to the Dutch in 1564, and to Sir Richard Hawkins in 1593. Even so an Admiralty order enjoining its use was not issued till 1795, and as late as 1779 the British Channel Fleet had over two thousand cases of scurvy after a ten-weeks' voyage. After this momentary consciousness on the part of the Admiralty in 1795, scurvy disappeared as if by magic. Only two years later Earl Spencer was unable to find a single case at Haslar, the great naval hospital. Woodall's second book was his *Viaticum,* which was really an appendix to *The Surgeon's Mate.* The two were later published together in an expanded form and governed the practice of surgeons on board ship for many years, becoming a sort of official textbook which every naval surgeon had to have. Woodall wrote on plague, on gangrene, inevitably on gunshot wounds, and also invented the form of trephine which in principle is still in use to this day. The old trepan which had long been popular was exactly like a brace-and-bit, the toothed bit being cylindrical. It had two great disadvantages. Both hands were needed to manipulate it, and the cylindrical drilling end once it had pierced through the bone was very apt to injure the underlying brain. Woodall's instrument overcame both these difficulties, and because of its three ends (*tres fines*), each of which had a variety of uses, he called it a "trefine". It was T-shaped. The long, transverse handle was so constructed that it could be used with one hand, and one end was a jagged and the other a smooth "levatory" for raising up the trepanned or fractured bone. Into this handle could be fitted any one of several bits, all conical in shape so that they could not possibly injure the brain and its coverings provided they were used with reasonable care.

A minor innovation of Woodall's was the suggestion that amputation of the leg could be successfully undertaken at the ankle. The operation was being practised rather more often than it had been in the past, but most surgeons removed the limb at, or just below, the knee. The death-rate associated with amputation was still high, and, despite all the teaching of Paré and others, it was still customary to undertake the operation in civil practice only when the patient was at the point of death, or in time of war only when the limb was already almost completely severed. In his travels Woodall had seen many natives in the Indies who had been punished by having both feet chopped off. A good proportion of them recovered, and were able to walk quite well with their stumps in crude bamboo baskets. This prompted his suggestion of amputation at the ankle, but, whatever the level of operation, he advised that the patient should be left in no doubt as to the possible results.

> If you be constrained to use your saw, let first your patient be well informed of the eminent danger of death by the use thereof, prescribe him no certantie of life, and let the worke be done with his owne free will and request, and not otherwise. Let him prepare his soule as a ready sacrifice to the Lord by earnest prayers; craving mercie and helpe unfainedlie; and forget thou not also thy dutie in that kinde, to crave mercie and helpe from the Almightie, and that heartily. For it is no small presumption to dismember the image of God.

Woodall had been a surgeon of St. Bartholomew's for twenty-four years, but in all that time had not performed himself or assisted at more than five or six amputations a year. He records with grim brevity the results of these hundred or more operations: "not above foure of each twenty dismembered, but lived to have beene healed". These results were not good, but they were no worse than those of Woodall's contemporaries, and he at least recorded them conscientiously. Woodall did for naval surgery what Gale and Clowes had done for military surgery in England. He died in 1643, not twelve months after civil war had broken out.

The Roundheads and Cavaliers each had their surgeons. James Cooke was a Puritan who edited the *Select Observations on English Bodies* by Dr. J. Hall. Hall had the doubtful distinction of being accused of destroying his father-in-law's manuscripts. His father-in-law was William Shakespeare. Cooke wrote the *Marrow of Surgery,* in which he described many of the cases he saw in the course of the war. There was the man who had three bullets through his chest as the result of his being mistaken by his friends for part of an enemy detachment, the officer's servant who sustained a fatal wound of the heart from a Scottish soldier's dirk—Cooke was justly proud of diagnosing the site of the injury and of verifying his diagnosis post-mortem—and many others. Cooke, however, was not a great surgeon, whereas his Cavalier prototype, Richard Wiseman, was.

Long naval service preceded Wiseman's attachment to the personal staff of the then Prince of Wales as a military surgeon. He went into exile with the Prince, joined the army again when Charles landed in Scotland, was captured at the Battle of Worcester in 1652, was imprisoned for a time, and then was freed to join the Barber-Surgeons' Company and practise in Old Bailey. This might have been enough of adventure for any ordinary surgeon, but Wiseman was no ordinary surgeon. He was soon back in the Tower for participating in a Royalist plot. Freed, he joined the Spanish navy and served for three years before the Restoration in England. Then he was justly rewarded by his appointment as Sergeant-Surgeon to the King. By that time he had collected the full notes of over six hundred patients he had treated. The publication of these cases, with a certain amount of mild moralizing and a few learned references to the older authorities, would have been deemed a fitting crown to his life's work by most of his colleagues. Wiseman was perhaps the first English surgeon to improve on this established practice by studying his collected cases, trying to find what was common to those that had done well, what feature had characterized those that had fared badly. From his many cases he produced sound generalizations and fundamental principles of the practice of surgery. He was not writing for students or for the inexperienced, as his predecessors had done. He made no attempt to cover the whole of a growing subject. He dealt with special branches of which he had wide experience and he wrote for educated surgeons, suggesting principles for them to consider in the light of their experience. He described, for example, a series of cases of injury to the brain. There was a soldier who at the siege of Taunton had his eyes, nose, and jaw blown away. With other corpses he was left for dead in an empty house, but later was found standing up, sightless, speechless, with macerated brain-tissue oozing out from a great wound of the cranium. Dressed daily by Wiseman he lived for a week, and then had to be left behind as the defeated Cavaliers retreated. Another man sustained a gunshot wound of the skull, fracturing the bone and injuring the brain. The wound was cleaned, the scalp being trimmed and the splinters of bone removed from the brain. "He lived seventeen days and walked a long distance, but became convulsed and died." From these and other cases like them Wiseman stated clearly and correctly that "the brain is of itself insensible"—that is, that touching, or cutting, or crushing brain tissue alone causes no pain. Pain which seems to be due to injury to the brain is actually caused by the associated damage done to the meninges, the three protective membranes which cover the brain. Again as a result of the careful study of his case records, Wiseman was the first to describe tuberculosis of joints as "tumor albus"—a white swelling. He also gave a full account of scrofula—the "King's Evil". Strangely enough, he was as credulous as any of his predecessors as to the healing power of the Royal touch in this condition. He wrote that His Majesty had cured more patients in one year by touching alone "than all the chirurgeons of London have done in an age". On other subjects into which the question of the divine power of kings did not enter Wiseman was literally centuries ahead of contemporary teaching. He advised immediate amputation in cases of severe gunshot wounds two hundred years before this practice was generally adopted. "In heat of fight, wether it be at sea or land, the chirurgeon ought to consider, at the first dressing, what possibility there is of preserving the wounded member; and, accordinglie, if there be no hopes of saving it, to make his amputation at that instant, while the patient is free of fever."

Surgery was advancing in every country in Europe. In England, half a dozen of the rugged, quarrelsome, war-trained Elizabethan surgeons had done their share, and were to be succeeded by men like Wiseman. Almost to the end of the sixteenth century Ambroise Paré was the doyen of French surgeons. Germany had two surgeons at this time who rose far above the barbers who let blood, set broken bones, and treated almost everything except constipation—a vast province to which the few physicians clung.

Bathing establishments were perhaps more numerous in sixteenth-century Germany than anywhere else in the world. A continuous five-day session in the baths was not an unusual cure for any general condition. During the five days there would be long periods spent in the heated water alternating with frequent cupping and bleeding, which was offset by the consumption of enormous quantities of food and drink. Thrown in with this, for good measure, were all the necessary facilities for the prevention of such evil humours as might have arisen from so long a period of continence. Of the two men who left their bath- and brothel-keeping colleagues far behind Fabry of Hilden was the first.

Wilhelm Fabry is really the father of German surgery. He was strongly conservative in his theories and beliefs, but in practice a bold and skilful surgeon. Before undertaking an amputation he diminished the blood-supply to the limb by an effective tourniquet, a circular ligature being passed right round the limb and then tightened by twisting a small stick passed underneath it. Amputation he always performed above the injured or gangrenous part of the limb, and not, as was advised by many surgeons, through the line demarcating the gangrenous from the healthy flesh. He knew that a head injury might cause insanity, and he wrote a work on lithotomy and a *Century of Surgical Cases*. He was reactionary in that he used the actual cautery in preference to the knife and still believed in the efficacy of the weapon-salve. This remarkable preparation had been popular for over a hundred years, and it remained a favourite prescription up to the early eighteenth century. It was compounded of human mummy, earthworms, powdered lodestone, swine's brain, and moss from the skull of a man either killed or hanged "gathered when the star Venus is predominate". This was applied not to the wound but to the weapon that had inflicted it. The importance of early treatment was recognized, and surgeons generally would refuse to undertake this particular treatment unless the offending weapon was brought to them while it was still bloody. If this was done, then the sword or other weapon was solemnly besmeared with the salve, covered with clean linens and bandaged carefully. The weapon-dressing was renewed every second or third day till the patient had recovered. Actually, the patients did recover simply because all attention was concentrated on the weapon, and, lest it should distract the surgeon or the patient, the wound was covered with a linen cloth and forgotten. Natural healing took place, and was cheerfully attributed to the efficacy of the weapon-salve and not to the absence of interference and the lack of pus-promoting dressings to which it was due.

Fabry's wife was also a surgeon, and it was she who first suggested that metallic particles embedded in the eye might be removed by a magnet. Despite the views which he held on weapon-salve and on the cautery—and it must be remembered that his views were those of the majority of surgeons—Fabry of Hilden stood head and shoulders above his German contemporaries. The only other German surgeon worthy of the name was Scultetus of Ulm. Fabry was born in 1560, Scultetus in 1595. Like Albucasis and Paré, Scultetus was one of the great illustrators of surgery. His *Armamentarium Chirurgicum,* which was first published at Ulm in 1653, has innumerable drawings showing the procedures adopted in treating fractures and dislocations, amputating limbs or breasts, and so on. He illustrated the application of an amazing variety of bandages, and among them the many-tailed bandage, which is still in use. It consists simply of a square of linen, to two sides of which are stitched short, wide bandages so that they can be passed across the patient's abdomen in criss-cross fashion to hold firmly an abdominal dressing. This could be undone and replaced without the necessity of lifting the patient up and passing a single long bandage round his body several times. Fabry and Scultetus were followed by other German surgeons, many of them trained in the Thirty Years' War, who made important technical advances.

With the gradual rise of surgery it was inevitable that more and more interest should be taken in the anatomy on which surgery is founded, particularly after the impetus that had been given to anatomical study by Vesalius. His chief pupil, Fallopius, discovered and described the ovaries, and gave his own name to the Fallopian tubes which conduct human germ-cells or ova from the ovaries to the womb. His chief opponent, Eustachius, gave his name similarly to the Eustachian tube which links the middle ear with the throat.

A fellow-lodger with Vesalius was a Cambridge graduate, Dr. John Caius, who was a Professor of Greek at Padua. He spent much of his time in hunting through the libraries for early editions of Galen's works, but the pioneer anatomists inspired him to turn from Greek and from Galen to pure anatomy. He returned to England, and in 1546 the Barber-Surgeons' Company appointed him its Reader in Anatomy. He held this office for seventeen years, and taught to the apprentice surgeons an anatomy which Thomas Vicary had not known. So well did he establish himself and so prized was his teaching that ever afterwards the Readership in Anatomy of the Barber-Surgeons'

Company was a coveted position, well paid, and always filled by a young university graduate, preferably one from Cambridge, for there John Caius refounded Gonville College to which his name was added and continued his teaching as the Regius Professor. It was to this College that there was attracted in 1594 young William Harvey, who, like John Caius, was to go to Padua, there to become a pupil of Fabricius ab Aquapendente, a pupil of Fallopius, chief pupil of Vesalius.

XII.   A One-Man Revolution

BY THE END OF THE SIXTEENTH CENTURY THE ANATOMISTS HAD begun to impress upon surgeons the importance of a knowledge of the structure of the human body.   The function of different structures and different organs had been the subject of speculation, and very occasional experiment, since the time of Hippocrates.   It was perhaps only to be expected that the heart should have been the organ about which there was most surmise and argument.   Hippocrates recognized that the heart was a muscle, and attributed the pulsing which can be felt at the wrist, and at any other part of the body where an artery is superficial, to a movement of the blood-vessels.   Aristotle regarded the heart as being the centre of the whole system of blood-vessels, the seat of all intelligence, and the internal radiator responsible for maintaining the heat of the body.   Erasistratus of the Alexandrian school, who had been accused of human vivisection, described the valves of the heart, but thought that the arteries, which carry blood from the heart, contained air.   This was one of the erroneous theories which Galen disposed of experimentally. He tied an artery in two places, opened it between the ligatures, and showed that it contained only blood.   Galen did not stop at this point, but went on to build up a theoretical masterpiece of pure speculation.   He modified Aristotle's view that the heart was the centre of the whole vascular system and regarded the heart as the centre of the system of arteries only.   The veins were very different from the arteries, and theoretical symmetry demanded that they too should have a centre.   The liver seemed an appropriate one, and the liver it was.   Taking, then, the two systems, arterial and venous, with their respective centres in the heart and the liver, Galen proceeded to his speculations.   According to him, the liver formed from the food which was eaten certain "natural spirits", which were taken up by tides of blood ebbing and flowing into the veins.   Part of this blood then passed through the right side of the heart and into the lungs, and here the act of breathing out relieved the blood of its impurities.   The remainder of the blood reached the right side of the heart in the same way, but passed through invisible pores in the septum dividing the heart into right and left upper and lower chambers, or auricles and ventricles, and so reached the left side of the heart.

Galen knew that the heart dilated and contracted regularly, and so postulated that the dilation sucked air into the left side of the heart from the lungs. Thanks to the presence of this air and the natural heat of the heart, the blood which had filtered through the invisible pores in the heart septum had the "natural spirits" with which the liver had imbued it converted into "vital spirits". The air which had been sucked in from the lungs had the additional effect of keeping this conversion a reasonably cool process. The arteries leading from the left side of the heart carried off the blood and its "vital spirits", which made possible the functions of the various other organs, such as the spleen, the kidneys, and the intestines. This was done by an ebb-and-flow process exactly like that in the veins. In the brain, however, the "vital spirits" generated the "animal spirits", which passed out along the nerves and made possible movement and the senses of touch and so forth.

The whole theory, though complicated in description, had the great virtue of an almost perfect symmetry. It presupposed that man was a neatly arranged mirror of a symmetrically designed Omnipotent, and so it found favour with all countries and all religions. Soon what Galen had regarded simply as a working hypothesis became an integral part of a pseudo-medical religion based on the divine rightness of Galen and all his works—a divine rightness which was to be venerated for just as long as the divine rights of kings, and to crumble with them.

Thirteen hundred years later Leonardo da Vinci hurled the first spanner into these complicated Galenical workings. He distended the lungs of a cadaver with air, and proved that none of the air entered the heart. He described the four distinct chambers in the heart, and recognized the fact that the valves at the roots of the two great arteries leading from the heart were so constructed as to prevent the blood which had been forced out of the heart regurgitating back into it. Vesalius continued the sacrilegious sabotage of which he was so fond when he wondered sarcastically at the handiwork of the Almighty—or the copyists' version of Galen's version of it—"by means of which the blood sweats from the right into the left ventricle through passages which escape the human vision". Vesalius was of course vilified for his attack on Galen, but he was at least wise enough to keep his realism within the limits of anatomy. Not so wise was Michael Servetus, who published in 1553 the *Restitutio Christianismi.* He described clearly how the blood in the lungs passed back into the heart after its colour had been changed from a dark bluish-red to a bright red by admixture with the air in the lungs. This idea provoked some criticism, but theological quibbles in the same book provoked much more than criticism, and led to the unfortunate author being burnt at the stake.

Six years later Realdus Columbus again described the route taken by the blood in the lungs in passing to and from the heart, and denied the possibility of the blood penetrating from the right to the left side of the heart through the dividing septum, though, on the other hand, he did not believe that the heart was a muscle. He insisted that his work was original, and it is possible that he had not seen Servetus's book, since all the copies that could be found at the time were used to set fire to the author. It is possible, too, and in fact probable, that he had had access to a copy and blatantly plagiarized Servetus just as he plagiarized Vesalius. Next in the field was Andrea Cesalpino, Professor of Medicine at Pisa and physician to Pope Clement VIII. He came near to the truth when he wrote, in 1571, that in contraction the heart forced blood into the aorta, the great artery arising from the left ventricle, while in dilatation blood from the great veins poured into the right side of the heart. The value of this contribution was almost completely negatived by the fact that Cesalpino also believed that the heart was not a muscle and that the septum was porous. Add to this the entire lack of any convincing experiments which would support his theory, and it becomes clear that Cesalpino was following in Galen's footsteps, the only difference being that the unfounded speculations of one were right and of the other wrong.

This was the state of knowledge in 1578 when, on the inauspicious April 1, William Harvey was born at Folkestone. England knew nothing of many of the Italian anatomists, and thought but little of those few it had heard of. There were a few more bodies available for dissection than there had been, but the instruments of investigation were still far from precise. There were no watches with seconds hands, and time was still quite often reckoned by the interval between the beginning and end of a psalm. There were magnifying glasses but no microscopes. It was the twentieth year of the reign of Queen Elizabeth, and her people were becoming a great trading nation. Francis Drake was at sea on the first English voyage round the world. Frobisher was setting forth on the third of his Arctic explorations. William Shakespeare was a boy of fourteen, and England was a merry place in which to rear a family of seven sons and a daughter.

William was the eldest of the eight young Harveys and was destined to be the greatest, though the material success of his brothers was considerable. Five of the younger sons were to make small fortunes as merchant adventurers, while John, the second of the seven sons, became Receiver for Lincolnshire and the Keeper of Sandgate Castle. At the age of fifteen William entered the college at Cambridge which had been refounded some forty years previously by John Caius. He had a scholarship of £3 0s. 8d. per annum, and after four years' study he obtained his B.A. Then, just as Caius had done, he went to the university at Padua which Vesalius had made famous. There were students of every nationality in the school of medicine, and on the governing student body Harvey was elected as representative of the English students, a distinction which fifty years later entailed being drunk at least forty times a year. In Harvey's time the students may or may not have been more temperate, but however bibulous the night, the early morning saw Harvey and his friends hastening to the great anatomical theatre, which the Seigniory of Venice had erected as a tribute to Fabricius ab Aquapendente, an anatomist in the direct line of descent from the greatest of anatomists, a pupil of Fallopius, who was a pupil of Vesalius.

In the centre of the theatre was a long table. Rising up all round were the circular galleries with railings of carved oak, tier upon tier almost to the high, dark roof. The students filed into these galleries. More candles were lit at either end of the long, bare table, enhancing rather than relieving the funereal gloom. A subdued mutter was stilled at last as the sixty-year-old professor entered the theatre. The stewards brought up the subject for dissection from the trap-door beneath the table, and the demonstration began. When it ended many of the students trooped down to inspect more closely the dissections, or to discuss with the lecturer some doubtful or controversial point. Young Harvey and his distinguished teacher became warm friends, and must have discussed the work which Fabricius was to publish in 1603, the year after Harvey gained his M.D. and returned home to take a similar doctorate at his old University. This work was on the valves in the veins, which had first been described by Erasistratus. Fabricius suggested that the valves were intended to prevent all the blood in the veins from flowing into the most dependent parts of the limbs, the hands and the feet. It was these discussions probably which first stimulated Harvey's interest in the movement of the blood, and which prompted the investigations he made.

A short two years after his return home Harvey was admitted, a candidate by examination, to the College of Physicians, and in the same year he married Elizabeth, the daughter of Dr. Lancelot Browne, who had been in turn physician to Queen Elizabeth and James I. Three years later Harvey became a Fellow of the College, and took a house close to St. Bartholomew's, to which hospital he was appointed assistant physician. In this office his stipend was £25 a year, augmented later to £33 8s. 6d., since he did not take the house the Governors provided for him. He began to build up a large practice, and at the same time made observations upon all kinds of animals, even his wife's tame parrot being subjected to a post-mortem examination when it died one day. This particular investigation at least established the bird as being a lady, though it had confidently been regarded as a male during its lifetime. All his dissections were general ones, but always Harvey must have had in mind a point which had perplexed him ever since his work at Padua and his talks there with his famous teacher, Fabricius.

The demonstration of the great anatomist that all the valves in the veins of the limbs pointed towards the heart, and his suggestion that they were intended to prevent the blood collecting in the extremities, as a result of the tidal ebb and flow from the heart, lent strong support to the fourteen-hundred-year-old theory of the great Galen. But what worried Harvey was that the short veins between the heart and the head also had valves, and these were also directed towards the heart. At this point the old theory fell down, for, carrying the argument to its bitter conclusion, either Providence had arranged these valves in the wrong direction—for if the blood flowed up the veins from the heart the nearest valve would open and prevent it reaching the brain, which was obviously absurd—or Galen's conception of an ebb-and-flow movement of the blood in the veins was wrong. The choice between God and Galen was an easy one for most men at that time. Galen would have won every time. Harvey was not like most men. He was neither more nor less religious or irreligious than his fellows, but he had studied at Padua, whence mighty shafts had already been directed by Vesalius and others at the Galenic concepts of anatomy and physiology, and he more than disliked any theory which did not fit the facts. It would have been quite normal and usual for Harvey, having taken the major step of doubting Galen, to follow Galen's own method of working, evolve another theory, and then try to fit the facts round it. Instead, Harvey advanced a mode of reasoning that Ambroise Paré had had thrust upon him. Paré believed implicitly in the John of Vigo theory of poisoned gunshot wounds. By accident Paré was faced with factual evidence that made the theory untenable, and so he adopted the only other theory possible—that gunshot wounds were not poisoned. Harvey was in a more difficult situation. It was not simply a question of deciding whether Galen's ebb-and-flow theory was correct or incorrect. If it was incorrect, and so it seemed to Harvey just because a few tiny valves were pointing in the wrong direction, then there was no other obvious theory to take its place. Some other explanation had to be thought out, but just as Galen's theory, based on pure reasoning, seemed faulty, so might any other theory similarly evolved have similar flaws. Harvey, therefore, simply abandoned the theoretical approach to his problem.

Patiently, over many years, he observed accurately and recorded in detail the results of innumerable dissections. He accumulated demonstrable facts instead of airy theories. He dissected or vivisected over eighty species of animals. All the facts pointed in one direction, all told the same story, and all of them added together to build up a theory which was indisputable. All the valves in all the veins always pointed towards the heart, and they always fitted so exactly together as to prevent completely any flow of blood away from the heart. The blood in the veins could only flow in one way—towards the heart. In the arteries there were no valves at all, except at the beginning of the two great arteries which arose from the heart, and here the valves were set away from the heart, and again they fitted so exactly as to prevent any possibility of blood flowing back into the heart. The blood in the arteries could only flow in one way—away from the heart. This much Harvey ascertained about the many venous and the few arterial valves. Then he turned his attention to the septum between the right and left sides of the heart. Like Vesalius, he found it quite solid. There was no evidence at all of the existence of the "invisible pores" which Galen had postulated. The picture seemed to be almost complete. The valves in the veins made it impossible for the venous blood to do anything other than flow into the right side of the heart. The thick septum prevented it from crossing to the left side, so it could only flow out of the right heart and into the lungs, and once it had flowed from the right heart the pulmonary arterial valves prevented it from returning. So from the lungs it flowed into the left heart, and thence into the great aorta, the huge artery, the valves of which prevented it from flowing back again. The ebb-and-flow theory was gone forever, but to the obvious solution of the problem there was one objection. Somehow the blood in the arteries had to pass into the veins, and yet there was no link between them visible to the naked eye—and there was not a microscope in existence.

Harvey took up another line of inquiry, and for the first time the fundamental science of measurement was applied to a problem in human physiology. Taking infinite pains, he estimated just how much blood all the blood-vessels in the body would hold. Next he measured as accurately as possible how much each compartment of the human heart would hold. The left ventricle, from which the blood was expelled into the aorta, would hold only a certain small quantity. Assuming that at each heart-beat only half of this was pumped out—this was a conservative under-estimate—then a heart beating at the normal rate, about seventy-odd contractions a minute, would by the end of ten minutes have discharged into the body between two and three times as much blood as all its vessels could possibly contain. Assuming that only a quarter of the fluid contents of the left ventricle was expelled, the result was the same, except that the time factor was increased, and similarly with a sixth or even an eighth part. If a more dramatic demonstration of this fact was needed, it could be obtained at any slaughter-house. Butchers had long known that if the large blood-vessels in the neck of an ox were severed, the whole carcass would be bloodless in less than quarter of an hour. It took a Harvey to link the lore of the slaughter-house with the science of medicine. On the same mathematical lines he showed that the amount of blood expelled from the heart in the course of a day was far greater than any amount which could possibly have been supplied by the meals taken in the same time, no matter how active the liver was in the production of "natural spirits". His experimental mathematics bore out the theory to which the observed facts had so obviously pointed. The only possible route for the blood to take was round and round, from heart to arteries, arteries to veins, veins to heart, heart to lungs, lungs to heart, heart to arteries, and so round the circle again and again.

These experiments and others like them Harvey repeated, seeking sources of error and finding only confirmation of the theory which had grown up experimentally. In August, 1615, he had been elected Lumleian Lecturer of the College of Physicians, a lectureship which was endowed by Dr. Caldwell and Lord Lumley in 1581, and which continues to this day. Harvey had clearly grasped the principle of the circulation of the blood even at the time of his appointment as a Lumleian Lecturer, but it was twelve months or more before, in the course of a lecture, he announced his discovery. Some of his notes have been preserved, and they show how Harvey was never at a loss for a turn of a phrase to illustrate a point he wished to make. He was of medium height, and had raven-black hair and small, dark, twinkling eyes. When he was lecturing he had a little wand of whalebone tipped with silver, with which he would indicate the precise structures in a dissected animal, or human cadaver, that he was discussing. A lecture on the liver, which might have been very dull, he transformed into a subject of vital interest by casual illustrative references to bear-baiting and cock-fighting, football and the ballet, and a strange bird in his Majesty's aviary in St. James's Park. Then he would conclude with a spirited attack on the fashion of lacing young girls till their waists were compressed to the requisite seventeen or eighteen inches and their livers were fantastically deformed.

It was in one such lecture that he made a first tentative communication, his own rough notes of which, in a crabbed and illegible form, have been translated by Charles Singer. They were brief and to the point.

> On account of the structure of the heart, William Harvey is of the opinion that the blood is constantly passed through the lungs into the aorta, as by two clacks of a water bellows to raise water. Moreover, on account of the action of a bandage on the vessels of the arm he is of the opinion that there is a transit of blood from the arteries to the veins. It is thus demonstrated that a perpetual motion of the blood in a circle is brought about by the beat of the heart.

Harvey, on one occasion, wrote deploring the precipitate rushing into print of "the crowd of foolish scribblers", whose observations were as inaccurate and inconsequential as their theories were wordy and improbable, and he himself had no intention of publishing any of his work till he had confirmed it in every possible way. He went quietly on with his experiments, but his practice was growing, and he had to devote more time to his patients than ever before. Such was his reputation that in 1618 he was appointed Physician Extraordinary to King James I. His relations with the King were those of a close friend, though he was never as intimate with James I as he was with Charles I. Despite this he was arraigned before the House of Commons a few months after the King's death in 1625. It had been suggested that James had been given poison, and Harvey was the most likely one to have administered it to him. Harvey can hardly have been popular with the Commons. He was too friendly with the King, for one thing, and it was probably well known that in one of his famous lectures he had described an acid belch as being comparable to a motion from the Lower to the Upper House of Parliament. However, there was not a shred of evidence against him, and he was completely exonerated of what seems to have been a mischievous and malicious charge.

Harvey attended Charles I when, as King, he went to Scotland for the coronation at Holyrood, and in the course of that visit Harvey himself was made a freeman of Edinburgh and of Aberdeen. He had the opportunity of demonstrating to the King many of the experiments in which they were both interested. On one occasion he showed him a patient who had a large sinus opening from his chest-wall down to the region of the heart. They both felt the exposed heart contracting and dilating, and were able to observe that their touching and manipulating the heart conveyed no sensation at all to the patient. Investigations on this man and on innumerable animals had at length convinced Harvey that the time was ripe for the publication of his views. So there appeared in 1628 a small quarto volume of only seventy-two pages, entitled *Exercitatio Anatomica De Motu Cordis et Sanguinis in Animalibus*. This anatomical dissertation concerning the motion of the heart and blood was printed at Frankfort, and is a brief masterpiece of sound inductive reasoning. It was, to effect a revolution in scientific method and procedure. It was, in fact, the first application of a true scientific method to medicine, the first attempt to make cold factual measurements assist in the solving of a vital, living problem.

The book opens with a graceful dedication to Charles I, in which the King, as the centre of the body politic, is aptly likened to the heart of man, and in the preface Harvey epitomizes all his work and gives the key to all his discoveries " . . . because I profess both to learn and to teach anatomy not from books but from dissections, not from the positions of philosophers but from the fabric of Nature". In succeeding chapters he outlines the older views on the vascular system, and disposes one by one of the beliefs which had so long prevented any progress being made. The theory that the septum between the two sides of the heart was perforated by invisible pores he dealt with very briefly. If it was perforated and blood was constantly flowing through all these pores, why was it necessary for branches of the coronary artery, which supplies with blood all the heart-muscle, to proceed also to this septum and supply it? At first he had been unable to analyse exactly the many movements which take place in a contracting mammalian heart at one and the same time, therefore he studied the "slower and rarer" movements in the hearts of cold-blooded frogs, toads, and serpents. Working up from comparative to human anatomy and physiology, he describes exactly the waves of contraction in the human heart, the upper or auricular chambers beginning their contraction a fraction of a second before the lower or ventricular chambers. In the eighth of the seventeen chapters he goes on to give his own view of the movements of the blood in the heart and blood-vessels. As he wrote this chapter he must have realized to the full just how he was going to flout all authority.

> But what remains to be said upon the quantity and source of the blood which thus passes, is of so novel and unheard-of character, that I not only fear injury to myself from the envy of a few, but I tremble lest I have mankind at large for my enemies, so much doth wont and custom, that become as another nature, and doctrine once sown and that hath struck deep root, and respect for antiquity influence all men: Still the die is cast, and my trust is in my love of truth, and the candour that inheres in cultivated minds.

How much "respect for antiquity" did influence his contemporaries it is almost impossible to realize. The works of Aristotle were still revered, though at that time they were taught from "a Latin translation of a Hebrew translation of an Arab commentary upon an Arab translation of a Syriac translation of the Greek text". Galen was still worshipped, for though Vesalius had revealed the feet of clay, he had barely ruffled the halo of antiquity. But Harvey literally put his trust in a demonstrable truth. He described his investigations and how they brought him to the point at which "I began to think whether there might not be a motion, as it were, in a circle". So he

gave meaning and force to a term which had been used before
—"the circulation of the blood". Further proofs followed,
enlisting for additional demonstrations innumerable different
species. For example, if a live snake was laid open, its elongated
heart could be watched slowly contracting and dilating for more
than an hour. The way in which the blood was flowing through
the heart could be seen clearly. If the great vein was pressed
tightly between the finger and thumb at the point where it
entered the heart, the contractions would become slower and the
heart would soon be pale in colour. On the other hand, if the
great artery was ligatured, then that part of it between the
ligature and the valves at the point where it left the heart would
be tremendously distended, and made a livid purple colour, by
blood which the heart continually pumped out and which could
not pass the ligature in one direction nor regurgitate in the other
direction, because of the immediate closure of the arterial valves.

From this description Harvey went on to consider facts that
must have been known, or known in part, to all the surgeons who
used ligatures, though never before had these facts been ex-
plicitly stated. He showed how the ligation of an artery could
be used in two ways: to stop bleeding as in an amputation, or to
cut off the blood-supply to a part of the body, and so cause slough-
ing and even gangrene, a method used in castration and for the
removal of warts or other fleshy tumours. The effects of a
ligature tied about an entire limb, an arm or a leg, varied according to whether it was tied tightly or only "middling tightly".
The tight tourniquet would compress both arteries and veins,
one less tight would not affect the arteries but would compress
the veins, so that the limb would become blue and swollen.
These last were practical points capable of immediate application. Of immediate interest, too, were other observations
helping to prove the fact of the circulation of the blood, notably
that of the way in which drugs applied externally would affect
internal organs—to which the blood had conveyed them. But
more important than any of these things were the two major
changes in thought and method which Harvey brought about
by his system of experiment, observation, and long-continued
investigation by the process of trial and error, and his method of
applying simple yet fundamental quantitative measurements to
a problem in physiology. From his time up to the present day
these interdependent principles of investigation have been at the
base of every advance in medicine and surgery.

Harvey's first communication to a small audience of his colleagues, as a Lumleian lecturer, had been greeted with approval and interest. The publication of his book, twelve years later, inevitably provoked criticism from the many more people who read of his views. He and his followers were called "circulators", which was hardly likely to have been complimentary in English for in Latin it meant quacks and charlatans. Two or three books and pamphlets virulently denounced the young upstart who dared assail the ancient authorities, but these attacks, and those of a few jealous contemporaries, disturbed him no more than did the disgruntled apothecary who once said he would not give threepence for a prescription of his. His practice diminished somewhat, but this was due as much to his too-close connexion with the House of Stuart as to the physiological revolution he had quietly effected. However, in the summer of 1630 he went off with the Duke of Lennox for a tour of France. This gave him a respite from his detractors, though they tried to have another physician appointed to the Court in place of him while he was away. They were unsuccessful, and Harvey enjoyed his tour, complaining only that France was so stricken by famine and poverty after its recent wars that he could find hardly a bird or an animal to dissect.

Returning home, he took up again another problem in which he was interested, and continued his work at St. Bartholomew's Hospital. There he proposed to a meeting of the President, Governors, Surgeons, and Apothecary of the hospital certain new rules and changes in old rules for "the good of the poore of this howse". Most of his recommendations were agreed to, among them being rules to the effect that only cases that were curable, or but a small proportion of incurables, should be admitted to the hospital; that any patient who refused to take his or her physic should be discharged or punished in some way; and that the surgeons, including John Woodall, should "in all difficult cases or where inward physic may be necessary" consult with a physician, the same rule as to consultation applying to any case for which a major surgical operation was proposed. The surgeons also agreed to have weekly consultations with the physicians about patients who had had "outward operations for inward causes"—cases presumably which the physicians had handed over to them. The surgeons protested vigorously and successfully, however, against the suggestion that their prescriptions for certain cases should be made known to the physicians. This last seems to have been in essence a reasonable proposal intended to give the physicians full information, so that there would be no possibility of the remedies they prescribed duplicating or conflicting with those the surgeons had ordered. Unfortunately, it was phrased rather baldly, and probably fell to the ground when Woodall, or some choleric colleague, drew attention to the fact that such a rule, which would have made surgical prescriptions semi-public, was suggested by physicians whose own prescriptions were jealously guarded—even to the extent of being recorded in a locked book.

In 1634 a single episode revealed Harvey's wise humanity, and the way in which he carried into every problem, no matter how remote from experimental physiology, the methods of observation and inquiry on which he had founded that new science. One Edward Robinson, a woodcutter's son with the lively imagination peculiar to small boys, had spent a day playing in Pendle Forest instead of going to school. To excuse his absence, he told a story which spread terror through all Lancashire. He had been kept from school by several witches. The accusation of witchcraft did not rest alone upon the slender evidence of their having kept him from school. He had seen them turn two greyhounds into a woman and child, and then the child had been transformed into a horse. Finding the witches was easy, and seven women were promptly flung into jail, where three of them died. The Bishop of Chester, who examined them, had no doubt that all were established concubines of Satan himself, cursed with devilish powers only a little inferior to those of their most hellish overlord. Harvey heard of this, and it was almost certainly at his suggestion that the King ordered the four surviving women to be brought to London, to the Shippe Taverne at Greenwich. Two surgeons chose a number of midwives to examine the women, and it is recorded that the midwives were to be instructed by "Mr. Dr. Harvey". Finally, the examination was undertaken by a panel of ten midwives and seven surgeons. They reported that the four unfortunate women were exactly like all other women, having none of the accessory organs with which witches were generally credited. So, thanks to Harvey, these four lives at least were saved.

On another occasion Harvey seized a golden opportunity of subjecting the theory of witchcraft to the same experimental criteria that had subjected the theories of Galen. He was at Newmarket with the King and heard that a lonely old woman, reputed a witch, lived near the heath. He visited her, and found her at first mistrustful and suspicious, but he quickly won her confidence by explaining that he was a wizard. Then he asked where her familiar spirit was. The old lady put a dish of milk down, made a chuckling noise, and pointed proudly to the fat toad which waddled out from under an oak chest. Harvey itched to lay hands on this bloated familiar, and at length suggested, as one wizard to another witch, that the odd pint of ale would seal their friendship. Neither wizard nor witch made any attempt to create the ale by magic, though the ale of that period was, from all accounts, a fluid to conjure with. Instead, the old beldam went off to the nearest tavern, and Harvey, abandoning the wizard's wand for the dissecting scalpel, opened up the toad. A thorough examination convinced him that the alleged familiar "in no ways differed from other toades". At that point the old woman returned and flew at Harvey, screaming curses and trying hard to scratch his eyes out. Harvey offered her money, and tried to explain that her beloved familiar was just another toad. Not unnaturally, this only served to make the bereaved old witch even more enraged. At length Harvey left her, assuring her that he was the King's physician, that he had been sent to find out if she really was a witch, and that if the toad had been anything remarkable in the way of toads, things would have gone hard with her.

Just about this time all London was agog at the strange conduct of Thomas Howard, second Earl of Arundel. The noble Earl was a curiosity-hunter, and on more than one occasion the citizens of London had been delighted by the exhibition of strange creatures he had brought back with him from his travels. His latest exploit was to have brought from the wilds of Shropshire a special litter, which was heavily curtained and closely guarded. Rumour had it that this contained a lady and that she was neither bearded nor obscenely fat. Rumour was soon proved wrong. The litter contained Thomas Parr, then entering serenely upon his hundred-and-fifty-third year of life. This "piece of antiquity" was shown to the King privately and then to the public at large. Parr seemed to be in good health, and not till his hundred-and-thirtieth birthday had he abated at all his activities as a farm labourer. With some support he could walk about quite well, and only his memory was at all impaired. His hearing was good and his eyesight only failed him in the last twenty years of his life. He answered questions readily and remembered quite clearly events of the previous three or four years, but of his early or middle life he had little or no recollection. Unfortunately, the change of climate and surroundings was too much for the aged but sprightly Thomas, and he died not long after his arrival in London. There was no proof of Parr's great age, other than his own statement, but he was buried in Westminster Abbey, and the ecclesiastical authorities, though they had never doubted Parr's estimate of his age during his lifetime, had his earthly remains interred right in the middle of that part of the Abbey devoted to those whose imaginative flights had brought them fame—Poet's Corner. Harvey's report of the post-mortem examination he undertook at the King's request showed quite clearly that the old man was healthy enough to have lived for quite a few more years had it not been for the abrupt alteration in his diet and mode of life. It also revealed the probable truth of the report that Parr had had to do public penance, after he had passed his hundredth year, on conviction of incontinence, and confirmed also the statements made by the woman he took to wife in his one-hundred-and-twentieth year.

Thomas Parr, post-mortem, may have been the means of bringing together the Earl of Arundel and Harvey, for soon afterwards Harvey became the Earl's physician and accompanied him to Vienna, whither the Earl had been sent by Charles I as Ambassador Extraordinary to the Emperor Ferdinand II. Harvey was fifty-eight years old at the time, and was still looking for new specimens. He took the opportunity of arranging to give a demonstration of the circulation of the blood to Caspar Hoffman, the Professor of Medicine at Nuremberg and formerly a fellow-student of his at Padua. Hoffman was interested in the anatomy and physiology of the heart, but clung to a mild modification of the old ebb-and-flow theory of the movement of the blood. The modification was his own, and consisted in likening the movement of the blood in the vessels to that seen when a wind ruffles the surface of a lake, rather than to the tidal to-and-fro movement. On the way to Vienna Harvey wrote to Hoffman, and on the return journey he gave a public demonstration in Nuremberg. The dissections and experiments he showed satisfied everybody except the old Professor, and since it seemed that nothing would convince the old man, Harvey at length threw down his knife and walked out of the theatre. The wandering diplomats reached England more than two years after they had set out for Vienna, and Harvey took up again the work on conception and generation on which he had been engaged ever since the publication of his *De Motu Cordis*.

The times were troubled, and in 1642, as the Parliament was preparing for war against the King, there were outbreaks of lawless rioting and pillaging in different parts of the country, but more especially in London. Harvey's official lodgings were in Whitehall, and he tells how they were broken into one day.

> Let gentle minds forgive me, if recalling the irreparable injuries I have suffered, I here give vent to a sigh. This is the cause of my sorrow: Whilst in attendance on His Majesty the King during our late troubles, and more than civil wars, not only with the permission but by the command of the Parliament, certain rapacious hands not only stripped my house of all its furniture, but, what is a subject of far greater regret to me, my enemies abstracted from my museum the fruits of many years of toil. Whence it has come to pass that many observations, particularly on the generation of insects, have perished with detriment, I venture to say, to the republic of letters.

Malloch believes that "the lost books of Galen . . . are not so much missed as are these writings of Harvey", and many will agree with him. Soon afterwards came the Battle of Edgehill. The two young princes were with the King's army, and Harvey was in charge of them. With the two youngsters, who were later to become Charles II and James II, he was sitting in a wide, grassy ditch, reading aloud from a book he carried, when a shot from a cannon landed within a few yards of them. This woke the single-minded Harvey to a realization of the fact that something of a war was in progress. His attention thus diverted from the physiology of the reproduction of man to the mechanics of man's destruction, he hastily put away his book and went to attend the wounded. His attentions were conspicuously successful, and particularly with one Adrian Scrope, whom Harvey succeeded in reviving after he had been stripped and left for dead on the field.

After this engagement Harvey accompanied the King to Oxford, where, after a few years, he became Warden of Merton College. He spent much of his time with the Reverend George Bathurst, in whose rooms a hen was kept to hatch eggs, one of which they opened daily to watch the development of the tiny chick embryo. The book which Harvey published on this work, in 1651, twelve months after Charles I was beheaded, shows again his remarkable powers of observation. Much of it was to be superseded with the coming of the microscope, but much of it remained valid, and is so to this day. There was, for example, his description of how a child, immediately it is born, stretches and dilates its lungs in taking the first breath of life. This changes the colour of the lung-tissue, and so it is possible to say with certainty whether a child was born dead or alive, even though it may only have lived for a few seconds.

Harvey had become a moderately wealthy man, and two years later he had built for the College of Physicians a library and museum, which last was almost filled by the instruments, specimens, and curiosities that he himself presented. Soon afterwards he was chosen President of the College, but had to decline this honour on the grounds of poor health and advancing age. Yet he was able to continue his Lumleian lectures until the July of 1656.

On resigning this lectureship he made over to the College his estate at Romney Marsh in Kent, the income from it being sufficient to provide an annual feast, an annual oration, and a salary for the College Librarian. The oration was delivered in Latin every year for over two hundred years, but since 1865 English has been the language used. Full of years and honoured through the length and breadth of his own and many other countries, Harvey died in June, 1657.

He had lived long enough to see his theory of the circulation of the blood generally accepted, and this despite the fact that barely a hundred years before the publication of *De Motu Cordis* the College of Physicians, which had sought to make him its President, had made an example of an unfortunate member who had had the temerity to doubt one of Galen's dicta, haling him before the Council and solemnly compelling him to recant this dreadful heresy. Harvey had taught physicians why their ointments and inunctions would affect the internal organs of the body, and why a local infection could give rise to symptoms which affected the whole body. He had taught surgeons the rational use of the ligature, which Paré had re-discovered. More important still, he had taught generations of students that speculation alone was valueless; that advances in knowledge would result only from patient experiment, patient measurement, patient application of the method of trial and error; and that the facts—if they were facts and if there were enough of them— would always speak for themselves.

His theory of the circulation—the first purely mechanical

explanation of a natural phenomenon—had only one missing link: that by which the blood passed from arteries to veins. His accumulated researches had made the existence of such a link as certain as anything which could not be observed could be. The link itself was discovered three years after his death. The microscope had been invented about the middle of the seventeenth century, but it was not until 1660 that it was sufficiently developed for Marcello Malphigi to be able to describe the minute vessels, the capillaries, which directly join the arteries to the veins. Thus, one of the earliest instruments of scientific precision, in the hands of a master microscopist, gave substance to the prophecy of Dr. William Harvey, a little man with twinkling eyes who achieved a precise knowledge of a vital function with a measuring-glass and a dissecting-knife.

XIII. Surgeons Forswearing Barbery

ONE OF THE IMMEDIATE RESULTS OF HARVEY'S WORK ON THE circulation was the rise of a new art—that of injecting coloured fluids into blood-vessels to make their dissection easier. Less immediate but far more important was his influence on midwifery in England. During the Middle Ages it was beneath the dignity of surgeons and physicians to take any interest in this neglected subject. Ignorant and untrained midwives did their worst, and if they did reach the stage of calling in a surgeon, mutilation of both mother and child usually resulted. The first sane book on the subject was *A Rose Garden for Pregnant Women and Midwives*, published in 1513 by Eucharius Roesslin, a physician of Frankfort. This was later reprinted as *The Byrth of Mankynde*. Roesslin may never have seen a child delivered, but he brought to light again the simple rules adopted by the Greeks for diet and exercise during pregnancy. He added to these sound directions advice of his own on the importance of lubricating the birth canal, manually and by giving various salves and oily preparations by mouth to the mother. To stimulate labour pains he suggested that the mother should be made to sneeze by smelling ground pepper.

It may have been Roesslin's book which stimulated Dr. Wertt of Hamburg to an interest in midwifery. Wertt realized that he could only study the process of birth at an actual labour, and knew well that as a man he would never under any circumstances be admitted to a lying-in room. He did the only thing possible —dressed himself as a woman and went boldly in to the next confinement in the district. For a brief while all went well, then somehow or other one of the midwives realized that he was a man, masquerading in a woman's garments. The mere idea of a male being present at a confinement raised a storm of protest. Punishment was swift and salutary. Wertt was burned to death. Other physicians watched him die and realized then, if they had not done so before, that midwifery was a woman's art protected by every possible taboo. The only men who dared even discuss the subject were cloistered and celibate clerics, for their motives only could be deemed pure. It was in 1522 that Dr. Wertt of Hamburg was led to the stake, so it is not surprising to find the next midwifery book published the work of a religious fanatic, one Jacob Rueff of Zürich. For no good reason he entitled the book he wrote in 1544 "*A Very Cheerful Booklet of Encouragement concerning the Conception and Birth of Man and its Frequent Accidents and Hindrances, etc.*" Anything less cheerful or encouraging it would be difficult to imagine. Most of the chapters follow closely the equivalent ones in the *Rose Garden*. There is, however, an additional section on monsters. Many of them represent abnormalities which may, and do, arise, others are simply the products of a too-vivid imagination, but all, according to Rueff, were the results of traffic with the devil. Similar beliefs were just as prevalent in England, and midwifery generally was just as neglected and just as bad, except perhaps in the hands of the Chamberlens. William Chamberlen, a Huguenot refugee, came to Southampton from France in 1569. He had two sons, Peter the Elder, and Peter the Younger, both members of the Barber-Surgeons' Company. It was probably the elder brother who invented midwifery forceps for the extraction of a live child in the course of a difficult confinement. Unfortunately, the Chamberlens kept their invention as a family secret. Against this major crime should be balanced the magnificent sallies they made against vested professional interests in their attempts to improve the education of midwives and the standard of their work.

Paré gave midwifery in France a tremendous stimulus. Harvey did as much for midwifery in England by the publication in 1651 of his *De Generatione*. His chapter on midwifery was the first original work on this subject to be published by an English author. The practical part shows an extensive personal experience, and is largely devoted to advising in favour of patient watchfulness and gentle assistance, and against any precipitate or unnecessary interference. Turning the child in the womb by grasping its feet, the method of assisting birth which Paré had popularized, was recommended in difficult labours. At the time this was almost the only effective branch of the obstetric art. Admittedly there were several fearsome instruments and innumerable methods of using them in difficult confinements to extract a dead child by literally hacking it to pieces. Such a procedure, when it did not presuppose, most certainly effected, the death of the child, and usually, too, it resulted in severe, if not fatal, mutilation of the mother. Methods for assisting mechanically the birth of a live child were, then as now, three in number. The child could be turned by inserting a hand into the womb, and this method was popular and usually

PLATE XI

Illustrations from the *Armamentarium Chirurgicum* of Schultetus of Ulm (*Amsterdam*, A.D. *1672*), showing, above, the trans-
fusion of blood from a dog to a man, who is being bled at the
same time; and, below, a method of draining fluid from the
abdomen.

PLATE XII

A surgeon about to perform Caesarean section, while a priest intones the last offices.

From the *Armamentarium Chirurgicum* of Schultetus of Ulm (A.D. 1672).

effective. If that failed, and one of the Chamberlens was at hand, a live child might be extracted with forceps. If the Chamberlens were otherwise engaged, perhaps in one of their periodical crusades in favour of the union of Scotland and England, national health insurance, or compulsory education— for all of which things Chamberlens were agitating centuries before anyone else thought of them—then Cæsarean section might be discussed. Rarely did the man-midwife get beyond the point of discussing it, for at that time every woman subjected to the operation died. In fact, Dr. Barlow of Chorley and Blackburn in 1793 performed the first Cæsarean operation in England from which the mother, though not the child, recovered. Jane Foster was the mother, and she was aged 40 at the time of, and lived some twenty-eight years after, the operation.

This method of extracting a live child from its mother's womb by opening the abdomen excites nowadays no more than polite interest at bridge-tables. It was first mentioned in the laws laid down by Numa Pompilius, over seven hundred years B.C., which forbade the burial of a pregnant woman before the child had been cut out of her abdomen. This was one of the few operations which had the whole-hearted support of the Church. It could do no harm to an already dead mother, and on occasion saved the life of the child. For over two thousand years there is no record of the operation being performed other than after the mother's death. Then, about the year 1500, the wife of a sow-gelder, Jacob Nufer of Sigershaufen, went into labour. For some reason or other she could not deliver herself of her child. The worried Jacob brought midwife after midwife to her assistance, but the thirteenth was just as little help as the twelve who had preceded her. At this stage, though not without comment from the other ladies of the village, decency and propriety were cast to the four winds of heaven, and the local lithotomists were brought to the rescue. However expert they may have been in removing stones from the bladder, these gentlemen were just as unsuccessful as the midwives in their attempts to separate the child from its mother. Jacob himself knew nothing about midwifery, but had been engaged in sow-gelding for some years. Feeling that he could be no more unsuccessful than the midwives and the lithotomists, Jacob took up a razor and did the obvious things with it. The end results of his impromptu performance have never been bettered. His wife recovered completely and at odd intervals later was delivered—naturally—

of one pair of twins and four other children, and the child which had resisted the combined efforts of thirteen midwives lived to the not unripe age of seventy-seven.   It was over a hundred years later, in 1637, that the first book on Cæsarean section appeared, and from that time onwards the operation was attempted more often.   Unfortunately, it was never done except as a last resort, when the mother was almost moribund.   The death-rate, not unnaturally, was so nearly 100 per cent. that even the most skilful surgeons and obstetricians hesitated to undertake the operation.   There was no credit to be gained from it, and bereaved relatives always had the feeling that the unfortunate mother might have lived had she been left alone.

Harvey and Paré advanced the art of midwifery appreciably, if only by indicating that they at least did not regard an interest in such a subject as beneath their dignity.   Pure surgery they lifted over the first great barrier which had barred its advance. There were three of these barriers: hæmorrhage, from which a proportion of the patients operated on always died; wound infection, which took its toll of the survivors; and pain, fear of which prevented many patients from submitting to operations which might have saved their lives.   Paré rediscovered the ligature, and Harvey placed its use upon a rational basis.   As the teaching of these two great surgeons became known and the principles they had emphasized were put into practice, there were fewer and fewer deaths from uncontrollable bleeding. Unhappily, the deaths after operation did not decrease.   Only the cause of these deaths altered, for instead of dying from hæmorrhage at operation patients died from infection of their wounds some days after operation.

The Barber-Surgeons' Company played its part in making midwifery a respectable occupation for Englishmen by granting licences for its practice.   As early as 1610 it is recorded that "this daie James Blackborne was examined touchinge his skill in the generatyve parts of women and bringenge of women to bedd in their dangerous and difficult Labours.   And he the said Blackborne was found fitt and alloued to practize (in that chirurgicall parte of Surgery touching the generatyve parts of women and bringinge them to bedd in their dangerous and difficult Labours) by letters under the seale of the house beinge the date above wrytten."   The Company gave no lectures in midwifery, though anatomical lectures were more frequent and more time was devoted to the teaching of pure surgery.

The Company was in financial straits at this period, and had reluctantly to reduce the number of public dissections to only one a year. These dissections were expensive. Trivial items like supplying linen for the body, perfume, wax candles, soap, and so on, cost very little, but the fees paid to the executioner and his assistants, the lecturer and his stewards, the clerk, the parson, and the sexton, were high. On top of this Kings were constantly requesting "loans" from the Company, which were never repaid, and successive Parliaments demanded increasingly high levies. Money was borrowed till no more could be borrowed, and at length the Company was reduced to pawning its gold plate. Had it not been for Mr. Alderman Arris, who founded the Arris lecture, the plate would have been sold. Even his generosity could not stave off the inevitable for very long, and in 1643 the Barber-Surgeons' Company declared itself bankrupt. In succeeding years the Company gradually recovered its financial stability, and was able to turn its attention again to its quarrels with the College of Physicians.

Up to 1616 the physicians and the Barber-Surgeons had been at peace, if not in amity. In that year, since the apothecaries had been created a separate company, the College of Physicians approached James I and received from him a new charter. This conferred several new privileges, notably that of being able to take proceedings against anyone who administered "inward medicines" and was not a member of the College. The result was that barely a meeting of the College passed without several barber-surgeons being brought before it and summarily fined for infringing this rule. The United Company took action at the first opportunity, which was presented when the offending charter came up before Parliament for ratification. After innumerable delays the matter was settled in 1624, when the House of Commons ordered that the College charter should be submitted to a committee of grievances which would hear also the views of the Barber-Surgeons' Company. The physicians let it go at that and there was comparative peace until 1629, when the Company took the initiative again. It obtained a new charter confirming old privileges and granting it new ones. According to this no one could practise surgery in London or Westminster or within a radius of seven miles without first undergoing an examination, which was to be conducted by the Company. No surgeon could be appointed to a ship leaving the port of London unless he and his chest of surgical supplies and instruments had been similarly examined. Apprentices had to have a certain basic knowledge of Latin. Lectures on surgery were to be arranged every week. These and other rules incensed the physicians, and three years later a most iniquitous Order in Council was promulgated. This was to the effect that no surgeon should amputate a limb, trephine the skull, open the chest or the belly, or undertake any operation more complicated than letting blood or opening abscesses except in the presence of one or more members of the College of Physicians. To have this order reinforced the physicians went to the extent of sponsoring a Bill in the Star Chamber. Against this the surgeons launched a successful campaign, and in 1635 Charles I had this singularly offensive Order expunged.

Expunged it might be, but it was not forgotten. War was declared in real earnest and hostilities were apt to break out on the slightest pretext. When the Protector triumphed, everyone had to subscribe to the famous Covenant. It was ordered that the President of the hated College of Physicians should call the Barber-Surgeons' Company and "tender the Covenant to them". Indignantly the Barber-Surgeons demanded that they should be allowed to subscribe to the Covenant in their own Hall and without any assistance from the physicians. They won their point.

The Company was still having difficulty in obtaining subjects for dissection. Time and again it protested bitterly to the Court of Aldermen of the City of London that "Aliens, fforeyners, Mountebanks, Imposters, and Empiricks" had bribed and corrupted the Executioner and his assistants and obtained bodies for private dissection. It hinted darkly—and probably correctly—that so high were the prices paid by private individuals for subjects that it was worth a murderer's while to create a supply of the material for which there was such a constant demand. The Court of Aldermen was sympathetic, and ordered that the bodies of all executed malefactors should be taken to the Barber-Surgeons' Hall. This order had no effect at all, so the Barber-Surgeons offered an additional 6s. 8d., over and above their usual fees, to the officers in charge of the execution. Theoretically this was for an additional service, the officers being supposed to escort the Company's Beadle, complete with body, to the Barber-Surgeons' Hall. Actually it was probably just a device for tipping the said officers. However intended, it still had no effect. Literal body-snatching became such a profitable business that in 1706, when several criminals were publicly executed at the same time, no fewer than one hundred and fifty soldiers seem to have been hired to create a riot, cut down all the bodies, and carry them away in coaches. The passing of twenty-odd years made the Beadle's task even more difficult. By that time the entertainment value of the executions and the riots which inevitably followed them had been realized by a few bright members of the community. Carts and waggons were parked all round the gallows, and seats on them were available at twopence, threepence, and sixpence. The Court of Aldermen did what it could by giving the Under-Sheriff of Middlesex full powers to read a minor Riot Act if more than twelve persons obstructed or hindered the execution or the carrying of the body to the Barber-Surgeons' Hall. As far as can be gathered, this intermittent reading merely added to the gaiety of London.

The Company must have obtained a proportion of the available bodies, for the Masters continued to give public lectures on the internal organs, the muscles, and the bones of the human body. Their material was still scanty enough to make them exploit every body to the full, but some material there must have been. It was easy to ensure that each body should assist in the teaching of the three main subjects—anatomy, pathology, and operative surgery. The cadaver was carefully prepared, coloured waxes being injected into the arteries and veins to show them up more clearly. One side of the body would be dissected to display the anatomical structures, while on the opposite side operations would be performed. How much pathology was taught from a particular body was a matter of chance, but every diseased or abnormal organ was demonstrated, and the lecturer would discuss the operations that might possibly have been performed to correct this or that deformity. The lectures were always advertised in the *Daily Post,* the *Daily Advertiser,* the *London Evening Post,* and the *St. James's Evening Post,* up to 1742, when this practice was discontinued in an endeavour to increase the teaching value of the dissections, which had tended, like the executions which preceded them, to become public entertainments. This giving up of public advertising and concentration on anatomical and surgical teaching was a sign of the times. Newly created hospitals were springing up all over London. At them a young man could learn more practical surgery in a month than in twelve months spent attending the Barber-Surgeons' lectures. The Company had had troubles enough in the past, with the physicians, with the Executioner, with Kings and Parliaments, with its own apprentices, with quacks and charlatans, and with the moneylenders, but never before had there been any competition in the province of surgical teaching.

The early eighteenth century saw a wave of philanthropy sweep over Britain. There was a revulsion of feeling following the last few decades of the seventeenth century, when social conditions in England were almost at their lowest. Hospitals founded by different religious orders had been in existence since the twelfth century. There were, for example, St. Bartholomew's Hospital, which had been founded in 1123 by Rahere, the jester turned monk, and on the opposite side of the Thames, St. Thomas's Hospital, which was burnt down in 1207 and rebuilt a few years later. At the time of the Reformation the nuns who had acted as nurses, and the Augustinian canons who had long attended the sick poor, disappeared, but many of the old monastic traditions still clung to hospital administration and practice. Each hospital had a church within its walls, and prayers were said twice a day. Devout men in their wills still disposed equal charities to the church and to the hospital. Physicians and surgeons were appointed for life, and, though allowed private practice, were resident in the hospital. Harvey was one of the earliest of the physicians of St. Bartholomew's to live outside the hospital. Prolonged negotiations and much discussion took place before it was finally agreed that he should be allowed to reside outside the hospital and should be given an increased yearly stipend in lieu of the house which might have been his, rent free, within the hospital grounds. The sisters who had charge of different wards were appointed for life in exactly the same way as the medical and surgical staff, and lost their identity just as completely as the nuns they had succeeded, for they were known by the names of the wards in their charge. The many great hospitals which came into being in the early eighteenth century often started as small dispensaries financed by a single charitable individual, or perhaps a small group of philanthropists. They were so obviously useful, and the patients attracted to them were so numerous, that they quickly expanded. A dispensary at Westminster, which was to become the Westminster Hospital, was founded in 1719. Guy's Hospital appeared six years later. In 1728 the Jervis Street Hospital was erected in Dublin. The following year saw the foundation of Edinburgh's famous Royal Infirmary. Within the next twenty years Winchester and Bristol followed Edinburgh's lead, and to the growing list of London hospitals were added St. George's, the Middlesex, and the London Hospital itself.

Surgery at this time was entering upon a new phase. Richard Wiseman, who died in 1676, was perhaps the last of the great military surgeons. Surgeons before him were trained on the field of battle, spent most of their lives with the army, and only in their declining years did they settle down and practise a desultory civil surgery which reflected very exactly their war surgery. That is, they confined their activities to dealing with wounds and amputating limbs. There were outstanding exceptions, of course, notably John of Arderne with his work on fistula-in-ano, but, in general, up to the end of the seventeenth century surgery was the surgery of war. Civil ailments, such as cataract of the eye, stone in the bladder, wryneck, and so on, were left to the itinerant quacks. Then the two oldest hospitals, St. Bartholomew's and St. Thomas's, began to expand their accommodation and appoint to their staffs young surgeons instead of aged war veterans. These men did the amputations that they had been taught to do, and treated on orthodox lines the wounds that were sustained in riots and free-fights. But in the hospitals there were so many patients that inevitably they found some with wrynecks, stones in the bladder, and similar conditions, who had escaped the far-flung net of the strolling mountebanks. The operations for these conditions had not been taught to the young surgeons, but they saw no reason why they should not attempt them. They did attempt them with increasing success, and the already great flow of patients to the hospitals was increased. Apprentices of the Barber-Surgeons' Company must have seen some of this work, which was then novel and exciting, and had in addition the exhilaration of being an invasion of quack territory. The surgeons of these hospitals were willing to teach, and needed no bond of apprenticeship and no seven years in which to convey their knowledge. Rough and ready operating-theatres had as many patients passing through them in a day as the Barber-Surgeons' Hall had bodies for dissection and demonstration in a year. Young men began to go direct to the surgeons of St. Thomas's and St. Bartholomew's rather than apprentice themselves to the Barber-Surgeons' Company.

The United Company of Barbers and Surgeons, in 1684 in common with many other guilds, had had to surrender its hardly won charter. Its power was ebbing, and it even entered into an alliance with another Company which had fallen upon evil days. That this Company should have been that of the Periwig-makers did little to appease the growing unrest of the surgical members. Fewer young men were apprenticing themselves to barber-surgery, and, apart from the unhappy alliance with the wig-makers, the reason was not far to seek. In October, 1695, a complaint was directed by certain of the barber-surgeons against St. Thomas's Hospital. It was alleged that St. Thomas's —and other hospitals—were breeding many illiterate and unskilful "pretenders to Chyrurgery", promising to have anyone at all well qualified as a surgeon within six or twelve months. Fees were paid for these short courses at St. Thomas's and at St. Bartholomew's, but were barely a quarter of the fees necessary for apprenticeship. This "subverting the very fundamentalls of ye Legall Education by way of apprenticeship" was made the subject of inquiry, and the surgeons of St. Thomas's explained to the Court of the Barber-Surgeons how the situation had arisen. They indignantly denied the suggestion that any of them had ever taken apprentices for a term of less than the usual seven years. But with conscious rectitude they admitted having allowed to act as their "dressers"—that is, assist them at operations and dress their patients' wounds—young men who had had the misfortune to be apprenticed to country surgeons. These young men wished to supplement their experience by an intensive six or twelve months at hospital, and it was surely a public service to assist them in this laudable desire. The Company could not doubt the word of the surgeons of St. Thomas's. It could not ask these surgeons to inquire closely into the history of the young men they took as their dressers, and to make sure that they had been apprenticed to provincial surgeons. However, the Company could, and did, return the conscientious provincials to the provinces whence they came by sternly forbidding these young men to practise surgery within a seven-mile radius of London.

The Governors of St. Thomas's in 1702 officially recognized the system of teaching which had grown up rather haphazardly, and began to regulate it so far as their own hospital was concerned. They laid it down that no surgeon should take more than three pupils at a time or take any of them for less than twelve months. In this way, despite the opposition of the

Barber-Surgeons' Company, great medical schools came into being. The dissatisfaction of the surgeons with their colleagues, the barbers and their associated periwig-makers, was growing. Surgeon members of the Company who were in the Army or Navy were occasionally captured and held prisoner. Sometimes they were in the honourable captivity accorded to surgeons. More often they were treated as barbers, and this annoyed them exceedingly. Surgeons at home felt just as strongly about the growing unhappiness of a marriage which had been celebrated merrily enough two hundred years previously. What rankled most was the way in which the superior College of Physicians still treated them as if they were barbers, or worse, enforcing always the rule that no surgeon could give "inward physic". This disability was not to be completely removed till the early nineteenth century, but the surgeons felt that they would have a better chance of meeting the physicians on equal terms if they could cut adrift from the barbers. As early as 1684 they petitioned the King to this end, but it was not until 1744 that they were really strong enough to effect a separation. In December of that year the surgeon members of the Court of Assistants of the United Company of Barbers and Surgeons gave formal notice of their desire to separate. They presented the case which they proposed to put before the House of Commons, and a committee of both barbers and surgeons was set up to consider this document and report to the next full meeting of the Court of Assistants in January. The barbers opposed the separation, but, at the end of the month, the surgeons presented their petition to Parliament. A committee examined it and heard the barbers' arguments against it. The committee reported favourably to the House, and leave was given to bring in a Bill. Amendments were made to the Bill in the course of its passage through the House, notably one to the effect that the new Surgeons' Company should be responsible for examining all candidates for surgeoncies in the Army. The licensing of naval surgeons had, of course, been in the hands of the United Company ever since its incorporation in the reign of Henry VIII. Finally, on May 2, 1745, having passed successively through the House of Commons and the House of Lords, the Bill received the Royal Assent and became law.

The newly-created body of The Masters, Governors, and Commonalty of the Art and Science of Surgery carried away from the parent Company two bequests and little else. One was the annuity of £16 bequeathed in 1655 by John Gale, himself a surgeon and one of the grandsons of the great Thomas Gale, for an osteological lecture. The other was the interest on the sum of £510 left by Mr. Alderman Arris. Jasper Arris had been a barber practising some surgery. His son, Mr. Alderman Edward Arris, was a surgeon who did no barbery, while of Mr. Alderman Arris's twenty-three children one became a surgeon and another a Fellow of the College of Physicians. These two bequests are to-day administered together as the Arris and Gale lectureship. The Hall of the United Company, the library, and all the fine plate remained with the barbers. The advantages the surgeons gained, however, were appreciable financially quite apart from the increase in prestige. Fees for apprenticeship could be fixed upon a much lower scale. The expenses of the new Company were far less, and so fines could be correspondingly reduced. The old Company had been exempted from serving in certain expensive city offices, but the exemptions rested upon insecure and debatable rulings of different Kings and different Parliaments. The new Company was expressly and unmistakably exempted from the duty of filling the offices of constable, overseer of the poor, and all parish and ward offices. In brief, those who joined the new Surgeons' Company had all the privileges of the old Barber-Surgeons' Company, and certain additional ones, for about a quarter of what these same privileges would have cost them as members of the old United Company.

The move for the creation of a new and separate Company had been approved by almost all the surgeons, but two men were particularly active in bringing about this advance: Mr. John Ranby, then Principal Sergeant-Surgeon to King George II, and Mr. William Cheselden, who had been surgeon to Queen Caroline, and was surgeon to the Chelsea Hospital and surgeon and lithotomist to the recently founded St. George's Hospital. John Ranby was the last Sergeant-Surgeon to follow the example of Henry Morstede and accompany his King into battle. Just as Morstede had been with Henry IV at Agincourt, so Ranby was with George II at the Battle of Dettingen in 1743. He linked Wiseman and all the surgeons before him who were trained in battle with the surgeons of the eighteenth century who were purely civil surgeons.

Ranby was born in 1703, the son of an inn-keeper, in the parish of St. Martin's-in-the-Fields. At the age of nine, for the sum of £32 5s., he was bound apprentice to a member of the Barber-Surgeons' Company. Ten years later the Company examined him and passed him as fit to practise surgery. After that his rise was rapid, for 1738 saw him appointed Surgeon-in-Ordinary to the King's Household, 1740 Sergeant-Surgeon to the King, and 1743 Principal Sergeant-Surgeon. His influence with the King did much to effect the long-desired separation of the surgeons from the Barber-Surgeons' Company, and as a result he was nominated as first Master of the new Surgeons' Company, while Mr. Cheselden took office as his Warden. At the end of his year as Master, Ranby presented to the Surgeons' Company a silver loving-cup, which is still preserved at the present Royal College of Surgeons of England. He was re-elected Master in 1751, and again in 1752.

He published, soon after his return from the German campaign, *A Method of Treating Gunshot Wounds*, and several short papers, of which the most interesting by far is an account of the last illness of Sir Robert Walpole, the great Prime Minister who was brought to power by the bursting of the "South Sea Bubble"—a wildcat speculation which ruined thousands of families, and in which all classes from paupers to the Prince of Wales, and from begger-women to the King's blowsy German mistresses, were involved. Walpole had so many stones in his bladder that they must have been accumulating for years. On one occasion at least they led to his political undoing. Walpole had had imprisoned in the Tower of London a well-known physician, Dr. John Freind, Member of Parliament for Launceston. The so-called "Bishops' Plot" had just been discovered, and those involved were promptly imprisoned. Freind was attending one of the Bishops implicated, and for that reason—and apparently no other—Walpole ordered his arrest. Soon afterwards the Prime Minister was laid low by an intense pain caused by his vesical stones. Dr. Mead, the most distinguished physician of that day, was sent for to relieve the Ministerial agony. Mead expressed the indignation of the whole profession at Freind's wrongful arrest, and refused to do anything at all for his patient until an order for Freind's release was signed. It is doubtful if any Prime Minister, before or since, has ever signed an order more rapidly.

These same stones were at last responsible for Walpole's death. He was attended by Ranby, Dr. Crewe, and Sir Edward

Hulse. From the surgeon's own account it appears that he had a fierce quarrel with the two physicians. They wished to give their patient a "Lithontryptic Lixivium", an elixir which would dissolve the stones. Ranby rightly condemned this fearful mixture, which was said to be four times stronger than the most powerful alkali used in the making of soap. If it was so, then it would certainly have dissolved the stones, and also the patient's bladder and any other organs with which it happened to come in contact. Ranby was said to have been a man of strong views, vain disposition, and inelegant manners. Whatever his disposition or his manners, he did a great deal to advance his profession, not only directly by playing a leading part in effecting the separation of the surgeons from the barbers, but also by himself reaching a stage at which he could quarrel with physicians. Quarrelling with physicians is not, and never was, an ideal to be aimed at, but that of being on an equal footing with physicians— of which quarrelling was but an outward and visible sign—was an ideal which the eighteenth century was to see almost realized. Ranby helped a great deal in this direction, but the two men who were to do most to establish surgeons as being equal with physicians in the public eye were his friend and contemporary William Cheselden, and, later, Percivall Pott.

XIV. Surgeons Become Gentlemen

WILLIAM CHESELDEN WAS THE MOST OUTSTANDING FIGURE IN English surgery during the first half of the eighteenth century. His general education, the high esteem in which he was held by the best-known men of his day, and his varied talents as something of an architect, as a pugilist, a *bon viveur,* a wit, and above all else as an original and amazingly skilful surgeon, gave him a social standing and a degree of personal popularity greater probably than those achieved by any surgeon before him.   The descendant of an old and wealthy family, he was born at Somerby, in Leicestershire, in 1688.   He was apprenticed for some time to Mr. Wilkes, a surgeon of Leicester, and then, at the age of fifteen, he became a pupil of William Cowper, a noted anatomist, before finally being bound apprentice to Mr. James Ferne of St. Thomas's Hospital.   Ferne was surgeon and lithotomist to the hospital, having been specially licensed to cut for stone, and it was probably this early association that led Cheselden later to take such an interest in lithotomy.   The young man made rapid progress as a surgeon and as an anatomist, accumulating in his spare time no little reputation as an amateur pugilist.   He was admitted to the Freedom and Livery of the Barber-Surgeons' Company in 1710, and a few months later obtained the "great diploma" of the Company, which entitled him to a specialized practice in surgery.

Twelve months later he was giving a series of lectures on anatomy, which in the course of a few years proved popular enough to bring down upon his head the grave displeasure of the Barber-Surgeons' Company.   He was solemnly accused before a Court of Assistants of procuring bodies from the public executioner, dissecting them at his own house—which was still forbidden—and so making it difficult for the Company to obtain bodies, and giving lectures on the same days as the Company's public lectures, thereby drawing away from the Company's dissection many who might otherwise have attended. This last naïve admission gave an early indication of Cheselden's considerable success as a lecturer and demonstrator.   On promising not to dissect without the permission of the Governors of the Company, and never at a time when the public lectures were being held, the offender was let off with a severe reprimand. With these provisos the lectures continued for some time at

Cheselden's own house in Crane Court, Fleet Street, and later at St. Thomas's. There were four courses a year, and each consisted of thirty-five lectures. They were advertised in the *Daily Courant*, and the advertisement had a footnote:

> N.B.—This course being chiefly intended for gentlemen, such things only will be omitted as are neither instructive nor entertaining, and care will be taken to have nothing offensive.

These lectures may have prompted Cheselden's election as a Fellow of the Royal Society in 1712, and his publication in 1713 of an *Anatomy of the Human Body*, which was popular enough to run through thirteen editions, the last appearing forty years after his death. This book he dedicated to Sir Richard Mead, the famous physician. Cheselden applied twice for the post of Assistant Surgeon to St. Thomas's before he was finally appointed in 1718, becoming a principal surgeon in the following year. There he was able to continue Ferne's work on cutting for stone.

Lithotomy, the operation for removing stones from the bladder, was known to the Egyptians, and was also extensively practised by the Hindoo surgeons. The situation of the bladder is such that it may be opened into from above, through the lower abdomen, or from below, through the perineum in men or the vagina in women. The Hindoo surgeons seem to have used the approach through the abdomen, while the itinerant charlatans with whom they were in competition extracted stones through the perineum. In women both used the same technique, performing the lithotomy through the vagina, which is in intimate contact with the bladder. Hippocrates neither practised nor taught lithotomy. Celsus, however, described a method of removing stones without needing to cut the patient. A small blunt hook was passed into the bladder and behind the stone so as to hold it firmly in place. The stone was then pounded into little pieces by another instrument, and the pieces were removed with a slim spoon or else passed in the urine. For over a thousand years the cutting operation was neglected by surgeons but practised by quacks. Just as the operation for the plastic reconstruction of the nose was a technique handed down from father to son by families of travelling mountebanks, so was lithotomy a journeyman craft practised in different ways by different families, though almost always by the perineal route, but for hundreds of years without any assistance from orthodox surgery. In the sixteenth century the Colot family took up the operation and made it respectable again. France at this time, under the inspiring influence of Ambroise Paré, was a nursery for good surgeons. A young contemporary of Paré's was Pierre Franco, who improved the operation of perineal lithotomy by inventing instruments for it better than any devised before, and rediscovered the suprapubic or abdominal type of operation. It was Franco, too, who made a great advance in hernitomy when he pointed out that in trying to cure a double rupture it was not necessary to remove both testicles—as had been the accepted practice for many years. Another Frenchman was Frère Jacques, the greatest of the unqualified journeyman lithotomists. At first a labourer and later a soldier, Jacques joined the Franciscan monks and became Frère Jacques. He was famous throughout Europe for his skill in both suprapubic and perineal lithotomy. He preferred the latter method, and made an important improvement in its technique. Previously the incision into the perineum was always in the mid-line. Long experience and a study of the anatomy of the parts made it clear to Frère Jacques that the mid-line incision divided or endangered important structures unnecessarily. An incision perhaps an inch lateral to, that is, to one or other side of, the mid-line had none of these disadvantages, and allowed the stone to be extracted just as easily. In this way he devised the so-called lateral lithotomy. Knowledge of Frère Jacques's technique spread slowly, till a Dutchman, Rau, studied the method and himself improved on it in certain respects.

In England in the middle of the seventeenth century a few surgeons were venturing to cut for stone, the cut being in the mid-line through the perineum. Thus was extracted the famous stone which had troubled Samuel Pepys. Pepys had his stone mounted in an elegant box, which would show it off to the best advantage. Every year on May 1 he gave a party to those of his friends who had gone through the same ordeal. Stones and notes would be compared, and a good time was had by all. The operation was practised with increasing frequency, and wandering charlatans who had had a monopoly of it for hundreds of years were gradually ousted by vested professional interests. Surgeon Ferne of St. Thomas's had been also lithotomist to the hospital, and, as his pupil, Cheselden took up the same operation when he was at last appointed to the staff in 1718. Five years later he published his *Treatise on the High Operation for Stone* and later

still, in 1733, the *Osteographia, or the Anatomy of the Bones*.
The *Osteographia* was one of the best illustrated books on this
subject ever published. It contained full and accurate descriptions of all the human bones, and also of the bones of many
animals. The whole book and all its illustrations reveal how
Cheselden, and the artists and assistants who worked with him,
did all they could to infuse a breath of life into the old dry bones.
The frontispiece, for example, shows Galen meditating upon the
skeleton of a bandit, who had been very properly killed by the
wayfarers he would have robbed. The skeleton of a crocodile
is shown paddling peacefully along the borders of the Nile,
towards an undoubted oasis, while in the background is one of
the pyramids. A skeleton heron has a skeleton fish in its bill,
and a skeleton cat with tail erect and back superbly arched is
retreating from a ferocious structure of canine bones.

The *Treatise on the High Operation for Stone* described
Cheselden's method of performing suprapubic lithotomy, a
method which he was soon to abandon. Both books were
violently attacked by Dr. John Douglas, a Scot who was surgeon-
lithotomist to the Westminster Hospital. Douglas had just
published a book—describing the same operation—which, with
Scotch modesty, he had entitled *Lithotomia Douglassiana*. He
accused Cheselden of plagiarizing his work, quite unmindful of
the fact that Cheselden had praised his book and his work, and
acknowledged, too, his indebtedness to Pierre Franco and other
lithotomists. When the *Osteographia* appeared, Douglas attacked it with equal venom, not for any good reason but just
on general principles. The only effect his animadversions had
was to increase the interest in, and the sale of, both books. The
treatise on suprapubic lithotomy dated quickly, for on March 27,
1727, Mr. William Cheselden performed a lateral lithotomy
more rapidly and yet with a better technique than any lithotomist
before him.

The patient was brought into the operating-room. A thick
blanket was doubled several times and placed at the end of a
flat table about three feet high. Two young assistants helped
the man to perch himself upon this blanket. Then they made
him lie back, and deftly tied him so that his knees were raised
high but kept apart. One of them passed the staff, a slim,
grooved rod curved at its blunt end and about nine inches long,
into the man's bladder. It was held there by the other assistant.
Mr. William Cheselden had been arranging five innocuous-

looking instruments in the order in which he would use them. He sat on a low stool and took up a scalpel. The two assistants watched him intently. He was pale and anxious, his heavy face drawn. Then Mr. Cheselden's full lips tightened almost imperceptibly. The razor-sharp scalpel sank deeply into taut flesh, and was drawn downwards and outwards. Two fingers of the surgeon's left hand pressed deep into the long wound, which was well to the left of the mid-line of the perineum. The assistant holding the long staff felt how unerringly the forefinger of his right hand sought and found the tip of the staff. The scalpel cut on to it, held so that the second and deeper incision was from below upwards. By what was almost sleight of hand a long gorget was passed down the groove in the staff, and at the same time blunt forceps were passed through the wound and into the bladder to meet both staff and gorget. The forceps were moved slowly, opened quickly, pressed deeper into the wound, closed, and then dextrously withdrawn, the blunt ends holding firmly a large, chalky-white stone. Stone and forceps were put on one side. A crooked needle, ready threaded, passed quickly beneath still-spurting blood-vessels, being prevented by the two fingers of the left hand from endangering the gut. The ligatures tied, a piece of lint deliberately besmeared with blood was applied to the wound. Mr. Cheselden turned and examined the stone, then went over to the apprentices who had been watching. One of them had a huge watch in his hand.

"One minute, fifteen seconds, sir."

There was a murmur of awed approval.

Mr. Cheselden left the theatre to begin his tour of the wards, and the young men walked the hospital with him. The one with the watch was able to record before his apprenticeship ended that Mr. Cheselden could, and on a score of occasions did, perform his perfected operation for lateral lithotomy in exactly fifty-four seconds.

This operation established Cheselden's reputation. In December of 1727 he was appointed surgeon to Queen Caroline. Paris, which from the time of Paré had been the hub of the surgical world, recognized his greatness. He was made a Corresponding Member of the Royal Academy of Sciences of Paris, and he was the first foreigner to be elected to the French Royal Academy of Surgery on its establishment in 1732. In 1734 he was appointed to the staff of the newly-founded St.

George's Hospital. There he worked for four years, before resigning this and his other hospital appointments twelve months after he had taken up the post of surgeon to the Chelsea Hospital. Always, wherever he was and whatever operation he undertook, he was sick and pallid with anxiety before he began operating. One of the French surgeons who came over to see his work laughed at this disability. Cheselden said nothing at the time, but he took his French guest to see a boxing-match and thoroughly enjoyed his discomfiture as two pugilistic friends of his proceeded with bare fists to batter each other's faces into pulp.

Cheselden published the results of his operation of lateral lithotomy as he had practised it on the patients of St. Thomas's. The many operations he had performed in private practice he did not include in his statistics, since they were not "sufficiently witnessed". The operations at St. Thomas's had all been more than enough witnessed—by his pupils and apprentices, and by surgeons from every country in Europe—and there were no fewer than two hundred and thirteen of them. The death-rate from the operation was amazingly low. In Cheselden's own words:

> . . . Of the first fifty only three died; of the second fifty, three; of the third fifty, eight; and of the last sixty-three, six. Several of these patients had the smallpox during their cure, some of which died but I think not more in proportion than what usually die of that distemper; these are not reckoned among those who died of the operation. The reason why so few died in the two first fifties was that at that time, few very bad cases offered; in the third, the operation being in high request, even the most aged and the most miserable cases expected to be saved by it. One of the three that died out of the first fifty was very ill with whooping cough; another bled to death by an artery into the bladder, it being very hot weather at that time. But this accident taught me afterwards, whenever a vessel bled that I could find, to dilate the wound with a knife till I could see it.

That so few should have died was directly due to the skill and speed with which the operation was performed, so that hæmorrhage was slight and shock hardly appreciable, and to the fact that "all the dressings during the cure are very slight". Had he wished, Cheselden could probably have spent the rest of his life doing lateral lithotomies and nothing else, but he was too original a surgeon to devote himself to that which he had perfected. He operated successfully upon a child of thirteen for congenital cataract, and gave a vivid account of the boy's sensations when he was able to see for the first time. He described, too, the operation of iridectomy, or slitting the iris and so making an artificially enlarged pupil to relieve certain eye conditions.

Another operation showed how he applied anatomical knowledge to surgical problems. The upper jaw has to either side a large cavity—an antrum—in which pus occasionally collects. Cheselden examined many of these bones carefully, and realized that extraction of the last, or last two, molars would usually make an opening into the lowest part of the cavity. He advised such extraction to drain pus from the antrum. The simplicity of his instruments is well shown by his concluding remarks on this operation. He pointed out that occasionally the drawing of a tooth did not leave the desired opening. If this was so, or if the opening made was not large enough to drain off the pus effectively, he advised that the opening should "be made or enlarged with a carpenter's nail-piercer or gimblet which is as good an instrument as can be for the purpose".

Excess of scientific zeal cost Cheselden his appointment as surgeon to the Queen. There was a deaf criminal, Charles Ray, who had been sentenced to death. Cheselden wanted to perforate this man's ear-drums to see if it improved his hearing. The man was told that he could submit to the operation and receive a free pardon, or else be hanged. Had all gone well, Cheselden might have advanced the surgery of the ear as much as he had that of the eye and the bladder. Unfortunately, the man developed a fever and was in no state to be subjected to operation. While he was being nursed back to health news of the projected experiment leaked out. There was a public outcry. The Court had to bow to public opinion and the operation was forbidden. As usual, public opinion was not satisfied and demanded, in effect, that somebody should suffer something. Cheselden was the selected sufferer, and in 1733 when the Queen died from the strangulation of an umbilical rupture Cheselden was not among those present.

The loss of Court favour meant little to Cheselden. Patients still crowded to his rooms to have their stones dealt with, despite the fact that his fee was always £500. Money then had a value almost three times as great as to-day, but private patients were not wanting. Men who could not afford his fee he treated for nothing, admitting them to his wards at

St. Thomas's or St. George's Hospital. So it was not unusual for gentlemen to wait their turn at the great charitable hospitals, and then donate as much as £100 to the hospital charity box. Cheselden's friends cared not a whit about his dismissal from Court. Sir Isaac Newton was one of them; Cheselden attended him on his death-bed in 1727. Sir Hans Sloane was another. Sloane had succeeded Newton as the President of the Royal Society, and was one of the most popular and successful physicians of his day, being President of the College of Physicians for many years. It was his own collection of plants, animals, fossils, manuscripts, and curios that, as a bequest to the nation, formed the nucleus from which grew the British Museum. A closer friend and an even more distinguished one was Alexander Pope, the poet. In a letter to Swift, dated March 25, 1736, Pope indicated something of the esteem in which he held Cheselden:

> As soon as I had sent my last letter, I received a most kind one from you, expressing great pain for my late illness at Mr. Cheselden's. I conclude you was eased of that friendly apprehension in a few days after you had despatched yours, for mine must have reached you then. I wondered a little at your *quaere,* who Cheselden was. It shews that the truest merit does not travel so far any way as on the wings of Poetry; he is the most noted and most deserving man in the whole profession of Chirurgery; and has saved the lives of thousands by his manner of cutting for the stone.

This same esteem prompted the reference to Cheselden and to Sir Richard Mead, the great physician who handled Sir Robert Walpole in such cavalier fashion, in the *Epistle to Lord Bolingbroke*:

> Late as it is, I put myself to school,
> And feel some comfort not to be a fool.
> Weak though I am of limb and short of sight,
> Far from a lynx and not a giant quite;
> I'll do what Mead and Cheselden advise
> To help these limbs and to preserve these eyes.
> Not to go back is somewhat to advance,
> And men must walk at least before they dance.

Another letter from Pope to Cheselden himself reveals how friendly they were:

> DEAR SIR—You know my laconic style. I never forget you. Are you well? I am so. How does Mrs. Cheselden? Had it not been for her, you had been here. Here are three cataracts ripened for you (Mr.

Pierce assures me). Don't tell your wife that. . . . Adieu. I don't intend to go to London. Good-night; but answer me.

Yours A. POPE.

Bath, Nov. 21st.

Shew this to Mr. Richardson, and let him take it to himself—and to his son—he has no wife.

Two other men whom Cheselden knew well were Voltaire and John Ranby. As a member of the Barber-Surgeons' Company, Cheselden, after being forgiven for his illegal dissecting and competitive lecturing, went through the usual offices, and was Junior Warden in 1744. Then Ranby and he effected the long-wanted separation from the Barbers, and Cheselden, rightly, succeeded Ranby as Master of the new Surgeons' Company. At that time he was continuing his anatomical and surgical lectures at the Chelsea Hospital. Among his pupils was Thomas Cadwalader, a young man from Philadelphia who wrote the first medical monograph to be published in America. James Lloyd was another American; he introduced in Boston the method of lithotomy he had learnt from Cheselden, and the technique of amputating limbs by making skin-flaps rather than by a circular incision. Most famous of all his pupils was John Hunter, who worked under Cheselden until 1751, when an apoplectic seizure forced the great lithotomist to retire to Bath. There he died twelve months later. He was interred on the north side of the Chelsea Hospital Burial-ground, where his tomb can still be seen. More lasting than any tombstone were the Old Putney Bridge, for which he drew the plans, the Surgeons' Company he helped to create, the lateral lithotomy he perfected, and the prestige he gave to surgeons and to surgery. In the seventeenth century France had led the world of surgery. In the early eighteenth century leadership in surgery was taken by Cheselden, and from then onwards through that century the best surgical teaching and practice in the world centred in London.

Cheselden was quickly succeeded as the greatest surgeon of his day by a young contemporary. Percivall Pott was born in 1715, the year in which George I succeeded Queen Anne, in a house in Threadneedle Street where the Bank of England now stands. Mr. Pott, a scrivener in the City, died when his infant son, Percivall, was only four months old, and Percivall and his mother were taken under the immediate care of a distant relative, Dr. Wilcox, the Bishop of Rochester. Financial aid was also given them by the Houblons, for Mrs. Pott's first brief marriage had been to a Lieutenant Houblon, who was killed in action only a few months after. The Houblons were a family of great merchant princes, who, with others like them, founded the Bank of England. With their help and that of the Bishop, young Percivall received an excellent early education. Chances of preferment in the Church were assured the boy, but he would have none of them. He wanted to be a surgeon, and since surgery was now a respectable profession—though not yet as respectable as the Church or the Law—there was no reason to force him into holy orders. Accordingly, at the age of sixteen, Percivall was apprenticed to Edward Nourse, one of the two surgeons then on the staff of St. Bartholomew's Hospital, for a fee of two hundred guineas. Nourse had a private school, where he lectured on anatomy and surgery. His lectures were largely attended by pupils and apprentices of St. Bartholomew's, just as Cheselden's lectures attracted students from St. Thomas's. Pott was soon busy preparing the subjects for his master's dissections—subjects obtained probably just as Cheselden's were. Later he was given much of the dissection to do himself. At the same time he was accompanying Mr. Nourse round the wards, watching and perhaps assisting at his operations, and reading many of the established surgical works. The works of the older authorities he read avidly, but rightly regarded them as "more valuable for their accurate descriptions of diseases than for their practical value". The books of Ranby, Cheselden, and others he must have read as they appeared. His apprenticeship ended, Pott was admitted to the freedom of the Company of Barber-Surgeons, and on September 7, 1736, he was publicly examined by the Court of Examiners.

The Court first of all debated as to whether they should examine him. It was customary at that time for the candidate to call formally upon all the Governors and Examiners and "desire the favour of their presence at his examination". The custom persists to this day in a modified form, for woe betide the applicant for a position on the staff of a London hospital who neglects to call upon every member of the medical board. Pott had failed in this duty, but since he had been called out of town, "to attend Sir Robert Goodsall's Lady", and had been so long detained that he had not had time to make the calls, and had explained this circumstance to one of the Wardens, it was finally resolved "That the Court would proceed to the examination of the said Mr. Pott notwithstanding his default in attending the Examiners, but this is not to be a precedent in time to come to any other person". The said Mr. Pott acquitted himself well, and was granted the "great diploma", which testified to his skill in surgery and empowered him to practise. So the young man took a house in Fenchurch Street and engaged in active practice, though continuing to assist Nourse at his lectures and actually delivering some of them himself, after Nourse had stopped teaching at his home and was giving a recognized course at St. Bartholomew's. Pott was elected assistant surgeon to the hospital in 1745, being made full surgeon four years later. In the interval his mother had died and Pott had married Sarah, the daughter of Joseph Cruttenden. At the first meeting of the new Surgeons' Company Cruttenden had been appointed Clerk to the Company.

Pott was small and rather spare of figure. His disposition was lively, and he was fond of talking and of society. He was clean-shaven, wore a wig, and usually a plum-coloured velvet coat with ruffles at wrist and throat, and on special occasions a dress sword. He had all the qualities necessary to a successful surgeon, and successful he was. In the first forty years of his life he had published only a short account of an unusual case of a tumour which had produced softening of the underlying bones. Then in 1756 an accident gave him enforced leisure in which he discovered that he could write and that he had, in fact, rather more than a taste for it. He was riding down the Old Kent Road to visit the Lock Hospital, on a frosty morning in January, when his horse slipped and he was thrown. He sustained a compound fracture of the leg, the broken bone being forced through the flesh and the skin perhaps an inch away from the actual site of the fracture. A coach was brought and the crowd which had gathered were anxious to lift him into it. Pott refused to be moved. He knew just how serious a fracture he had sustained, and how much more serious it would become if improperly or roughly handled, or if subjected to the jolting of a coach. Despite the bitter cold he lay where he was till two chairmen had been brought from Westminster with the long poles which they used for carrying sedan chairs. Then he purchased the door from a nearby house, had it torn from its hinges, and instructed the chairmen to nail it to their poles. When this had been done to his satisfaction, he was laid on the door and carried gently and slowly through Southwark and over London Bridge to his home, with the least possible disturbance to his broken limb. His colleagues, hastily summoned, decided on immediate amputation. Pott consented to this and the instruments were got ready. Then Pott's old master, Nourse, arrived. He examined the limb and thought there was a chance of saving it. Pott was convinced that no one could judge his own case, and so he left it to his colleagues. Nourse argued that the opening through the skin being some distance away from the fracture, there was less likelihood of infection of the wound spreading to the bone itself than if the bone had pierced the skin immediately over the break. He convinced his colleagues. They reduced the fracture, splinted it, and left it alone. Nourse was right. The wound healed quickly and the broken bone united, but the surgeon become patient had to lie up for a long time. He began to write a book, a *Treatise on Ruptures*, which was published a year later.

This book set a standard for his later works. In it Pott described fully the anatomy and the surgery of his subject as it was known at that time. Its great value lay in the refutation on anatomical grounds of many of the old theories of the causation of rupture, and methods of treatment based on those theories. Pott cleared the ground for other surgeons, and in addition described for the first time, though he was not the first to observe it, congenital hernia, a rupture which is present at birth. He recorded many of his own cases including, over and above the usual types of rupture, hernia of the liver, of the spleen, of the ovary, and of the bladder. He dealt with the possibility of a rupture which included a part of the intestine becoming twisted and strangulated, and urged the importance of early operation in these cases. The success of his first book encouraged Pott to continue his literary endeavours, and from then onwards he was publishing books every two or three years. In 1758 he wrote his *Observations on that Disorder of the Corner of the Eye commonly called Fistula Lachrymalis*. Tears are always flowing from the lachrymal glands, but except under emotional or other stress they are conducted down a minute duct into the nose. If this becomes blocked, then "crocodile tears" flow perpetually and inflammation of the eye and the eye-lids may soon result. Pott described this condition exactly, and on anatomical grounds made it clear that the cause was always some degree of obstruction of the duct leading into the nose. He advised against the passing of a probe down the duct, believing that this simply introduced inflammation or made an existing inflammation worse. In the simplest cases he insisted that no surgery was needed, and where the obstruction was more advanced he always tried first to syringe fluid down the duct and clear it in that way.

Two years later came another book, this time on *Injuries to the Head from External Violence*. Here Pott described a puffy swelling of the scalp indicative of localized inflammation inside the skull, which has ever since been known as Pott's puffy tumour. This work again refuted many popular errors, and brought some system into the treatment of head injuries, if only by a careful classification according to the extent of the injury. It gives a glimpse of the way such injuries were sustained at that time. One case was that of a man who was unwise enough to resist the press-gang, another that of a girl who was tossed by a bull in Smithfield Market. Pott was giving a regular course of lectures in anatomy and surgery at this time, but still he kept on writing. In 1768 he published his treatise on *Fractures and Dislocations*, outlining methods of treatment which were to be adopted all over the world. Two most important points he made in this book were the necessity for immediate setting of a fracture, and the need for relaxation of the muscles if the setting was to be done properly. He described in detail, too, the fracture of the ankle which is now known as Pott's fracture. Another condition associated with his name, which again he was the first to describe accurately, is Pott's disease, that is, curvature of the spine due to a tuberculous "caries" and causing some degree of paralysis of the lower limbs. He treated this condition simply and conservatively, applying plasters and poultices to the back and using supports to relieve the diseased spine of any weight-bearing. The treatment usually adopted in his time, by means of "back-board collars, steel bodices, screw-chairs, and other pieces of machinery" he condemned roundly.

At this stage of Pott's career his consulting-rooms in Watling Street were permanently overcrowded, David Garrick, the actor, and the great Samuel Johnson being among his many patients. The next appreciable book he published was a sort of omnibus volume, *Chirurgical Observations relative to the Cataract, the Polypus of the Nose, the Cancer of the Scrotum, and the Mortifi-*

cation of the Toes and Feet. In this book Pott plunged into industrial medicine, and was the first to associate cancer of the scrotum with the occupation of chimney-sweeping. The sweeps themselves called the condition "soot-wart", but most physicians regarded the ulcer on the scrotum as due to venereal disease, and treated it accordingly. Pott drew attention to its malignant character, and indicated clearly what caused it.

> The fate of these people seems singularly hard. In their early infancy they are most frequently treated with great brutality, and almost starved with cold and hunger; they are thrust up narrow, and sometimes hot, chimneys, where they are bruised, burned, and almost suffocated; and when they get to puberty, become peculiarly liable to a most noisome, painful, and fatal disease . . . which seems to derive its origin from a lodgement of soot in the rugæ of the scrotum.

Pott resigned his position as Surgeon to St. Bartholomew's in July, 1787, and was able to say that he had served the hospital, man and boy, for half a century. He was then a Fellow of the Royal Society. He had received the first honorary diploma ever granted by the College of Surgeons of Edinburgh, and a similar mark of appreciation from the College of Surgeons of Ireland. As a teacher, a surgeon, and a writer, he had excelled, and his great virtues as a surgeon were his simplicity and his humanity. He taught again many of the lessons of Ambroise Paré which England had not learnt fully enough. The actual cautery, which even Cheselden had often advised for many very different conditions, Pott completely abandoned. He brought up successive generations of students in the same school of thought. He laid it down as an axiom that at any operation the least possible number of instruments should be used and those should be of the simplest possible design. He put this teaching into practice himself, and actually simplified many existing instruments which were cumbrously or badly designed. He stressed the fundamental importance of a knowledge of anatomy and of keen observation. He advised his students to read the old authors and to criticize them in the light of their enhanced anatomical knowledge, but told them frankly that reading alone would never make surgeons of them. Two things he condemned roundly, quacks and all their works, and the artistic bandages which to this day are beautifully depicted in many first-aid books. Bandaging a dressing in place over a scalp wound has always been a subject for artists and a sore trial to whoever had to follow designs which are perfect on paper. Pott was brief and to the point about these involved and difficult exercises. "All that can possibly be wanted in these cases is to keep the dressings in their place without any degree of pressure or confinement, and this purpose will always be better accomplished by a loose cotton or yarn nightcap than by the nicest and most elaborate bandage that was ever invented." Pott did away with superfluous bandages, supernumerary splints, and an excess of instruments, and he tried in all his works to achieve simplicity by a rational classification based on anatomy.

Beyond receiving his "great diploma" from them, Percivall Pott had but little to do with the old Barber-Surgeons' Company, for he was barely thirty when the new Surgeons' Company was founded. The new Company had allowed the anatomical lectures of the old days to lapse during the transitional stage and pending the building of a new Hall, but in 1753, encouraged by an Act of the year previous "for the better preventing the horrid crime of murder", they were started again. The Act expressly ordered that the bodies of all criminals executed at Tyburn should be handed over to the Surgeons' Company. The late effect of this Act was to convince the public that dissection after death was an even worse punishment than hanging, but the immediate effect was good. Assured of a supply of subjects, the Surgeons' Company revived the old practice of appointing six anatomical officers, two Masters of Anatomy, two Wardens, and two Stewards. The first two Masters were Percivall Pott and William Hunter—not his younger brother John, as has often been wrongly stated—and they held office for twelve months. Later, Pott served on a committee which considered the vexed question of whether surgeons retired from the Army or Navy could settle down in civil practice without further examination. Later still, he was involved in a more personal problem. His wife's father, Mr. Cruttenden, had been Clerk to the Company since its foundation. Unfortunately, Cruttenden had not kept the Company's money separate from his own, and, when at last the matter was looked into, it was found on March 2, 1780, that whereas the Company should have had £837 7s. 5d. cash in hand, it had only £74 8s. Joseph Cruttenden was an old man and had served the Company for thirty-five years. In addition, he was Pott's father-in-law, and Pott was one of the most distinguished members of the Company, and had been a Governor in 1765. Pott was given the delicate task of interviewing his defaulting father-in-law, and at length, after considering all the circumstances, the Company simply accepted the old man's resignation and left it at that.

After his retirement from St. Bartholomew's, Pott continued to practise for the brief eighteen months before his death. The day before he died of pneumonia he said: "My lamp is almost extinguished. I hope it has burned for the benefit of others." The epitaph engraved on his tombstone in Aldermary Church, Bow Lane, was written by his son, who was archdeacon of St. Albans, and more than answers his last question:

IN MEMORY OF

PERCIVALL POTT, ESQ., F.R.S.

SURGEON OF ST. BARTHOLOMEW'S HOSPITAL

DURING FORTY-TWO YEARS,

WHO DEPARTED THIS LIFE DECEMBER 22, 1788,

AGED 75.

He was singularly eminent in his Profession, to which he added many new Resources, and which he illustrated with matchless Writings. Let Posterity revolve the Sum of his Experience, that the World may still enjoy the Benefit of his Successful Practice. He honoured the collective Wisdom of past Ages; the Labours of the Ancients were familiar to him; he scorned to teach a Science of which he had not traced the growth; he rose, therefore, from the Form to the Chair. Learn, Reader, that the painful Scholar can alone become the Faithful Teacher. But his studies had a double Issue; whilst he gathered the Knowledge of his Predecessors, he perceived their Errors, and corrected them; he discovered their Defects, and supplied them. Original in Genius, prompt in Judgment, rapid in Decision, he directed Knowledge to its proper Ends; but pursued them when the Aids of Information were exhausted; the last Steps, therefore, and great Improvements, were his own.

His integrity is before his Judge; Without it, his Skill might have profited Mankind, but could have claimed no Record within these Walls. His private Virtues, his signal Tenderness to his Family, completed an Example, Amiable, Useful, Great.

XV.   The Quacks and the Brothers

WILLIAM CHESELDEN AND PERCIVALL POTT RAISED THE PRESTIGE
of surgeons to a point where they could rank almost, if not quite,
equal with physicians.   They did this directly, by their work in
the Surgeons' Company and by helping to raise the standard of
surgical education, and indirectly, by example.   At this time
there was a natural tendency for physicians and surgeons to work
in greater amity, for in eighteenth-century England there was a
plague which threatened both their houses.   The divided ranks
of physicians and surgeons were faced, right, left, and centre, by
a monstrous army of quacks and mountebanks.   In self-defence
physicians and surgeons drew together.   Contact with men like
Pott and Cheselden made the physicians realize that surgeons
were not necessarily boors, and physicians like Mead equally
impressed the surgeons.   Cheselden had defeated the quacks on
their own ground in perfecting lithotomy.   In the surgery of
the eye, however, the few advances he made affected not at all
the standing and reputation of Sir William Read, the best-known
quack of that time.

He and a Dr. Grant were entrusted with the care of Queen
Anne's weak eyes.   Roger Grant had been a tinker and an
Anabaptist preacher.   How either his profession or his hobby,
whichever was which, fitted him to become an oculist is not
known, but an oculist, and a royal one, he became.   Much of his
success was due to his magnificent and well-attested testimonials.
He obtained these quite simply.   Some poor person with imper-
fect vision was procured, preferably a half-wit, and treated with
medicines and with crowns and half-crowns.   A final lump sum
was given him at the end of about six weeks or so for signing a
document to the effect that he had been born stone-blind, had
been treated unsuccessfully by everybody under the sun, and had
at last had full vision restored to him by the medicines of Dr.
Grant.   This certificate the local clergymen were asked to attest.
If they would neither sign the document nor accept the generous
contribution to their funds which Dr. Grant offered, then Dr.
Grant had no compunction about forging their signatures.

William Read had a slight advantage over Dr. Grant in that he
started life as a tailor, but Grant on the other hand could read
and write—two minor qualifications which Read never attained.
His tailoring was in as little demand as Grant's tinkering, and he

took to the road as an itinerant quack. For some seven or eight years he wandered all over the country, boasting everywhere of his remarkable cures. Then in 1694 he came to London and settled in the Strand. He issued a series of the most blatant advertisements and soon became well known. Eye diseases were his avowed speciality, but he was also willing to cure cancers, wens, hare-lip, wry-neck, and deafness. He was knighted in 1705 for his "services done in curing great numbers of seamen and soldiers of blindness gratis". This free treatment for Her Majesty's Army and Navy was one of the brightest propaganda stunts ever devised. As a further mark of royal favour Queen Anne soon afterwards appointed him her Oculist-in-Ordinary. Read celebrated the event by hiring a Grub Street poet to turn out some verses worthy of the occasion. The first verse is the most modest of the three:

> Whilst Britain's sovereign scales such worth has weighed
> And Anne herself her smiling favours paid,
> That sacred hand does your fair chaplet twist
> Great Read, her own entitled oculist.

Addison, Steele, and Swift attacked him roundly in the *Spectator*. Read countered by entertaining them all at his house and giving them an admirable punch served in golden vessels. He could never do as much for another poet, for no one knew who wrote the four-line epigram which went round every coffee-house in London:

> Her Majesty, sure, was in a surprise,
> Or else was very short-sighted,
> When a tinker was sworn to look after her eyes
> And the mountebank Read was knighted.

Another eye specialist of the same calibre was the Chevalier John Taylor, whose career, according to the great Dr. Johnson, formed a striking example of how far impudence could carry ignorance. The Chevalier, who always went about dressed in black and sported a magnificent carriage and four, claimed to have had no less than fifty royal personages among his patients. He also claimed to have treated all the best families in England, and among them the Walpoles. Horace Walpole replied promptly:

> Why Taylor the quack calls himself Chevalier
> 'Tis not easy a reason to render,
> Unless blinding eyes, that he thinks to make clear,
> Demonstrates he's but a Pretender.

Taylor, unlike his fellow-quacks, was surprisingly well qualified. The son of a surgeon of Norwich, he had received the orthodox medical education of his day, acting as assistant to a London apothecary for some time and then studying the surgery of the eye under none other than William Cheselden. Returning to Norwich, he set up in practice as a surgeon with a complete lack of success, so he became an itinerant oculist. There is no doubt that he was a skilled operator, and he invented several instruments for operations on the eye which came into general use. His advertisements were imaginative flights of the highest order, and the speeches he made at every town he visited were gems of grandiloquency. For example, his lecture to the University of Oxford started like this:

> The eye, most illustrious sons of the Muses, most learned Oxonians, whose fame I have heard celebrated in all parts of the globe—the eye, that most amazing, that stupendous, that comprehending, that incomprehensible, that miraculous organ, the eye, is the Proteus of the passions, the herald of the mind, the interpreter of the heart, and the window of the soul. . . .

In 1736 Taylor was appointed Oculist-in-Ordinary to George II. He developed then a mode of speech which he called "the true Ciceronian, prodigiously difficult and never attempted in our language before". A good sample of the true Ciceronian was "Of the eye, on the wonders, lecture will I", all of which helped to bemuse his hearers and increase their faith in him. Patients of his at this time included Gibbon, the historian, and, on one of his frequent trips to Germany, Handel, with whom even Taylor admitted a lack of success. He wrote several works on diseases of the eye, but attracted far more attention with the autobiography he published in 1761. Taylor realized to the full the value of whetting the public appetite before actually publishing a book. A preliminary announcement therefore appeared in the *Gentleman's Magazine* and gave a glowing indication of what was to be expected from the autobiography. This advertisement included references to bull-fighting, torture, embalming, the history of Persia, and "every female nunnery in Europe"—the Chevalier hastening to explain that he was in the nunneries for purely professional reasons. Towards the end of his life Taylor became blind, and he died in Prague in 1772. His son followed the same profession and developed a lucrative business in Hatton Garden, while his grandson maintained the family tradition by becoming oculist to George III and later to George IV.

Cheselden need hardly have been ashamed of this particular pupil, but he was probably thoroughly upset at being completely duped on one occasion by a far less able quack. This was Joanna Stephens, who announced about 1736 that she had a sovereign remedy for stone in the bladder. She raked in the golden guineas from peers, dukes, bishops, and merchants for several years. Then when she had reached the retiring age she announced that she would sell her famous secret for £5,000. A public subscription was raised and the list of donors rapidly took on the appearance of a *Burke's Peerage*—the Earl of Pembroke £50, the Duke of Rutland £50, the Earl of Godolphin £100, Viscount Lonsdale £52 10s., the Duke of Richmond £30, Earl of Clarendon £25, the Duke of Leeds £2, the Bishop of Oxford £10 10s., and so on till finally £1,356 was raised. Joanna wisely refused to haggle. She wanted £5,000 and had every intention of getting it, but by way of a first instalment she took the £1,356. The Government of the day was approached, and it agreed to find the £5,000 if the report of a Special Commission was satisfactory. Cheselden was a member of that Commission along with other surgeons, several physicians, and representatives of the Lords and the Commons, and the Commission reported favourably on Joanna and all her works. £5,000 was duly handed over from the public funds, and the public received the famous secret:

The medicines are a Powder, a Decoction, and Pills.

The Powder consists of Egg-shells and Snails—both calcined.

The Decoction is made by boiling some herbs (together with a ball, which consists of soap, swine's cresses burnt to blackness and honey) in water.

The Pills consist of Snails calcined, wild carrot seeds, burdock seeds, ashen keys, hips and hawes—all burnt to blackness—Alicant soap and honey.

Joanna's success led inevitably to the marketing of scores of other infallible remedies for stone. Sir Robert Walpole, who died of his vesical calculi, took up one form of treatment with alicant soap and lime-water. Sergeant-Surgeon Ranby, who presided at the post-mortem examination of the Prime Minister, must hardly have wondered at the mass of stones he found, for it is calculated that in the last few years of his life an otherwise

PLATE XIII

A surgeon at work in the time of William Cheselden. The surgeon is opening an abscess, and one of his apprentices is letting blood.

From Johannes Muys's *Praxis Rationalis* (Amsterdam, A.D. 1695).

PLATE XIV

Mary Toft the Rabbit-breeder.

From an engraving of 1726 attributed to Hogarth.

intelligent Prime Minister had consumed 180 lb. of soap and not less than 1,200 gallons of lime-water.

Another lady, less successful financially than Joanna, with whom Cheselden came into contact was Mary Toft, the Woman of Godlyman. Mary was quite illiterate, had been married six years, and had borne three children. One day, whilst weeding in a field, a rabbit sprang up and startled her. "This set her a-longing for Rabbets, being then, as she thought, five weeks gone with Child." Some five months later she was delivered of a rabbit. Other rabbits followed. Most of the delivering was done by a Mr. Howard, and the initial publicity was handled by a Mr. Davenant. His account of this remarkable birth came to the attention of Mr. Nathaniel St. André, surgeon and anatomist to George I. The Prince of Wales was also interested and instructed his secretary, the Hon. Mr. Molyneux, and St. André to investigate. André himself delivered most of another rabbit, and some hours later the midwife in attendance on Mary Toft retrieved the rest of it. In the next few days more rabbits arrived till finally the grand total was brought up to fifteen. (*See plate facing* p. 241.) By this time most of London was on its way to Guildford, where Mary Toft was having her remarkable confinement, and the whole country was in an uproar. At this stage Sir Richard Manningham saw the woman. He was not as fortunate as other observers, for no rabbit was brought forth in his presence, but he did find a piece of membrane. Mr. Howard thought this was a part of a fifteen-fold afterbirth. Lacking his simple faith, Sir Richard suggested that it probably was exactly what it looked like—a hog's bladder. Not content with this aspersion on the lady's character, Sir Richard insisted on having her brought to London, where she could be kept under close supervision.

This was done, and soon after her arrival Mary Toft started another mimic labour. James Douglas was dragged out of his bed and asked to examine her. James Douglas, like Manningham, was an experienced obstetrician. He stated his profane opinion—namely, that both womb and vagina were quite empty, and that the labour pains were hysterical. This displeased St. André and annoyed Howard. St. André insisted that the womb still contained a few rabbits and that the King had commanded that they be delivered. Not anxious to incur the Royal displeasure, Douglas and Manningham reported for duty again, and this time brought Cheselden with them. The great lithotomist put a few leading questions to Howard, and the consultation soon threatened to develop into a free fight.   However, the whole party stayed the night with the hapless Mary, and were rewarded by observing only "rolling of her eyes, and great risings in her Stomach and Belly".   Wearily, they left her to it, but Douglas called again the next day, on this occasion taking care not to bring his friend Mr. Cheselden.   Even so he was refused admission, at which indignity he became enraged, and, snorting that presumably "some new Monster was breeding", stalked away.

This was the beginning of the end.   Mary Toft was so closely watched that she found it impossible to procure rabbits, and even had she, or her nurse, or her husband, done so, she would have had difficulty in making the necessary preparations for their birth without being observed.   Sir Richard Manningham had become very tired of the whole business.   He had seen not only the piece of hog's bladder, but also the intestines of several of the rabbits.   These intestines contained hay, straw, and corn, which rather suggested that the rabbits were of very normal origin and accustomed to a usual rabbit dietary.   Accordingly, Manningham went to the woman one day and explained very clearly that he wanted a confession from her.   Mary brightly responded that there was nothing to confess.   Sir Richard insisted that the whole matter needed clearing up, and added, thoughtfully, that this could only be done by performing a really appalling operation.   Mary confessed, and was for a short time imprisoned. London christened poor St. André the rabbit doctor, and neither he nor Howard ever lived down the deception that had been practised on them.   The whole country rocked with laughter at their discomfiture, and of all the people connected with the case only Manningham, Douglas, and Cheselden were unscathed by the satirists and cartoonists.

The quacks who took it upon themselves to treat surgical conditions annoyed the surgeons.   The many more quacks who promised cure for every known, and many unknown, medical ailments annoyed the physicians just as much.   A particular thorn in their flesh was Joshua Ward, usually called Spot Ward from a birthmark on his cheek.   He began life as a drysalter, was returned to Parliament as the member for Marlborough, was rapidly turned out of Parliament when it was learnt that actually he had not received a single vote, and fled to France. There he began to make various drops, pastes, and essences.

Returning to England, he cured George II of a pain in his thumb, and became famous overnight. The House of Commons gave him a vote of thanks for relieving the royal thumbache, and he was granted protection from any interference in his practice by the College of Physicians. This thoroughly incensed the College and those members of it who were attached to the Royal household expressed their feelings very freely. Among them was Cheselden's friend, Mead. Queen Caroline was particularly impressed by Spot Ward's nostrums, and, discussing his remarkable cures one day with General Churchill, she asked if it were true that Ward's medicines were so powerful that they had made a man mad.

"Yes, Madam," replied the General, "and his name is Mead!"

While one quack annoyed Mead and another duped Cheselden, a third brought down upon her head a few well-phrased comments from Percivall Pott. This was Mrs. Sarah Mapp, of whom Pott wrote:

> Even the absurdities and impracticability of her own promises and engagements, were by no means equal to the expectations and credulity of those who ran after her, that is, of all ranks and degrees of people from the lowest labourer up to those of the most exalted rank and station, several of whom not only did not hesitate to believe implicitly the most extravagant assertions of this ignorant, illiberal, drunken, female savage, but even solicited her company or at least seemed to enjoy her society.

Crazy Sal was trespassing on Pott's own speciality of bones and joints, for she took up her father's work as a bone-setter. Her sister achieved fame in another sphere, for she was the original of the famous Polly Peacham, who afterwards married the Duke of Bolton. Crazy Sal settled at Epsom, but drove into London once a week to the Grecian Coffee-House, where there were always queues of patients waiting for her. Sir Hans Sloane frequented this same coffee-house, and Crazy Sal so impressed him that he entrusted a niece of his to her care. Sal cured the niece of a "back . . . broken nine years and stuck out two inches".

Bone-setting was almost entirely in the hands of quacks at that time, and so was dentistry. Perhaps the best known of the quack dentists was a little man with a long grey beard, who every morning rode solemnly up and down Rotten Row on a white pony painted with purple spots. This was Mr. Martin Van Butchell, who made "Real or Artificial Teeth from one to an Entire Set, with Superlative Gold Pivots or Springs, also Gums,

Sockets, and Palate fitted, finished and fixed without drawing stumps or causing pain". Butchell had a magnificent house in Mayfair, which attracted even more attention than the Gold Pivots or the purple-spotted pony. Butchell's wife died, in January, 1775, and he had her body embalmed. The embalming was done by packing the abdominal cavity with camphor, and injecting into the blood-vessels a preservative made of oil of turpentine and camphorated spirit of wine. A more than life-like reality was finally achieved by two glass eyes and the injection of a carmine solution into the vessels of the head and neck, so that the lips were bright red and the cheeks rosily flushed. This greatly improved edition of Mrs. Van Butchell was arrayed in fine linen and lace, placed in a glass-lidded case, and kept in the sitting-room. The lady was formally introduced to each and every visitor as the "dear departed", and not unnaturally the visitors were many. Mrs. Van Butchell the first remained in the sitting-room till she was displaced permanently by Mrs. Van Butchell the second. This embalming was done so perfectly for the quack dentist by Dr. William Hunter, a young Scotchman who had already made a name for himself in London.

William Hunter had come to London in the early November of 1740. Born in 1718 at Long Calderwood, East Kilbride, to the south of Glasgow, he was the seventh of a large family. From the age of thirteen he studied theology for five years, which was long enough for him to decide that the ministry was not for him. About this time he had become acquainted with a surgeon of Hamilton, William Cullen, the patron of Burns and later Professor of Medicine at Edinburgh University, and with him William Hunter lived as a resident pupil for the three happiest years of his life. Then it was decided that he should continue his studies in medicine and surgery, first at Edinburgh and later in London, after which he would return to Hamilton and go into partnership with Cullen.

The barber-surgeons of Edinburgh had been dissecting their "ane condampnit man" and enjoying their monopoly of the distilling and selling of whisky since 1505. With these two privileges was conjoined the responsibility for providing the citizens of Edinburgh with a sufficiency of barbers licensed to "clip, cow, and shave", and such barbers were not permitted to practise any branch of surgery. Later, this regulation was relaxed, and as a first stage in development the barbers and the surgeons were soon outnumbered by barber-surgeons. So what had been predominantly a "Barber-Craft" became a "Craft of Chirurgeons"—though the "chirurgeons" were actually barbers practising surgery. The first deacon of this new and more powerful craft was Gilbert Prymross, an ancestor of the Earl of Rosebery. Later still, just as in London so in Edinburgh, surgeons who had gained strength from a union with the barbers and then had been swamped by the barber-surgeons began at length to demand separation. This was effected in 1722; incidentally, the Society of Barbers created in that year met for the last time one hundred and seventy years later, when a father and son formally elected each other to the two highest offices. Soon afterwards the father died and his son left the country. All that remained was an aged clerk, an oak treasure-box, sundry minute-books, and a few mildewed documents.

It was four years after the separation of the barbers and surgeons that the University of Edinburgh, which had been granted a Charter of Erection as early as 1582 by James VI, created a Faculty of Medicine and appointed as Professor of Anatomy Alexander Monro, the first of an academic dynasty. His father, John Monro, had been largely instrumental in persuading the authorities to arrange a complete medical course within the University. A favourite pupil of William Cheselden, Alexander Monro had early had his interests directed towards pure anatomy. Young William Hunter attended his lectures on anatomy, and his occasional demonstrations of operations and the use of various splints, in the winter of 1739, and then went on to London in November of the following year.

He had letters of introduction from Cullen to several fellow-Scots who had already achieved distinction in London. The first of these he presented to William Smellie, with whom he lived for nearly twelve months. Smellie was born just forty years after the death of William Harvey, and was one of the first to achieve anything approaching his eminence in midwifery. The obstetric forceps, which had been a secret of the Chamberlen family, he popularized and improved upon as well as extending their usefulness in application, and he published a set of anatomical plates showing the various positions of the unborn child, and its delivery naturally or by forceps, better than any produced previously. William Hunter was among the first of some nine hundred pupils of Smellie, and must have received from him a sound training in midwifery. At the same time he attended other courses in anatomy and in natural philosophy.

Hunter left Smellie's house in September, 1741, and went to live with James Douglas, to assist him in his dissections and superintend the education of his son. Douglas also arranged that Hunter should attend St. George's as a surgical pupil. James Douglas was the brother of John Douglas who attacked Cheselden so vehemently, but James himself was very friendly with the great lithotomist. He was a distinguished anatomist, obstetrician, and bibliophile. He described in detail the peritoneum, the membrane lining all the abdominal organs, and its most dependent fold has ever since been known as the pouch of Douglas. Douglas died twelve months after William Hunter had come to live with him, leaving a seventeen-year-old son, William George, and a daughter, Martha Jane, with whom Hunter had fallen in love. Unfortunately, she died two years later at the age of twenty-eight. Meanwhile William Hunter had communicated to the Royal Society a paper on the structure and diseases of joint cartilages. In this paper the source of the blood supply to the cartilages of the knee and other joints was described correctly for the first time. Later that year he visited France and studied for a while at Paris with his young pupil, William George Douglas. On returning from France, Hunter continued to live with the Douglas family, and he spent his time studying and making anatomical preparations. Then in the *London Evening Post* of September 16, 1746, it was announced that there would begin in October ". . . a course of anatomical lectures to which will be added the operations of surgery with the application of bandages, by William Hunter, Surgeon. Gentlemen may have the opportunity of learning the art of Dissection during the whole winter season in the same manner as at Paris. . . ."

In starting to teach anatomy privately Hunter was following the example of a score of pioneer teachers, among them being the Douglas brothers, Cheselden, Ranby, Edward Nourse, and Percivall Pott. He advanced on them, however, by introducing the Paris method of allowing each pupil to dissect an entire body under his supervision. How popular his teaching and his methods were is shown by the increase in the number of his pupils. Two years after he had started lecturing they numbered twenty, and after ten years about a hundred. Most of the lectures were given at 5 p.m., the morning and afternoon being devoted to preparing dissections, seeing occasional patients, studying, and attending the British Lying-in Hospital, to which he had been appointed Surgeon-man-midwife in 1749, soon after taking up a similar appointment to the Middlesex Hospital.

It was in the year before this that William's young brother, John, the last of a family of ten, asked if he might pay a visit to London and perhaps assist him in his anatomical researches, or, failing that, join the Army. London now has a population of eight millions, a university, and twelve medical schools. The London that received this short, thick-set, red-haired young man had a population of three hundred thousand, and its first real school of medicine was being brought into existence by the young man's brother. Once John had arrived, William soon took the opportunity of finding out if he had any dissecting ability. John was given two arms and asked to prepare one so as to show the muscles, and the other to show the muscles and the blood-vessels, which had been injected with coloured wax. Despite his inexperience John acquitted himself well, and was soon actively employed in the dissecting-room. He was instructed by his brother and his assistants, and was at the same time a pupil of Cheselden's at the Chelsea hospital. After Cheselden had left for Bath, the young man continued his studies at St. Bartholomew's, and some years later may have attended Percivall Pott's lectures. At about this time William moved his whole establishment to a large house in the Great Piazza, Covent Garden, and soon afterwards Percivall Pott and he were elected the first Masters of Anatomy of the newly-created Surgeons' Company.

John, meanwhile, had transferred his allegiance to St. George's Hospital, on the long-sighted advice of his elder brother. St. George's had two advantages over St. Bartholomew's, Guy's, and St. Thomas's. One of the senior pupils was each year selected to act as a sort of resident house-surgeon, whereas no such appointment existed at the other hospitals, and the staff appointments to St. George's were open to all-comers, while those at other hospitals were restricted to those surgeons who had been apprenticed for a minimum of five years to some senior surgeon on the staff. John also went to Oxford, as a gentleman commoner at St. Mary's Hall, perhaps for reasons of health, perhaps to acquire a little classical knowledge and a university polish. Whatever the reason, John hated Oxford and stayed there for less than two months. Years later he said of this brief experience,

"They wanted to make an old woman of me; or that I should stuff Latin and Greek. . . ." He returned to Covent Garden and there dissected several fœtuses and infants, studying particularly the testicles and the sites of congenital rupture. Then in 1756 he was duly appointed to take up residence in St. George's. His duties were very much the same as those of a present-day house-surgeon. He was to see that the surgeons' instructions as to the care of their patients were carried out; deal with any emergencies, such as hæmorrhage from an amputation stump; attend to any accident cases, preparing and applying the necessary dressings; dress patients' operation wounds; apply fomentations and plasters whenever necessary; bleed those patients who needed bleeding; and finish off all the stitching up and dressing that the surgeons thought fit to leave with him. Substitute blood-transfusion for bleeding, and the picture is quite a modern one, especially as John Hunter lived in, received no salary, paid £10 a year for his board, and was treated generally as an "upper servant". In this office John Hunter was succeeded by John Gunning.

While John was well on the way to becoming a surgeon, William was fast abandoning surgery and becoming a physician. To do this he had first to be disfranchised from the Surgeons' Company, paying forty guineas to the Company to effect this, before being admitted a Licentiate of the College of Physicians in 1756. William took another house in the same year, this time in Jermyn Street, and lived there while continuing the dissections and lectures in Covent Garden. The next four years saw John's health failing. Three sisters and a brother of his had already died of tuberculosis, and John had spent almost eleven years working hard in the dissecting-rooms, with only one brief holiday at home, a short stay at Oxford, and five months in residence at St. George's by way of recreation during this time. Some change was necessary, and so John procured a commission as an army surgeon and joined the expedition against Belleisle which sailed from Spithead in March, 1761. The commission was actually granted him on October 30, 1760, by the then Inspector-General of Hospitals, Robert Adair.

Robert Adair, "the fortunate Irishman", was to become Sergeant-Surgeon to George III and surgeon to the Chelsea Hospital, but his fame rests not on his surgery, but on a song. He had no sooner landed in England from the boat which had carried him from his native Dublin than he saw a lovely lady thrown out of her overturned carriage. This was Lady Caroline Keppel, a young beauty, who was so impressed with his prompt ministrations, his good looks, and his charming roadside manner that she insisted on Adair's accompanying her to London. She recommended him to her many friends, usually the male ones, for he was always said to have "played the devil with the women", set the seal on his success by marrying him, and wrote a song about him. It was to the tune of *Eileen Aroon*—Eileen, secret treasure of my heart—that she set "Robin Adair", and gave her husband a more lasting fame than any Inspector-Generalship of His Majesty's Hospitals ever brought.

The taking of Belleisle was just a sideshow in the Seven Years' War, and not very long after it had been taken it was to be returned to France along with other spoils in exchange for Canada. Nevertheless, eight ships of the line and several frigates were needed to escort an expedition of ten thousand troops, which took the island at the second attack. One attack would probably have sufficed had it not been for the ingenuity of the redoubtable French Governor. He made his tiny garrison appear exactly twice as numerous by dressing the ladies of the island in scarlet uniforms and making them gallop round the ramparts on horses. Since the horses were few, many of the ladies did just as good work mounted on equally serviceable, if less mettlesome, cows. Once the island was occupied, an epidemic of fever broke out, and hospitals had to be improvised. John wrote of his work there and of his future intentions to William, and in one letter conveyed very succinctly his opinion of his hospital colleagues and his immediate superiors: ". . . My fellow-creatures of the hospital are a damn'd disagreeable set. The two heads are as unfit for their employment as the Devil was to reign in Heaven. . . ."

A later epistle showed no change in these opinions. "I hear that Dr. Blyth is to go to Portugal; I suppose that Mr. Young goes as Surgeon-General; God help the hospital when directed by such two. . . ." War having been declared with Spain, Mr. Young did go to Portugal, and John Hunter succeeded him as Chief Surgeon and Director of the Hospital at Belleisle. Then some months later, after just over a year in Belleisle, Hunter, too, went to Lisbon, where he spent another twelve months as an army surgeon. In February, 1763, peace was declared, and in May of that year John Hunter returned to London with

Robert Home, surgeon to the Sixteenth Dragoons, whom he had met in Lisbon. Hunter quickly became acquainted with Home's family, and as quickly fell in love with his daughter, Anne. Quite apart from this meeting with Home, however, the two years in the Army had not been unprofitable. His health was fully restored, he had a great deal of material for the *Treatise on Gunshot Wounds* he was to write, and at Lisbon he had spent much of his time making observations on the hibernation of animals and on the hearing organs of fishes.

William, after seeing his younger brother off to the wars, plunged happily into several minor wars he was conducting on his own account. The tear-ducts in man had been fully demonstrated for the first time by him in 1757. Alexander Monro Junior, another member of the famous Edinburgh family, had attended William's lectures on the subject, but refrained from mentioning this when he published in 1758 his own description of the lachrymal ducts. That was not his only sin of omission. William and John in 1752 had described the seminiferous tubules in the testicle. The young Monro completed his work on these structures twelve months later, but claimed priority. William attacked him roundly on both claims, and hurled not a few shafts at Donald Monro, another of the clan who was a physician at St. George's. A further publication of this persistent young plagiarist, which again did not mention the Hunters, was concerned with the lymphatic vessels. These minute vessels had long been regarded as continuations of the arteries. William Hunter had been teaching for six years before young Monro burst into print again that they were a separate system of absorbent vessels starting from all the exernal and internal surfaces of the body. His indignation at young Monro can well be imagined and was, in point of fact, frequently and forcibly expressed. Also in the line of fire was Percivall Pott, who in his monograph on congenital hernia, published in 1757, did not mention the preparations and dissections showing this condition that had been demonstrated to him by John Hunter some months previously.

William, what with these and other discussions, was fully employed, especially as his private practice in midwifery was growing rapidly, his lectures were still continuing, and he was in addition in attendance upon the Queen. It was on August 12, 1762, that the Queen was delivered of a son who was to become George IV. On that day William Hunter wrote to Cullen:

". . . I am very happy, and have been so for some time. I owe it to you, and thank you from my heart for the great honour I now have and have had for some time, though very few know anything of it—I mean having the sole direction of her Majesty's health as a child-bearing Lady." The delivery was uneventful and was conducted by a midwife under Hunter's supervision, and in the following September he was rewarded by being appointed Physician-Extraordinary to her Majesty. Earlier in the same year he had published his *Medical Commentaries*, Part I of which contained "A Plain and Direct Answer to Professor Monro Junior Interspersed with Remarks on the Structure, Functions, and Diseases of Several Parts of the Human Body". Actually this was a plain and direct account of several interesting investigations, interspersed, very liberally, with remarks on Professor Monro Junior.

William Hunter was a relatively wealthy man by this time, his patients ranging from the Queen down to the poorest of her subjects, and including the wives of such notable men as Pitt and Thomas Coutts, then a rising young banker, and he conceived the idea of building a museum for the advancement of anatomy and surgery and the allied sciences. He petitioned the First Lord of the Treasury asking for a grant of land to this end. After a delay of two years his request was refused. Disappointed, but with the same plan still in mind, he bought a house in Great Windmill Street for over £6,000 and spent a further £2,000 rebuilding it and constructing a large museum, a lecture theatre, and several dissecting-rooms. Once this was ready for occupation he took up residence there, while John moved from Golden Square to the Jermyn Street house. William had been elected a Fellow of the Royal Society in 1767, and George III had appointed him Professor of Anatomy to the Royal Academy in the following year. In 1780 he was made President of the Society of Physicians of London, and later became a foreign associate of the Royal Academy of Sciences of Paris. Earlier he had arranged for a printing-press to be set up at the building in Great Windmill Street, and from this were produced the plates for his monumental work on *The Anatomy of the Gravid Uterus*, thirty-four of them, superbly engraved. The book itself is the only medical publication of the famous Baskerville Press. This epitomized his dissections of the previous twenty-four years of the bodies of pregnant and recently delivered women.

Other works of his were *On the Uncertainty of the Signs of*

Murder in the Case of Bastard Children, and *On Encysted Dropsy of the Ovarium.* He was the first to describe retroversion of the uterus, a condition in which the womb is deflected backwards instead of forwards, as it should be normally, and the first to record a case in which an aneurysm communicated with both an artery and a vein. He was also among the first to suggest that a large cyst of the ovary could be treated simply by tapping—making an incision in the swollen abdomen only big enough to admit two fingers, and then driving a sharp-ended hollow tube into the cyst itself, so draining off all the fluid in it and relieving the symptoms which were due largely to the bulk of the cyst.

His lectures continued, and were always well attended, until March 20, 1783, when, against the advice of his colleagues, he got up from a sick-bed to deliver the first lecture of his course on operative surgery. He fainted from exhaustion and had to be carried home, to die ten days later. He was buried quietly at St. James's, Piccadilly, but there were many who brought forward his claim to a public funeral. He had accumulated at Great Windmill Street a unique museum of preparations and dissections, and with them an amazing collection of coins, shells, and books. The coins alone were said to have cost £22,000, and on many of his specimens of different diseases and abnormalities it would have been impossible to place a price. He had excelled as a teacher and as an anatomist. He was a good but not a great obstetrician, for his contributions to the art were all anatomical rather than purely obstetrical. He left no record of his actual cases, but his treatment was always very conservative. At that time it was a common practice to remove the afterbirth by hand immediately after the delivery of the child. Hunter rightly opposed this, but went to the other extreme, leaving alone for far too long afterbirths which were not expelled naturally after the usual twenty or thirty minutes. It is believed that at least one of his patients, the Countess of Suffolk, died from this over-conservatism. Only occasionally did he employ forceps, in fact he often produced the pair he possessed and showed them to be covered with rust from disuse, saying also that "where they save one they murder twenty". So strong were his views and so great his influence that for years afterwards obstetricians in England tended to carry his policy of masterly inactivity to dangerous lengths.

For example, in 1819 Princess Charlotte's obstetrician left her in labour for fifty-two hours. The result was the birth of a dead child and the death of the mother a few hours later. Realizing too late his mismanagement, the unhappy accoucheur —who had merely done what any one of his colleagues of that time would have done—shot himself. Hunter's teaching of conservative obstetrics was fundamentally sound, but he carried that teaching too far, and his immediate successors erred even more excessively in the same direction. To-day the pendulum has swung perhaps too far the other way.

William Hunter was described by a contemporary as "a polite scholar, an accomplished gentleman, a complete anatomist, and probably the most perfect demonstrator, as well as lecturer, the world had ever seen". He was all these things and more. A friend of Samuel Johnson, James Boswell, Tobias Smollett, Joshua Reynolds, David Garrick, Hogarth, Gainsborough, Oliver Goldsmith, and many other famous men, he built up a remarkable private library, collected many works of art, and founded a school which was to be a cradle for great anatomists and surgeons for well over sixty years. He was too jealous of his reputation and plunged too readily into controversies on priority of discovery, but he was none the less a great anatomist and a popular teacher. One of his greatest virtues was his insistence upon the necessity for experiment and observation. This was another quality which did not commend itself to all his contemporaries: ". . . there be many that hate him, he having a damnable way of never offering a Suggestion on matters Medico-Physical until he has proved it privately by Experiment beforehand; the which is Highly Exasperating to those that prefer to browse on the Windy Heights of Pure Discourse." He made two great contributions to surgery, one direct and one indirect. He revolutionized the teaching of anatomy and sur-gery, and set up a model school which was only displaced when the modern hospital schools of medicine arose—and he brought to London, and trained and educated, his younger brother, John.

XVI. John Hunter

JOHN HUNTER HAD RETURNED FROM PORTUGAL IN 1763. HE went into lodgings in Covent Garden and entered then into a brief partnership with a fashionable dentist, Spence, who seems to have graduated from barbery to dentistry, moving at the same time from a small shop in Gray's Inn Lane to the largest house in Soho Square. The partnership was a successful one. It allowed John Hunter to accumulate some much-needed capital, and it provided the material for a treatise on *The Natural History of the Human Teeth*. This was the first scientific study of the teeth ever made, and in it Hunter recommended for the first time the complete removal of the pulp from teeth which were to be filled. In 1765 he applied unsuccessfully for an appointment to the staff of St. George's. The appointment was given to John Gunning. Hunter had been senior to Gunning in terms of the period of residence as a house-surgeon, but while Hunter was ill in 1760 Gunning had been appointed assistant to one of the senior surgeons, and was therefore preferred when the time came for the election of a full surgeon. John Hunter was quite determined that he would succeed to an appointment at St. George's sooner or later. He had still no surgical diploma, and though his experience as an anatomist was vast, his experience of surgical practice was confined to that which he had obtained in the Army. These considerations did not deter him from buying some land, rated at £5 per annum, in Earl's Court, which was conveniently near St. George's. He was teaching anatomy to a few pupils at Golden Square at the time, but soon began to build on his newly-acquired property, though to do this he had to mortgage the lease he had just bought. In 1767, "after dancing", he ruptured a tendon in his leg, and turned this accident to good account by demonstrating in dogs the union of tendons. Earlier in the year he had been elected a Fellow of the Royal Society. This was three months before William's election, and in itself gives some indication of the distinction he must already have attained.

In May of this same year he quite deliberately inoculated himself with pus from a patient suffering from gonorrhœa. The veneral diseases were still not properly distinguished one from the other, and he wanted to find out whether the poison producing gonorrhœa was, or was not, identical with that causing syphilis. A theory commonly held was that the two conditions were simply different manifestations of the same disease, gonorrhœa appearing when a mucous membrane was infected, syphilis when the skin was attacked. Unhappily, the pus with which Hunter inoculated himself contained the spirochætes of syphilis as well as gonococci. The inoculation was on to a scarified skin surface, and so the organisms causing gonorrhœa simply died, while those responsible for syphilis multiplied and spread through his system. The ulcers which formed were cauterized and soon healed. But inevitably after a few months a skin rash appeared, and at the same time the right tonsil ulcerated. The syphilitic nature of the condition was recognized, and treatment with mercury ointment was begun and continued intermittently for three years. This disability necessitated the postponement of Hunter's marriage, but did not upset his other plans.

On July 7, 1768, soon after leaving Golden Square to take possession of his brother's house in Jermyn Street, William having moved to the new premises in Great Windmill Street, he was admitted a member of the Surgeons' Company and received its diploma. December saw him elected surgeon to St. George's at last, and about this time the first of the buildings at Earl's Court was finished. The election to St. George's brought Hunter a share in the surgical pupils' fees, and allowed him to take apprentices. He had, too, an increasing number of resident pupils. Thanks to these pupils, if not completely free from debt, Hunter was at least in a position to marry, but the treatment for syphilis had to be completed first, and so it was not till 1771 that he penned a brief note to William:

> DEAR BROTHER,
>
> To-morrow morning at eight o'clock and at St. James's Church, I enter into the Holy State of Matrimony. As that is a ceremony which you are not particularly fond of, I will not make a point of having your company there. I propose going out of town for a few days; when I come to Town I shall call upon you. Married or not married, ever yours,
>
> JOHN HUNTER.

It was typical of John that Sunday morning at eight was the only time he could afford away from his work. He was forty-three at the time of his marriage, and Anne Home was twenty-nine. The brief honeymoon was spent at Earl's Court before John Hunter plunged again into the investigations he was making. He read a paper before the Royal Society on the changes which take place in the stomach after death. Other papers followed this in bewildering succession. There was one on the electric organs of the ray, another on the bones of birds, another on the gillaroo trout. He used to get up each morning about six and work till nine. After breakfast he would see the patients who had come to consult him, before going off to do a round of visits. At four he dined, and then in the winter he would go off to his lectures or demonstrations, while in the summer and at the week-ends he would prepare lectures or papers, or go on with his dissections till one or two in the mornings. Four hours sleep each night seemed to be all he needed. At least three months in every year were spent at Earl's Court, and it was there that Hunter had rushed to him by coach the corpse of O'Brien, the Irish giant, whose skeleton still stands in the Hunterian Museum of the Royal College of Surgeons of England. Two of the larger works he was preparing at this time were his *Treatise on the Venereal Diseases,* which was published in 1786, and his *Observations on the Animal Oeconomy.* This last included his original description of the nerves of smell, notes on the differences between warm-blooded and cold-blooded animals, a method of artificial respiration, and records of innumerable other investigations.

For the course of nearly a hundred systematic lectures which he gave each winter he charged four guineas. Deliberately, he broke away from the established method of teaching surgery by describing various diseases individually and going on immediately to discuss the operations needed for their cure. He tried instead to give a general view of the whole practice of surgery and the principles upon which it was established. Once the principles were clear, they could be applied to any disease, and would help to explain its pathology and indicate the line of treatment to be followed. He hammered into his pupils his belief that to know the effects of disease was to know very little. To know the cause of those effects was to understand them, and to know at the same time how best to treat them. Only thus could a man learn how to prevent disease or, if disease did arise, when best to operate and when to leave well alone. It was essential to know the anatomy of the human body, but more important even than the simple mechanics were the mechanisms involved. Structure was important, but function was even more important. Any operation was to his mind a reflection on the healing art. Surgery marked always the failure of medicine. The lithotomist could remove stones from the bladder easily enough, but the stone should never have formed, and would never have formed had the surgeon known how to prevent it. The amputating knife could save a man's life, but the gangrenous limb should have been kept healthy, and would have been healthy had the surgeon known how to prevent the onset of gangrene.

This teaching was compounded of equal parts of sheer heresy and rank revolution. Those of his pupils who understood John Hunter formed the next generation of great surgeons, and they handed down the Hunterian teachings and ideals like twin torches, which burn as brightly to-day as ever they did. Those of his pupils who did not understand him—and in the early days they were many—stopped attending the lectures and never got their four guineas' worth. It is easy to realize how there arose the famous fable of the size of his classes. It was said that so few students came to hear what Hunter was talking about that on one occasion he had to have a skeleton brought into the lecture-room, so that he could properly open his discourse to one solitary student with the usual "Gentlemen"! Fable this certainly was, for classes which had numbered twelve or sixteen pupils soon included as many as fifty.

John Hunter was appointed Surgeon-Extraordinary to His Majesty the King in 1776, and in the same year he published a paper on methods to be employed to assist the recovery of persons apparently drowned, and began a series of six Croonian lectures on muscular motion to the Royal Society.

It was in 1780 that he quarrelled with William. The relationship of the two brothers was never a normal one. When John came to London William was already a busy consultant of considerable reputation. Everything of John's came from William, from ideas to work out to such pocket-money as could be spared. William had long had to provide for his brothers and sisters. The woman he was to have married died. The discoveries he made were derided, and the claims he put forward were opposed. His had been a hard fight. For John it was much easier. William found him employment, arranged for him to be taught by Cheselden, procured an Army commission for him, saw that he was appointed to St. George's, and inevitably was always conscious of what the younger brother owed him. It was natural enough for William, in his *Atlas of the Gravid Uterus,* to refer generally to the help he had received from his younger brother. It was just as natural for John, once his own efforts had established his position, to claim the discoveries which were rightly his. In a paper on the structure of the afterbirth in 1780, he told of how he and Mackenzie, then Smellie's assistant, had made the important discoveries which had first been recorded in William's book. There had been minor quarrels between the two brothers at different times, but this particular communication marked the parting of the ways. John went on producing papers on every natural phenomenon from which something might be learnt. The effect of smallpox on pregnancy was investigated at the same time as the changes in the plumage of hen pheasants. His fame was spreading and he was made a member of the Royal Society of Gothenburg; later he was elected to the Royal Society of Medicine, later still to the Royal Academy of Surgery in Paris.

In 1783 William had his fatal seizure. John was called in to see him just as were other distinguished colleagues. He was not mentioned in his brother's will, and did not attend the funeral. Instead he delivered his usual lecture to his students, but prefaced it by a formal reference to the great loss which anatomy and surgery sustained in the death of William Hunter. John could not be as insensible as he wished, however; he had to pause for a long moment and turn his face away from his pupils before he could proceed. William Hunter just before he died said, "If I had enough strength to hold a pen I would write how easy and pleasant a thing it is to die. . . ." John, when he heard of this, said, "Aye, 'tis poor work when it comes to that."

Soon after his brother's death John sought better accommodation for the vast collection of specimens and dissections he had already accumulated. In the early years of his married life he had been making perhaps £1,000 a year, but this had gradually mounted to about £5,000 a year—which to-day would be the equivalent of about £15,000. He could well afford the new premises, which he urgently needed. Not only was the lease of the Jermyn Street house ending, the family were being literally forced into the street by the ever-growing collection. It was perhaps fortunate for his patient wife that the surgeon whom Hunter sent to Greenland, at his own expense, brought back no more than a few representative portions of the whale he had been commissioned to procure. What Hunter did, finally, was to buy two houses and the land between them, one house fronting on what is now Charing Cross Road, the other on Leicester Square, just south of where the old Alhambra used to be. It cost him most of £6,000 to build a lecture theatre and museum connecting the two houses, to buy the leases which had only twenty-four years to run, to set up printing-presses, and so modify the houses as to provide all the accommodation he needed for his assistants and for preparation-rooms and dissecting-rooms. The whole scheme was just as ambitious as that which William had undertaken in Great Windmill Street. It was 1785 before the building was completely finished, though he and his small family had moved there almost as soon as the leases were taken over. Hunter's interests were as catholic as ever. During this time he was doing some work on colour-blindness, in the intervals of dissecting cuckoos and compiling a paper on phlebitis. His collections were actually transferred from the old to the new museum while he was at Bath, taking the waters there. He had had an almost disabling recurrence of heart attacks which had worried him for over ten years past.

It was on his return, in December, 1785, that he performed at St. George's the first high operation for aneurysm of the popliteal artery. This great artery which runs behind the knee was ligatured actually in the thigh, in what has ever since been known as Hunter's Canal, several inches above the large swelling which had formed in its course. The operation was deliberately planned upon three principles, which he had proved experimentally: that the gradual swelling was due to the repeated impulses of each heart-beat conveyed along the arteries, which impulses could be cut off simply by tying the artery at a point between the heart and the aneurysm; that the apparent solidity of the aneurysmal sac was due to coagulated blood, which would be absorbed and disappear if no fresh blood were admitted; and, most important of all, that the tying of an artery to a limb would not affect the circulation in the limb as a whole, for other smaller arteries collateral with the large ones would enlarge and take up the function of supplying blood to the limb. The recognition of this last principle made possible this and other operations which were to save the lives of thousands, and provided a final answer to his many critics, who had wondered, scornfully, what was to be gained from a study of birds, fishes, and beasts, ranging from mice to leopards.

John Hunter had noted, while studying the growth of antlers in deer and the way in which they were shed and grown again, that when a main artery was obliterated, its function was rapidly and effectively taken up by small side-vessels. Never did a man spend long afternoons in Richmond Park to better purpose. In the following year, 1786, he published the two books on which he had been long engaged, the *Observations on the Animal Œconomy* and the *Treatise on the Venereal Diseases*. They came from his own printing-presses, for only by printing a book himself could an author at that time hope to escape the piracy of the Dublin booksellers, who threw cheap editions on to the English market as soon as possible after the appearance of any important—and usually expensive—original work. In this year, too, he became Deputy to Adair, then Surgeon-General of the Army.

Fame was his, and patients flocked to him. Sir Joshua Reynolds painted his portrait; the American Philosophical Society elected him a member; the Royal Society awarded him its Copley medal. At this time also St. George's allowed him and John Gunning each to take an assistant, and Hunter saw elected as his assistant Everard Home, his wife's young brother, who had been his own pupil. It was Home whom Hunter entrusted with his lectures when in 1790 he himself gave up lecturing. Adair had died that year, and Hunter had become Surgeon-General and Inspector-General of Hospitals. In addition he was anxious to complete his *Treatise on Inflammation,* and to see that the contents of his great museum were catalogued fully. He was ill again, too, suffering from attacks of giddiness, occasional loss of memory, and sleeplessness. So Home began to lecture for him, and more and more of the work of directing the museum and the activities of nearly fifty people, who had year by year been pressed into Hunter's service, devolved upon him and William Clift, Hunter's chief assistant.

"The dear man", for so all his nearest friends called John Hunter, was failing, but he obstinately refused to abate any more of his activities. In fact, he was active enough to bring to an explosive and tragic crisis a quarrel at St. George's which had been boiling up for many years. A custom had grown up at St. George's, as at other hospitals, whereby the surgeons divided equally the fees charged the surgical pupils of the hospital, though each surgeon was responsible for the teaching of those pupils entered under him. All the instruction given was at the bedside, though Hunter had pressed for many years for the institution of a definite series of lectures, a method of teaching which had been introduced at St. Bartholomew's by Percivall Pott as early as 1765. Gunning and his other colleagues opposed this suggestion. Their opposition was not lessened, when the proposal was brought up a second time, by the comments Hunter had made in the meantime. He was at his mildest when he wrote: " . . . one gentleman said he did not choose to lose any reputation he might have in surgery by giving lectures, which was at least modest, and another confessed that he could not see where the art could be improved, the natural conclusion from this declaration being that such a man would never improve it".

Defeated in his attempts to change the order of things by constitutional methods, John Hunter deliberately precipitated an open quarrel, knowing that it would lead to investigation of the whole problem of the admission of pupils and the methods to be adopted in teaching them. He stated in a letter to Gunning and the others his intention of keeping for himself, instead of dividing with them, the money which had accrued to him from new pupils. He pointed out that in the twenty-three years he had been associated with the hospital 449 pupils had entered under him, as against 103 with Mr. Gunning, and 284 with the three other surgeons. Stated bluntly, Hunter had attracted more than four times as many pupils as any other surgeon, had in consequence been involved in four times as much work, yet had received the same remuneration as them. This letter had the desired effect. Gunning and his fellows announced their entire disapproval of this flying in the face of established if inequitable custom, and referred the dispute to the General Board of the hospital. The General Board supported the long-established custom, as was to be expected, but soon afterwards appointed a committee to consider how best to improve the education of the surgeons' pupils. This was almost certainly what Hunter had hoped for, but he was never given the opportunity of communicating his views to the committee. The proposals made by this body took up his idea of courses of lectures being delivered at the hospital, and carried it much too far. They advised that lectures should be given on every subject in the medical curriculum, a proposal which at that time was quite impracticable. They ruled, too, that on entering the hospital pupils should submit certificates "of their having been bred up to the profession, and of their good behaviour". This was a wise revival of a rule which had been forgotten. Their other proposals concerned the regular attendance of the surgeons at the hospital, twice a week to visit their patients, and once a week personally to superintend their dressings. Operations were to be performed on Mondays, Wednesdays, and Fridays, and every Friday the surgeons were also to meet for consultation. In addition, post-mortem examinations were to be performed by the surgeons, and one lecture was to be delivered every week by each of them. This was an arduous and time-consuming list of duties, probably calculated to make Hunter resign, for his activities outside St. George's had increased as steadily as his health had deteriorated. Attacks of disabling pain were affecting him almost every other day, and were liable to be brought on by any exertion or emotional stress. Grimly, the "dear man" agreed to conform with these rules, which were finally given effect on June 14, 1793, refusing his opponents the satisfaction that would have been afforded them by his resignation. Almost exactly four months later, on October 16, he brought before the weekly Board Meeting a statement concerning two young men, who wished to enter the hospital as his pupils but had not the necessary certificates of having been "bred up to the profession".

Hunter urged that they should be admitted. Two of the hospital physicians present at the meeting disagreed. An argument which started moderately soon became heated. The chaplain of the hospital, who was in the chair, tried to keep the peace. He failed. Someone flatly contradicted a statement of Hunter's. Hunter glared at his interrupter, tried vainly to control his anger, then, abruptly, he struggled from the Board room and collapsed. Within the space of seconds he was dead.

A few days afterwards he was buried in the vaults of St. Martin-in-the-Fields, though more than fifty years later his body was to be re-interred in Westminster Abbey. His executors were his widow, his brother-in-law, Everard Home, and his nephew, Matthew Baillie, and as directed by the will they petitioned Parliament, asking the House to consider buying Hunter's collection for the nation. Pitt was aghast at the idea. "What! Buy preparations! Why, I have not enough money to purchase gunpowder." A second petition had the same fate as the first, and it was 1799 before it was finally resolved "that a sum not exceeding £15,000 be granted to His Majesty to enable him to purchase the Collection of Natural History belonging to the late Dr. John Hunter, for the use of the public". The collection had actually cost Hunter somewhere about £20,000, quite apart from his forty years of inspired labour on it. Once bought it was taken over by the College of Surgeons, and in 1806 was transferred to Lincoln's Inn Fields. His executors were also responsible, in the year after his death, for publishing perhaps his greatest work, *Blood, Inflammation, and Gunshot Wounds.* This was a study of physiology, pathology, and surgery, which had been begun in Belleisle more than thirty years previously.

Everard Home took upon himself another duty, which does not as a rule fall to the lot of an executor. He deliberately burned many volumes of Hunter's manuscripts. It was fortunate that William Clift, Hunter's chief assistant, had copies he had made himself of no less than nine volumes of notes on the dissections Hunter had undertaken, and some twenty-six other monographs. Still in existence, too, were the notes successive generations of pupils had made of his lectures. Controversy has long raged about this holocaust of Home's, and the accusation has often been levelled at him that he pilfered Hunter's discoveries, announced them as his own, and then burnt the evidence of his iniquity. The view taken by Sir Arthur Keith seems nearer the truth. Hunter was an undoubted pagan, "he silently and resolutely thought and wrote as if the Book of Genesis had never been in existence". Perhaps the last paper he wrote was "Observations on the Fossil Bones presented to the Royal Society by His Most Serene Highness the Margrave of Anspach". In this paper, which was, as usual, submitted to the Council of the Royal Society before being read, Hunter explained certain changes in the structure of bones as having taken place by a process which had been in operation for thousands of centuries. The Council was horrified to find a distinguished Fellow seriously suggesting that anything at all could have been happening for thousands of centuries. Hunter died, and the Council were saved from having to decide whether to reject the paper, which was impossible, or to persuade Hunter to alter it, which was just as impossible. Everard Home was then consulted, and agreed to have the phrase changed to "thousands of years" and brought safely within the limits of Biblical chronology. Sir Arthur Keith suggests that the same honest and well-meaning, if mistaken, piety prompted the burning of so many other manuscripts, which must have contained similar pagan suggestions. This is the more charitable and surely the more correct view.

Controversy there has been about Everard Home's conduct, but there has been even more discussion about the cause of Hunter's death, which has so often been attributed to angina pectoris. Sir D'Arcy Power has made it clear, however, that the heart pains and fainting attacks from which John Hunter suffered were not due to disease of the heart alone but to a generalized syphilitic disease of the blood-vessels. Hunter inoculated himself with syphilis, thinking he was dealing only with gonococcal pus, in May, 1767. Purposely he delayed treatment to study the condition in himself. Then he played with the disease, controlling it with inunctions of mercury ointment for a while and then letting it return. The spirochætes of syphilis took a hold of him that was never to relax. Hunter died as a direct result of this disastrous experiment, and the accurate account he gave of his condition, which he thought was due to gonococcal pus, led to a confusion of syphilis and gonorrhœa which was not to be cleared up till nearly fifty years after his death.

John Hunter founded the sciences of experimental and surgical pathology. He found surgery little more than a trade. Harvey had pointed out a method of simple investigation, which a few of his successors were following. Cheselden and others had raised the standards of craftsmanship in surgery, and the prestige of surgeons. John Hunter showed that there were processes of disease which could be studied just as Harvey had studied the processes of nature, and that only by investigating the changes due to disease in the light of a knowledge of the functions of normal tissues and organs could surgery be properly applied. He provided the surgical pathology which was to weld Cheselden's craftsmanship and Harvey's physiology into a single instrument, which could be applied scientifically to the relief and cure of disease. Like Harvey's, his experiments were always simple, and in fact the only new instruments he had were a not very good microscope and a somewhat erratic thermometer, which Fahrenheit had invented in 1720. He dissected and described over five hundred different species of animals, seeking in animals, birds, and fishes ultimate truths of natural functions.

Anatomists before him had always held that natural actions and processes reflected the structure of the organs which gave rise to them. Hunter made it clear that structure is always an expression of function, and abnormalities are due to retarded or arrested development, or to misuse or malfunction. He showed how much a study of the lower animals could contribute to the study of man, how the physiological activities of lower forms of life are but simplifications of those same activities in higher forms. His contributions to embryology, biology, anatomy, physiology, pathology, surgery, dentistry, and medicine, were legion and were all arrived at by the same route, patient observation, then painstaking inquiry. These methods he taught to his pupils, and he founded a tradition and a school of thought which were to be the mainsprings of surgical advance. The surgery of his time was a manual version of the medicine then practised. If a patient had this, that, and the other symptoms, then his disease could be labelled, and according to the label so was the patient treated. If no label could be found, then he would be bled by the surgeons, or purged by the physicians, and he might live or he might die. John Hunter shattered the faith his fellows had in this empirical treatment. He asked not what was the name of the man's disease, but why that man had become diseased, what could have been done to prevent the disease, and, if it was established, why was he bled, why purged, why subjected to operation? He said once, and was derided for playing with words: "It is the cause producing inflammation which is the disease and not the inflammation itself, for all inflammations that can be called diseases have specific causes". Hunter's methods were inductive. He never argued by deduction from the general to the particular. He noted every facet of any given function in every form of flesh or fish upon which he could lay hands, then from his mass of particular instances he formulated the general principle which governed them. Inevitably, he made errors of inference, when his particular instances were not sufficiently multiplied, or when his few crude instruments failed him, but he never erred in observation.

The little man with the stubborn chin and the inquiring eye found a trade and left a philosophy, mastered a mechanic art and made of it a science. Upon everything he touched, and not least upon his immediate pupils, he left the stamp of his genius. These pupils were to make his mode of thought a tradition. Their pupils were to make that tradition a living inspiration.

XVII.   After Hunter

JOHN HUNTER'S PUPILS BECAME THE LEADERS OF THE NEXT generation of surgeons.   To the hospitals at which they worked they brought the Hunterian ideals and teachings.   These they had learnt at the finest private medical school in Europe.   By their efforts teaching was centred around the great hospitals with their wealth of clinical material.   Sir William Blizard, one of Hunter's first pupils, as early as 1785 saw the private school he had founded become the London Hospital Medical School. Two other pupils were the natural successors of Cheselden and Percivall Pott, Henry Cline at St. Thomas's and John Abernethy at St. Bartholomew's.   Abernethy championed Hunter's theories and continued the work his master had started on the ligation of arteries.   He was the first to tie the external iliac artery for aneurysm.   On four occasions, twice successfully, he did this operation on the great blood-vessel which supplies the entire lower limb.   The common carotid artery, so deeply seated in the neck that it had been almost immune from surgical inter-ference, he also tied successfully.   Kind-hearted and generous though he was, Abernethy affected a brusque and masterful rudeness at the bedside, in the belief that this would inspire confidence in his patients.   The brusqueness was carried to remarkable lengths with those patients who had nothing much the matter with them and were simply wasting his time.   A farmer consulted Abernethy and allowed the surgeon to waste nearly half an hour eliciting, pint by pint, the fact that his only trouble was an acquired thirst, which could only be quenched by a daily intake of over a gallon and a half of ale.   Abernethy threw the thirsty farmer out of his consulting-rooms and bellowed after him: "Go home, sir, and let me never see your face again!   Go home!   Drink your ale and be damned!"   In 1790 Abernethy was appointed professor of anatomy to the Surgeons' Company at the same time that John Gunning was made pro-fessor of surgery.   Other pupils of Hunter were Astley Cooper at Guy's, Anthony Carlisle at the Westminster Hospital, Hey, who was to found a great school of surgery at Leeds, and Philip Syng Physick and his nephew, John Syng Dorsey, who were to carry the Hunterian tradition to Pennsylvania.

Philip Syng Physick was born on July 7, 1768.   He was John Hunter's favourite American pupil.   Though he studied

in London, he qualified in Edinburgh, and returned to Philadelphia in 1792. He performed his first operation for the extraction of stones from the bladder five years later, and soon was
an acknowledged master of the lateral lithotomy Cheselden had
perfected. Philip Syng Physick made innumerable advances
in surgical technique, devising and modifying instruments and
splints. Like all Hunter's pupils, he was an excellent anatomist;
his surgical skill rested firmly upon his anatomical knowledge.
He experimented for several years with different ligature
materials, trying to find some substance that would be absorbed
and not need to be sloughed out; buckstring, French kid, and
animal gut were among the ligatures he tried. He and Alexander
Monro of Edinburgh were the first surgeons ever to wash out the
stomach. Physick used for this purpose a long, flexible tube
and a syringe made of pewter. He devised a wire snare which
was used in removing tonsils, a splint for fractured thighs,
another for injured elbows, and a cannula which could be introduced through a trephine hole in the skull to drain off an excess
of fluid from the brain. He was the first full professor of
surgery at the University of Pennsylvania, and held that chair
for thirteen years. Then he took over the professorship of
anatomy until 1831, when failing health forced his resignation,
and he became emeritus professor of both anatomy and surgery.

Many of Hunter's students became famous surgeons, but a
general practitioner, Edward Jenner, was perhaps the most
distinguished of them all. Dr. Edward Jenner in introducing
vaccination for the prevention of smallpox made one of the
greatest single contributions any one man has ever made to
medicine. Smallpox was never more rife in England than in
the eighteenth century. Every year it killed thousands, blinded
thousands, and left those who escaped these major catastrophes
disfigured for life. So common was it that for a woman to be
free from pock-marks almost assured her fame as a beauty,
though it might not improve her chances of winning a husband.
A pock-marked bride might not be much to look at, but at
least she carried a guarantee that she would not suffer smallpox
again and put her husband to a great deal of trouble and expense.
At the age of twenty-one, after serving his apprenticeship to a
surgeon at Sodbury, near Bristol, young Jenner came to London
to live for two years as a house pupil of John Hunter. This was
the beginning of a life-long friendship based on one quality
the two men had in common—an insatiable curiosity. They

corresponded regularly for many years, Hunter always demanding all sorts of biological specimens—hedgehogs, cuckoos, eels, bats, salmon spawn, even a porpoise—Jenner going to endless trouble to supply his wants. Jenner in his turn was often asking for advice, Hunter always giving it. Jenner sent patients as well as specimens to Hunter. One letter of Hunter's, for example, thanks Jenner for "a Wapping landlady and two lizards". Jenner it was to whom Hunter gave the clue to his own mode of working when he wrote to him on one occasion "Don't think, but try; be patient, be accurate". But Jenner had put this maxim into practice before he ever met Hunter. It was during his apprenticeship that a young dairymaid told the younger apprentice, "Oh, I shall never have smallpox, for I've had cowpox". Jenner soon found that all the country folk held firmly to this belief, and all the local physicians laughed at it as an old wives' tale.

Jenner was patient, and for twenty-five years he studied the affections of cows' teats and udders. He found that true cowpox was rare, compared with the many other conditions simulating it which could be conveyed from the cow to the hands of the milkers. This spurious pox did not protect the patient against subsequent attacks of smallpox—so the local physicians were right. True cowpox once sustained did protect against smallpox —so the dairymaid was even more right. At length the time was ripe for a trial, and on May 14, 1796, this undistinguished country practitioner successfully inoculated a healthy lad of eight with cowpox from the lesions on the hand of a milkmaid. Sarah Nelmes and John Phipps then went their various ways for eight weeks, at the end of which time Jenner inoculated Phipps with true smallpox. Nothing happened. The cowpox had prevented the boy from contracting smallpox. Two years later Jenner wrote a book of seventy-five pages, *An Inquiry into the Cause and Effects of Variolæ, Vaccinæ, a Disease discovered in some of the Western Counties of England, particularly Glostershire, and known by the name of Cowpox*. Encouraged by Cline and others whom he had first met as students of John Hunter's, Jenner came to London. At first there was opposition, but John Hunter had left a generation of physicians and surgeons trained as Jenner was —to try. Gradually the idea was accepted in England, then in Europe, then America. Parliament voted £10,000, and later another £20,000 to Edward Jenner. The Empress of Russia presented him with a diamond ring. At the outbreak of war between Britain and France many Englishmen living in France were held prisoner by Napoleon. All the usual diplomatic requests failed to secure their release. Jenner wrote direct to Napoleon, and the Emperor immediately ordered the release of all the prisoners, saying, "We can refuse nothing to that man". Spain, Italy, and Denmark were at one in doing honour to the discoverer of vaccination. Fame and reputation were his, but great patients and large fees never came his way. Vaccination was a simple trick, which anybody could perform. Jenner went back to his country practice and worked quietly on till in his seventy-second year he died of apoplexy.

These men were John Hunter's friends and pupils. Two other men, if not avowed enemies, were never Hunter's friends. Jesse Foot, a contemporary surgeon, would probably never have been heard of had it not been for his virulent attacks on Hunter. These seem to have followed an assertion of Hunter's that a bougie Foot had invented for use in the treatment of venereal diseases was useless. Foot attacked Hunter on every possible occasion in books and in pamphlets. Hunter dealt with him briefly: "Jesse Foot accuses me of not understanding the dead languages; but I could teach him that on the dead body which he never knew in any language, dead or living".

John Gunning never descended to the depths of abuse which Foot reached, but he and Hunter became most unfriendly rivals at a very early stage in their careers. Gunning had entered St. George's as an apprentice three years before Hunter, yet Hunter became a resident house-surgeon there before Gunning. On the other hand, Gunning became a governor of St. George's two years before Hunter, and was later appointed assistant surgeon and then full surgeon before Hunter. Their intermittent quarrels, none of them very violent, were brought to a head in the last twelve months of Hunter's life, during the long controversy as to how the teaching of students should be conducted at St. George's. Unlike Foot, Gunning is memorable in his own right, quite apart from his relations with John Hunter, for the way in which he purged the Surgeons' Company of many abuses, which had been growing up slowly ever since its creation in 1745. In 1789 he was elected first an examiner, to fill the vacancy caused by the death of Percivall Pott, and later Master of the Company. He took his mastership seriously. The first thing he probed into was the number of expensive dinners given to the Court of Assistants and to the Court of Examiners each year. The expense of providing a dinner had in the past been 4s. a head, rising to 10s. in 1775. In the eight years previous to his taking office it had mounted steadily to 19s. a head, and the total cost to the Company during that period was no less than £1,300. He drew the attention of the Company to all these things and added, as a final thrust, that after the so-called annual audit, the dinner to the auditors cost 30s. a head.

These strictures had the desired effect. Rules were promptly laid down restricting the number of dinners each year to four for joint meetings of the Assistants and Examiners, and eight for the Examiners alone, the cost of the former not to exceed twelve guineas for any one dinner, and of the latter six guineas. Any expenditure in excess of this was to be met by the diners. The total saving Gunning effected in this way was over £200 a year.

At the end of his year of office the Master delivered what has come to be known as "Gunning's Philippic". He started off by saying that he had paid all the Company's bills, all the taxes, and the salaries of all officials, "that the Company may for once know what their necessary expences in one year really are", and added that some of the bills had been outstanding for one or two years. He went on to outline a method of checking and auditing the accounts, which he thought ought to be adopted. He suggested that the sending out of an agenda before each meeting, and careful minute-keeping at the meeting, would do no harm. Having dealt destructively, and then constructively, with the methods of conducting both business and finance, he went on to what he termed "a great indecency"—namely, that "Your Theatre is without Lectures, your Library Room with Books is converted into an Office for your Clerk, and your Committee Room is become his Eating Parlour". The servants of the Company were next in the line of fire. The Clerk to the Company had originally been appointed at a salary of £60 per annum. To this had been added, in successive years, an annual gratuity of £40, free rooms, free coals and candles, and an allowance for a servant. The Clerk managed to make his coals and candles cost £84 a year, and sundry other perquisites were in the same expensive disproportion. Gunning ventured to submit that it was neither wise nor thrifty for a poorly endowed Company to squander one quarter of its income on its Clerk. In a less degree but in the same way the Company's Beadle was doing well for himself. Gunning was next concerned with the provision of anatomy lectures. He admitted all the usual arguments about the rapid growth of both private and hospital medical schools, but pointed out that money had been left to the Company for the express purpose of providing lectures, and suggested that the Company would fill a gap in the existing arrangements by providing a course of perhaps fifteen lectures in anatomy and surgery in May and June, when the systematic courses of most schools had ended and before the students left the town to spend the summer months in the country. Finally, he suggested that each year a proportion of the Company's income should be set aside in order that books might be bought for the library, and a sum be allotted to charity.

A committee was appointed to consider his suggestions, and accepted many of them with little modification. The salaries of the Clerk and the Beadle were fixed and perquisites were forbidden them. The points Gunning had made about charity and the library were conveniently forgotten, but Gunning was made professor of surgery and Abernethy professor of anatomy. Gunning only held this office for a few months before resigning. Most of the reforms he suggested were sound. Most of them were enthusiastically adopted. Unhappily, their effect was short-lived, and within a few years the business of the Company was being conducted as slackly as ever. The Company's Hall, the lecture theatre, the library, and the committee-rooms lapsed again into a state of disrepair and desuetude. At length a surveyor was called in, and he reported that general repairs to the whole structure, which had only been built in 1751, would cost not less than £1,600. The tenure of the property in the Old Bailey had only another fifty-five years to run, and the ground-rent and taxes amounted to £240 each year. It was generally agreed that the most economic procedure would be to erect new premises on freehold ground. Under Gunning's chairmanship a committee of six was given plenary powers to deal with the situation. The Hall and Theatre were offered for sale unsuccessfully. On July 7, 1796, Gunning reported to a meeting of the Court of Assistants that the highest bid received was £200 less than the reserve price placed upon the property. The business was discussed at length, and Gunning was instructed to continue to search for a purchaser. The Court then proceeded to elect Mr. Henry Cline of St. Thomas's a member of the Court of Assistants, in order to fill the vacancy created by the death of Mr. William Walker, a Warden of the Company.

By so doing the Company unwittingly put an end to its legal existence. By the Act of Incorporation granted by George II the Company's Court of Assistants could not despatch any business except in the presence of the Master of the Company and one of the two Wardens. William Walker was dead and the other Warden, John Wyatt, lay dying at his home in Warwickshire. So all the actions of the Court, in the absence of either Warden, were illegal. Not realizing this and several other constitutional irregularities, the Company went ahead and bought from a Mr. Baldwin a freehold house in Lincoln's Inn Fields for the sum of £5,500. In October the City of London bought the Hall in Old Bailey from the Company for £2,100. The Court of Assistants met for the first time at the new house on January 5, 1797. The Company was still unaware of the illegality of its actions, but had been advised that there was some doubt as to the propriety of its holding freehold estates in mortmain. For this reason, and this reason only, it sponsored a Bill in Parliament to change its Bylaws. The same Bill suggested a change of name from Company to College, and the King had readily consented to the adoption of the prefix Royal.

The Bill, about which the general body of members of the Company knew little or nothing, progressed easily through the Commons, and after a first and second reading was sent to the Lords. The third reading was adjourned till July 17, 1797. At that point the Bill was bitterly attacked by Lord Thurlow, whose opposition was said to be largely due to his personal hatred for Surgeon-General Gunning. According to the noble Lord, Parliament had been taken by surprise. His own knowledge of the Bill was purely accidental. He had heard of it only when residents in Lincoln's Inn Fields protested about a house in that district being used for dissection. He objected to a bylaw which forbade any examiner or officer of the proposed College to practise midwifery or pharmacy being applied to a body which asked to be entrusted with the examining of all Army and Navy surgeons. How much value to the community would a surgeon who knew no pharmacy be? The clause extending the jurisdiction of the College to a radius of ten miles from London was iniquitous, merciless, and oppressive. Penal clauses in the Bill were indefinite and likely to lead to legislation. The fees proposed were too high. The members

PLATE XV

A man-midwife beneath a "modesty blanket."

From Santbergen's *Korte En Bondige Verhandeling Van de Voortteeling en Kinderbaren* (A.D. 1681).

PLATE XVI

John Hunter with three of his freaks.

of the College who were to be entrusted with the management of its business and finances were too few.

There was much more to the same effect, his lordship carefully pointing out that his concern was merely for the public interest, and the health and well-being of mankind. It may have been, but he was constrained to remark at one point: "There's no more science in surgery than in butchery". This was too much for Gunning: "Then, my lord, I heartily pray that your lordship may break your leg, and have only a butcher to set it, and then you'll find the difference between butchery and surgery". For the moment, however, Thurlow was successful, and his attack killed the Bill. One of the real objections to the Bill was that Lincoln's Inn Fields was so far from the usual place of execution that it was thought it might be difficult and inconvenient to convey the bodies of hanged felons such a considerable distance through the streets of London. A clause was inserted at the last minute to the effect that there would be provided "a convenient house or building as near as can be procured to the place of execution, to which house the bodies of all persons who shall be executed for murder, and shall be sentenced to be dissected and anatomised . . . according to the Act entitled an Act for the better preventing the horrid crime of Murder, shall be conveyed". This did not save the Bill, but the Company accepted the offer of Mr. Chandler's stable for the reception of the bodies of two murderers executed in June of that year.

It was customary to expose the body of a condemned criminal to the public for a day or so, and for some time past the Company had hired houses or yards in which this might be done. Thus six guineas was paid for the use of a house in which to expose the body of William Long, the murderer, and seven guineas for part of a stable-yard for the public viewing of the corpse of Marie Theresa Phipoe. When Laurence Shirley, the fourth Earl Ferrers and the cousin of Lady Huntingdon, after trial by his peers, was sentenced to death, "after which your body is to be delivered to Surgeons' Hall to be dissected and anatomized", he cried out "God forbid", which he hastily corrected to "God's will be done". His trial for the murder of his steward had been sensational, his execution was something of a public holiday, and the exposure of his body at Surgeons' Hall attracted enormous crowds.

The throwing out of the Bill which had been entitled "An Act for erecting the Corporation of Surgeons of London into a College, and for granting and confirming to such College certain rights and privileges", left the Company in a state of chaos. Members refused to pay their fees. Three Commissioners appointed by the First Lord of the Admiralty took away from the Company the old-established and remunerative duty of examining the instruments and drug-chests of would-be naval surgeons. They even disregarded the results of the Company's examinations of the naval surgeons themselves. One fortunate young man whom the examiners at Surgeons' Hall had classed as a third-rate second mate was examined again by the Commissioners and passed as a first-rate first mate. Lectures and meetings were suspended for a while, and the only activity which was not interfered with seems to have been that of adjudging naval compensation cases. Notable amongst these cases was that of Rear-Admiral Sir Horatio Nelson, K.B., who in 1797 was examined after receiving an injury to his eye, and a year later was seen again as to "£135. 1. od. for the chirurgical and medical expenses of the cure of his arm, which was thought reasonable and allowed". At length the Court of Assistants was gathered together again and appointed a committee to meet those members who had been opposed to the Bill. Provisional agreement was reached as to a new constitution. It was suggested that the new College should have a president, four vice-presidents, and a council of thirty members. There were to be three examining committees, one for surgery, one for midwifery, and one to examine in medicine candidates for the Army and Navy medical services. Jurisdiction was to be over the whole of England and Wales, and there was to be no disqualifying bylaw concerning midwifery and pharmacy. Lectures on anatomy and surgery were to be on a much more extensive scale. A library was to be formed, the transactions of the College were to be published periodically, and a museum was to be built up around the magnificent nucleus formed by John Hunter's collection, which had been finally taken over by the Company in December, 1799.

All these things were agreed on, and a new Bill was being made ready when it was realized that all that was needed could be achieved far more easily by a charter direct from the Crown. A prerogative charter cannot override an Act of Parliament, but since the Act of 1745 had been rendered non-operative by the irregular meetings of 1797 and the Company had legally no existence, there was no obstacle to the granting of a charter.

The Company was therefore able to profit considerably from its mistakes in procedure, which had automatically dissolved it three years previously. A petition was duly presented on the Company's behalf by the Duke of Portland, and His Majesty George III on March 22, 1800, established by Charter the Royal College of Surgeons in London. In 1821 a supplemental Charter from George IV sanctioned the use of the titles of president and vice-presidents, instead of master and governors or wardens. Queen Victoria in 1843 by a further Charter gave the College the name it holds to this day of the Royal College of Surgeons of England, and confirmed its constitution of President, Vice-presidents, Council, Fellows, and Members.

The old Barber-Surgeons' Company had tried first to harass and later to propitiate the quacks. The Surgeons' Company, in its brief fifty-odd years of existence, treated the problems of widespread roguery and charlatanism much as it treated most other problems, by quietly forgetting about them. For example, in 1785 William Blizard and another member complained that Mr. Pinkstan, a member of the Court of Assistants, had signed an advertisement recommending certain fever powders for the cure of white swellings. The Court was with them in disapproving the advertisement, but felt that it had no power to take any action in the matter.

Quacks still abounded in London, and there were three in particular, a German, an Italian Jew, and a Scot, whose names became household words. The German, Dr. Myersbach, revived the lost art of urinoscopy. This water-casting, or diagnosing a patient's ailments and prescribing treatment solely from an inspection of the urine, was a procedure of venerable antiquity. So-called physicians contemporary with Rhazes and Avicenna had no difficulty in forecasting the sex of an unborn child from the prospective mother's urine. Certain of the early writers of the School of Salerno produced long treatises on urinoscopy. In the Middle Ages the urinal was the emblem of medical practice, and was even used as a convenient sign-board device. Innumerable works of art testify the diagnostic importance of inspection of the urine at this period (*see plate facing* p. 288). In the early Renaissance period "uromancy" was still a popular diagnostic method, but towards the end of the seventeenth century it fell into a deserved disrepute. Myersbach was an M.D. of Erfurth in Germany. The exact value of this doctorate was not known in England, but a young man travelling in Germany had no difficulty in obtaining it for one Anglicus Ponto. After paying the necessary fees and receiving the degree in all solemnity, he revealed the fact that Ponto was his favourite mastiff. Myersbach reached London about 1774, and rapidly proceeded to accumulate a fortune. After two years of affluent immunity from all criticism, he was attacked by John Coakley Lettsom, then a young Quaker physician. Lettsom was one of the founders of the Medical Society of London, and played a large part also in the founding of the Royal Humane Society, which had as its immediate object "the Recovery of Persons who are suppose[d] Dead of Drowning." Lettsom, if he had never achieved anything at all, would have been remembered by Lord Erskine's neat rhyme, prompted by the way in which he signed himself "I. Lettsom":

> Whenever patients come to I,
> I physics, bleeds, and sweats 'em.
> If, after that, they choose to die,
> What's that to me? I. Lettsom.

Lettsom and his friends got a great deal of amusement out of Myersbach. They submitted a flask of port wine to him, and were assured that the case from which it came was one of serious disease of the womb. From the urine of a gelding the omniscient doctor deduced that the patient was a lady, and that she had a disorder of the womb, two children, and a bad temper. A cow's urine distressed him greatly. He explained that it obviously came from a young man who had been much too free with the ladies of the town. Lettsom wanted the College of Physicians to deal with Myersbach. They could have done so easily, for they had the power to prevent anyone who did not hold their licence from practising within seven miles of London. Like the Surgeons' Company, however, the College preferred to do nothing, and so Lettsom himself attacked Myersbach, in pamphlets and in letters to the Press. One shaft of his was to the effect that "Dr. Myersbach knew less of urine than a chambermaid and as little of medicine as most of his patients". Myersbach discreetly packed up his bags and retired to the Continent for some twelve months. Then he returned and had as great a success as ever. Eventually he died, the last of the "uromancers", and no one since has ever attempted to revive the art of water-casting.

It was Carlyle who labelled the Italian Jew, Count Alessandro

Di Cagliostro, the Quack of Quacks. Cagliostro started life as Joseph Balsamo and graduated early as a sneak-thief and forger. His nearest approach to earning an honest living was by faking old etchings. He came to London in 1771 with his wife Lorenza because there was more scope for his natural genius in capital cities, and also because he was wanted by the authorities, for forgery and kindred activities, in Rome, Barcelona, Madrid, and Lisbon. Soon the London police were seeking him as earnestly as their colleagues in Italy, Spain, and Portugal, but by that time Joseph was in Paris, as the Marquis de Balsamo, rejuvenating the aged, healing the sick, softening marble, making gold, transforming cotton into silk, and generally benefiting mankind at large. The authorities in Paris were incurable sceptics, as were the city fathers of Brussels. Naples was more receptive, and for a while Joseph stayed there, modestly confining his activities to making beautiful the very ugly, and causing diamonds and pearls to grow to twice their original size. Marseilles was the next city to be honoured by the Marquis and his lovely wife, and from there they went on to Cadiz. There Joseph sold a Spanish grandee the formula for the philosopher's stone, and left the next day for an unknown destination. Actually he was trying London again, but this time as Captain, later Colonel, and soon afterwards Count, Cagliostro. Unfortunately he was found out while indulging in his favourite relaxation of swindling the very wealthy, and languished for a while in an English prison. On being released he must have resolved to turn over a new leaf, and a bigger and better and brighter one at that. He was soon established in popularity as a nobleman, an illustrious scientist, and a great philanthropist. He started travelling again in a magnificent private carriage, surrounded by couriers, lackeys, and valets. His claims were as modest as ever. He could, for a considerable consideration, raise the dead, restore lost youth, foretell the future, and perform miracles. In Russia, Poland, and Germany he was received with acclamation and showered with presents. He would never take fees for healing the sick—and never refuse presents. Wherever he went the troops had to be called out to control the crowds. He was an honoured guest of every other princely family in Europe. He returned to Paris in 1785, to be promoted immediately to the pedestal from which Mesmer had just toppled. The Faculty of Medicine watched his every move, but Cagliostro was not to be caught napping. Two medical students were sent to him, one of them playing the part of a patient. He was inept enough to use one or two scientific terms in describing his symptoms. Cagliostro saw through the trick. He insisted that the "patient" should stay at his house for sixteen days, and added casually that it was essential that the youth should have only one ounce of food a day during that period. The "patient's" friend asked weakly what the diagnosis was. Cagliostro wrote a few words on a piece of paper and with much mysterious gesturing gave it to him. The student got away as quickly as he could and unfolded the paper. On it Cagliostro's accurate diagnosis was writ large: "Superabundance of bile in the gentlemen of the Faculty".

Cagliostro and his wife were mixed up—for perhaps the first time in their career innocently—in the affair of Marie Antoinette's diamond necklace. They were sent to the Bastille, but acquitted after trial. Their release provoked great popular demonstrations in their favour, but the King ordered them both to leave Paris within a week. The irony-of-fate cliché applies exactly. The one crime of which he was not guilty ruined Cagliostro. London would have none of him. Switzerland drove him from its frontiers, and he returned at last to Rome. There was no market even there for his love-philtres and elixirs. He took up again Freemasonry, in which he had long dabbled, and this soon brought him into the hands of the Inquisition. Five years later he died in prison.

Cagliostro was the genius of quacks. James Graham, the third of this trio, was no genius, but he had an instinctive knowledge of human nature and an inventive originality which brought him as much fame as any orthodox practitioner of his time. The son of an Edinburgh saddler, Graham was born in 1745. He studied medicine there for a short time under William Cullen, the friend of William Hunter, and the Monros, but it is doubtful if he ever took a degree or obtained a qualification of any kind. After practising for a short time at Pontefract, he went to America as a sort of itinerant specialist in diseases of the eye and ear. There he became acquainted with Franklin's discoveries and quickly saw the possibilities of using electricity for the exploitation of the public. He returned to England, and after practising for a while in the neighbourhood of Bath and Bristol he established what might be termed an electro-therapeutic practice in London. This first venture was not very successful, and so he returned to Bath, and soon had queues of patients waiting to spend a few minutes sitting on his "magnetic throne" or lying in an "electrical bath". In 1779 he went to Paris, where he met Franklin again, and then on to Aix-la-Chapelle. There he treated many aristocratic patients and accumulated a large file of glowing testimonials. One of his most ardent admirers was Georgiana, Duchess of Devonshire. He made a small fortune, and proceeded next to invest not less than £10,000 of it in a Temple of Health, facing the Thames on the Royal Terrace, Adelphi. The door of this Temple was always open, so that the poor might enter as freely as the rich. All that was demanded of the poor was a fee of £6, which was paid to one of two enormous porters clad in chain mail and flowing robes. Once this trifling formality was over, rich and poor males were alike conducted to the Great Apollo Apartment. Here the high priest himself lectured from 5.0 p.m. till 7.0 p.m. every day. Soft music always preceded his discourse, and at appropriate moments his audience received mild electrical shocks from the carefully wired chairs in which they were seated. As a grand finale an enormous spectre came up through the floor and handed to Graham bottles of his famous "ætherial balsam", which was guaranteed to promote fertility. The ladies were catered for in much the same way by a High Priestess, except that instead of a spectre they saw Hebe Vestina, the Rosy Goddess of Health and Hymen. It is said that Emma Hart, Lord Nelson's Lady Hamilton, once officiated as Hebe.

If, despite the guarantee, the ætherial balsam did not promote a successful conception and lead to the production of the loveliest possible children, Graham placed at the disposal of his clients his wonder of wonders, the innermost mystery of the Temple of Health. This was his Celestial Bed. The bed was in the centre of a spacious room pervaded always by rich scents and perfumes, and in which could be heard soft music from a string orchestra in an adjoining room. The bed was supported on six massive glass pillars and bedecked with blue satin. The slightest movement of the occupants made it oscillate rhythmically, and there ran through it electrical currents varying in intensity with the movements of the bed. According to Graham, once in the bed what he termed the *moment critique* became *l'heure critique*. This magnificent apparatus was at the disposal of any lady and gentleman, preferably married. The price for one night in the bed—presumably with breakfast—was £50. Graham was a shrewd investor, and he reaped enormous dividends. Anyone who had not slept in the bed was regarded by the world of fashion with the gravest suspicion. This vogue lasted for three most profitable years, at the end of which time Graham returned to his native Edinburgh, there to preach the virtues of the mud bath. In his declining years he became first religious and later maniacal. He died suddenly in 1794, falling short of his own boasted expectancy of life by exactly fifty-one years.

These three men were perhaps the last of the great quacks. As long as nothing is known about a subject it remains a happy hunting-ground for quacks. Harvey and Hunter had pointed the way to knowledge. Harvey himself made a great contribution to knowledge and to scientific method. Hunter did both these things and more. He left behind him eager pupils, trained in his mode of thought, accustomed to his methods of experimental attack. Philip Syng Physick and John Syng Dorsey were creating a school in the direct line of descent from Hunter in America. In London William Blizard, Henry Cline, and John Abernethy had carried the Hunterian teachings to their different hospitals, and with John Gunning had seen the old Surgeons' Company become a Royal College, firmly established on rational lines and a worthy custodian of the greatest single collection of pathological and anatomical specimens in the world. These men were among the early pupils of John Hunter. Following close in their footsteps were younger men, pupils of an older but still inspiring John Hunter. Perhaps the most distinguished of them was Astley Paston Cooper, and contemporary with him were two brothers, John and Charles Bell, the first of a series of great surgeons who took origin from the fast-growing school of Edinburgh.

XVIII.   Astley Cooper and the Bells

ASTLEY PASTON COOPER, THE FOURTH OF A FAMILY OF TEN children, was born on August 23, 1768, at Brooke Hall, some seven miles from Norwich.   He aspired to great heights even as a child, notably to the roof of the parish church, off which he fell.   At a very early age his tastes were directed towards surgery, partly by the success of his uncle, Mr. William Cooper, then one of the senior surgeons of Guy's Hospital, and partly by the local fame he achieved at about the age of eleven.   A son of the village woman who had been his nurse had a large artery severed when he was run over by a cart.   He would almost certainly have bled to death, had not Master Astley Cooper been quick-witted.   He tied a handkerchief tightly round the lad's thigh, above the wound, so as to stop the bleeding, and took effective control of the situation until a surgeon could be sent for. Consequently at the age of sixteen Astley became an articled pupil of his uncle's.   For some reason or other William Cooper was unable to take his nephew into his own household, so he arranged for him to live with Mr. Henry Cline, who was just beginning to make a name for himself at St. Thomas's.   Cline had attended the first course of lectures ever delivered by John Hunter, and was soon teaching revolutionary surgical principles to young Astley.   Cline was also a political revolutionary, that is to say he believed in democracy and thought some good might emerge from the French Revolution.   How heinous such beliefs were, particularly in one who was a surgeon and seemingly a gentleman, is shown by Astley Cooper's nineteenth-century biographer, his nephew, who says of Cline's political views and the effect they had on the young man ". . . so baneful an influence . . . at one time threatened . . . to blast all his future success in life".   Astley Cooper was soon comfortably settled in Cline's house in Jefferies' Square, St. Mary Axe, and enjoying himself thoroughly, being "led into those dissipations which the metropolis so readily afforded, and into which young men of his age and inexperience are too apt to be ensnared".

After a few months as his uncle's pupil Astley asked if he could change over to Mr. Cline.   Cline was undoubtedly the more brilliant surgeon, but the request was probably prompted not so much by this fact as by the knowledge that Cline was not a strict disciplinarian, whereas Mr. William Cooper was.

Whatever the reason the change was made, and the young man who had done as little work as possible under the watchful eye of his uncle began to work hard in the hospital and in the dissecting-room as the pupil of Cline, who was well known for caring not at all whether his charges worked or not.   He spent most of two years in the dissecting-room, attended Cline's lectures and later John Hunter's, and soon began to undertake anatomical investigations on his own.   In the autumn of 1787 he went to Edinburgh to continue his studies there for seven months.   On the way he spent a few days in Staffordshire, visiting the potteries there with none other than Mr. Wedgwood.   At Edinburgh he had a pleasant and profitable session. Cullen, who had done so much for William Hunter, impressed him greatly, old man though he was at that time.   Of him Astley Cooper wrote: "Physic may have much improved since his time, but if Hippocrates was its father, Cullen was its favoured son".

He returned to Cline's house in the autumn of 1788 and again attended John Hunter's lectures.   Often he would watch Hunter dissecting, and he saw him preparing those portions of the whale which had been brought from Greenland for him.   In the following year he was appointed Demonstrator of Anatomy at St. Thomas's, and not long afterwards, though his seven years' pupilage was not quite ended, Cline made him his assistant and arranged for him to deliver part of his course of lectures. Astley Cooper married in the December of 1791 Ann Cock, the daughter of a wealthy merchant.   The bride's father had only recently died, and for this reason the marriage was a quiet one and the honeymoon was postponed till June, when the young couple went to Paris.   Astley attended the meetings of the National Assembly and at different times heard speeches by Brissot, Danton, Marat, and Robespierre, and took advantage of the introductions he had from Cline and other bloodthirsty rebels to see the practice of several of the leading French surgeons.   He and his bride remained in Paris for several months, till after the attack on the Louvre, the massacre of the Swiss Guards on August 10, and the butchering of the prisoners in the Abbaye on September 2.   Astley's mother and father were glad to have them both back unharmed, but deeply distressed to find their favourite son as low-browed a democrat as ever.

Ann had brought her husband a house and a fortune of £14,000, so for three years he was able to devote himself to further study rather than to the building up of a practice. To increase his experience he gave his services gratuitously to those sick poor who came or could be brought to his house, even doing his own dispensing for them. At the same time he was lecturing at St. Thomas's to large and attentive crowds of students. He would select a series of similar cases from the patients in the wards and lecture on them, teaching Hunterian principles and their application more lucidly than ever John Hunter himself could. Hunter and his chief pupils were still regarded by most surgeons and students as of a race apart. They were physiological philosophers whose discussions provided academic amusement but nothing more. Astley Cooper was the great interpreter of Hunter. He showed his pupils, in a way they could understand, that the Hunterian doctrines were immediately applicable to the treatment of disease. When Hunter demonstrated certain principles by the dissection of rabbits and mice and hedgehogs, those that could understand him thought it all most interesting—and no more. When Astley Cooper, a forcible and impressive lecturer, demonstrated the same principles as applied to living patients, they realized at last that the aggressive little Scotchman, only recently dead, had been almost always right. Thirty years after Hunter's death Astley Cooper remembered well "that the surgeons and physicians of his day thought him a mere imaginative speculator, and anyone who believed in him a blockhead and a black sheep in the profession".

In the summer of 1793 he was also delivering at Surgeons' Hall a short course of anatomical lectures and he was an active member of the Guy's Hospital Physical Society. Guy's and Thomas's at this time were administered together as the United Borough Hospitals. Astley Cooper was re-elected Professor of Anatomy of the Surgeons' Company in the following year, and then was succeeded in this office by Thomas Blizard. In 1797 he took over Cline's house in St. Mary Axe, with a large warehouse next door to it, which he converted into a dissecting-room for his own pupils. By this time he had an established reputation as an anatomist and a lecturer, and he was recognized by his colleagues as one of the most competent of the younger surgeons, though he was barely known to the general public, excepting perhaps the poor of the district in which he lived. Private practice in the first year Astley Cooper was established on his own brought him exactly five guineas, in the second year £26, in the third £64, and then, successively, £96, £100, £200, £400,

£610, and £1,100. In this last and most successful year he succeeded his uncle, William Cooper, as surgeon to Guy's Hospital. Astley Cooper had been assistant lecturer in anatomy and lecturer in surgery to the hospital for nearly ten years, but his appointment was not recommended to the Governors by the then Treasurer until an assurance had been received that his politics would not be allowed to interfere with the discharge of hospital duties. After that it was simply a matter of making a personal call upon each of the Governors of the hospital—there were seventy-two of them—and awaiting their decision, which was arrived at in the course of the October board meeting of 1800.

The two other surgeons at Guy's at the time of Astley Cooper's appointment were Mr. Forster, "a gentlemanlike man in his appearance, but not so in reality, for, at dinner, he would swear at waiters and abuse them"; and Mr. Lucas, who made "£300 per annum by bleeding". At St. Thomas's at the same time were Mr. Chandler, who "was so quick that even before the dressings were removed from an old woman's back, I have heard him say, 'Nothing on God's earth, my good woman, can be looking better', and at once pass on to another patient"; Mr. Birch, "a sensual man—clever, but a bad surgeon"; and, of course, Henry Cline. Astley Cooper himself was responsible for the above descriptions, but perhaps his most amusing pen-picture is of a physician of St. Thomas's Hospital.

> Dr. Fordyce was a coarse man, a bad lecturer, got drunk every evening, and Mr. Cline said, was not over careful about truth.
> He himself said he was the only Scotchman he ever knew that had entirely lost his native dialect, and this he would assert in the broadest Scotch it could be spoken in.
> His best paper was on "Purgatives".

At this period Astley Cooper was following zealously in the footsteps of John Hunter, dissecting every fish, bird, or animal he could procure. He had an arrangement with a menagerie, then housed near the Tower of London, and they sent him the bodies of all the rare beasts which died there. Notable among them was a large elephant, which it was quite impossible to introduce into the warehouse dissecting-room. Enormous crowds had gathered to watch the fate of the elephant, and finally it had to be dissected in the open air, by Astley Cooper and about half a dozen of his pupils, while carpets thrown over the gates and railings surrounding the courtyard at St. Mary

Axe more or less concealed this remarkable spectacle from the crowds outside.

In the same year Astley Cooper made his first individual contribution to surgery. Since he was not himself a Fellow, he persuaded Everard Home to read for him two short papers to the Royal Society. The first concerned a resident pupil of his and a patient. Both had had their ear-drums ruptured on both sides, and both could hear ordinary conversation fairly well. The mere reporting of these cases exploded a long-cherished belief that destruction of the ear-drums led inevitably to complete deafness. The second paper recorded twenty more cases of this type, and described a simple operation for deliberately making an opening into the drum of the ear. This was the operation which Cheselden had wanted to perform upon a condemned man, and in a proportion of selected cases it undoubtedly relieved deafness. For these two papers the Royal Society awarded Astley Cooper the Copley Medal, which John Hunter himself had won only fifteen years previously. The award was made in 1802, and early that year the young Copleian medallist became a Fellow. His admission to the Royal Society was sponsored by William Blizard, Everard Home, and John Abernethy. He published in two parts, in 1804 and 1807, a *Treatise on Hernia* which represented the result of several years' work in the dissecting-room, in the operating-theatre, and in the post-mortem room. The first part was dedicated to Cline, the second to Alexander Monro of Edinburgh.

Astley Cooper always valued his friendship with Cline. He quoted Cline at his former pupil, Mr. Travers, on one occasion. Astley Cooper was going to deliver a lecture at the hospital one winter evening when he slipped and sustained a fracture of the fibula, the long, slim bone which runs from the knee to the outer ankle. He managed to limp into a shop close at hand, and ordered his coach to be brought. Once safely home, he sent for Travers. Travers was delayed a little, and when he arrived found Astley Cooper in bed with his leg resting on a pillow and covered with a loosely folded damp cloth. Travers was anxious to handle the limb. Astley Cooper had already satisfied himself that the fracture was the simplest it is possible to sustain. He laughed at the anxious Travers and told him that he proposed to follow Cline's policy. Some years previously Cline had injured his ribs. Astley Cooper was called to attend him, and, like Travers, wanted to make an examination and find out just how many ribs were broken. Cline said briefly that "he was quite satisfied of the fact that some of his ribs were broken, and he had no further curiosity about the matter, as the same bandage was required, whether there were half a dozen or only one injured".

In the years intervening between the publication of the two parts of the *Treatise on Hernia,* Astley Cooper and many other surgeons and physicians became very dissatisfied with the management of the Medical Society of London, to which they all belonged. Accordingly they broke away from this society and formed another one, the Medico-Chirurgical Society, in 1805. This became the Medical and Chirurgical Society, linked itself to other London medical societies, in the course of time was granted a Royal Charter, and is to-day the Royal Society of Medicine.

Just about this time Astley Cooper was involved, professionally, in two cases of murder. These and other incidents made him much better known to the general public than he had been before. Wealthy patients were attracted to him and the income from his practice grew steadily. For several years a merchant of Croydon paid him £600 a year for visiting him there at regular intervals. A merchant from the West Indies had Lettsom as his physician and Astley Cooper as his surgeon. After he had completely recovered from the operation performed for the removal of stones from his bladder, he gave Lettsom £300 and threw his nightcap to the surgeon, saying, "There, young man, put that in your pocket". Astley Cooper extracted a rolled-up script from the nightcap. It was a draft for a thousand guineas. Patients such as these made it easy for him to forgo his fees in the case of more needy patients or when attending wounded officers and men who had returned from the Peninsular War. Soon his fame was such that four quacks in the provinces made a very good living by moving from town to town and advertising the presence of "Dr. Ashley Cooper, Dr. Monro, Dr. Daniells, and Dr. Duncan". As was intended, the "Ashley" was always mistaken for "Astley" and patients flocked to them.

Sir William Blizard was the first Professor of Comparative Anatomy of the College of Surgeons. He gave the first of the series of lectures in connexion with John Hunter's Collection, which was not properly housed and arranged until 1810. There was then a gap of two years, during which time building alterations were in progress at the College, but in 1813 the second course was delivered by Sir Everard Home. He and his colleague resigned their professorships in the spring of that year, and on June 18 two new appointments were made. John Abernethy became Professor of Surgery, and Astley Paston Cooper Professor of Comparative Anatomy. For his first lecture Astley Cooper drew not only upon John Hunter's collection, but himself provided some thirty additional specimens, including dissected parts of lions, hyenas, monkeys, seals, porpoises, kangaroos, otters, and deer. The menagerie at the Tower was still proving a valuable source of supply. One of the experiments he recorded in a lecture on the power of the stomach to digest various foods was amusingly illustrated. He had obtained several pieces of bone and painted upon them the names, John Hunter, William Blizard, Everard Home, and Henry Cline. These bones were passed into the stomach of a dog and left there for various periods. The black paint was of such a nature as to protect the underlying bone against digestion by the gastric acids. The white bone between the letters, being unprotected, was eaten away to a depth varying with the length of time the bone had been allowed to remain in the stomach. The end result was a series of bones with the black-lettered names of the surgeons in progressively bolder and bolder relief. These lectures, which came to an end in the June of 1815, were nearly always attended by as many people as the theatre would hold, actually three hundred or more. Since he was still lecturing at St. Thomas's on anatomy and surgery, was full surgeon to Guy's, and had a huge practice, the time taken in preparing the lectures had reduced the hours Astley Cooper slept to exactly four a night. Two years of this took a heavy toll, and he decided that if he was to preserve his health he would have to move into the West End of London, where he could take some exercise in the parks in the early morning and where he would be nearer the hospitals and his patients. He could well afford to do so, for the income from his practice alone in 1815 was just over £21,000, and he accordingly took a large house in New Street. It was in the following May that a single operation spread his fame as a surgeon from this country to the whole of Europe and the New World.

Just over thirty years previously John Hunter had performed at St. George's his first operation for the high ligation of an artery which was affected by an aneurysmal swelling. In that relatively short time his pupils had successfully ligated most of the other arteries which were at all accessible to the surgeon's knife. There remained inviolate only the arteries in the brain and in the chest, and the largest arterial trunk, the aorta, in the abdomen. From this huge vessel, which lies immediately in front of the spinal column, every other artery in the body takes origin, directly or indirectly. Astley Cooper had convinced himself that even the aorta could be successfully ligatured in certain animals. The blood supply to that part of the body below the ligature was short-circuited by the enlargement of collateral vessels, which took up the function of the aorta itself.

The condition of aneurysm of the aorta or of the common iliac arteries, the terminal divisions of the aorta, was recognized increasingly often, but there was no treatment for it. A porter who had a huge aneurysm of the common iliac artery was admitted to Guy's. Nothing could be done for him, and the swelling in his abdomen grew steadily larger and larger. Astley Cooper was interested in the case, and one day went down to the dead-house with a few of his pupils to try to discover how quickly and how best the operation of ligature of the aorta could be performed. Even in the dead bodies on which he attempted the theoretically possible operation the difficulties were so great that he abandoned the attempt. The next day the porter's aneurysm ruptured and blood began to pour from it. One of Astley Cooper's apprentices was in the ward at the time, and by promptly applying pressure to the aneurysm prevented the man's immediate death from loss of blood. Astley Cooper saw the patient a little later. It was impossible to stop the bleeding completely, and the man was slowly dying. He had a chance in a million of surviving, if the surgeon was courageous enough to give him that chance. Astley Cooper had turned away from the man. To operate on him would be near murder, yet not to operate would be to deny the man his last hope of even a few hours more of life. The surgeon turned to the students who pressed about him: "Gentlemen, this only hope of safety I am determined to give him".

The operation took only a few minutes. The aorta was ligated just above the aneurysm. Three hours later the man was fairly well. The next morning he was sitting up in bed smiling at the innumerable surgeons who had come to see him. In the afternoon, however, he died. His body was dissected before an audience which included practically every surgeon in London. Examination revealed two things: that the disease of the aorta was so extensive that he could never have recovered from it, and that the ligation of the aorta had been so performed that with any less degree of disease the man would almost certainly have recovered. This feat of surgical skill made it clear that one more operation based on John Hunter's much-scoffed-at theories could be both technically and clinically successful.

In 1820, though he had at that time no official appointment to the Royal household, Astley Cooper was called in to remove an infected sebaceous cyst—a wen—from the scalp of George IV. Cline assisted at the operation, and Sir Everard Home, who was actually Sergeant-Surgeon at the time, was there. The operation was not easy, for the cyst was adherent to the skin, and some time had to be spent dissecting it out. However, a fortnight later the King was completely well again and Astley Cooper was a baronet. Two years later he was appointed to the Court of Examiners of the College of Surgeons. For years he had been having recurring attacks of giddiness, and largely for this reason he resigned in 1825 the lectureship at St. Thomas's, which he had held for thirty years. At that time Guy's Hospital and St. Thomas's Hospital were administered together as the United Borough Hospitals, all the lectures for the students of both hospitals being delivered at St. Thomas's. On his resignation from the lectureship at St. Thomas's, Sir Astley Cooper was given to understand that his own nominees, his nephew Bransby Cooper and Mr. Key, would be appointed to the lectureships in surgery and anatomy, respectively. This was not done, and general indignation was aroused at this slight to the great surgeon. Before St. Thomas's knew what was happening the United Borough Hospitals was no more. Guy's Hospital had established its own school of medicine and it had Mr. Key and Mr. Cooper as professors, the patronage of Sir Astley, who acted as consulting surgeon to the hospital, and most of St. Thomas's pupils.

Sir Astley was elected President of the Royal College of Surgeons in 1827, and in this capacity had some hand in the founding of another new medical school. Henry Cline died in this year, at the age of seventy-six, just three days before the Duke of York, on whom Sir Astley Cooper had been in attendance for several months, and so did Lady Cooper, whose health had been failing for some time previously. For a while Sir Astley Cooper retired from practice, but time hung heavily on his hands and soon he was back in the West End. In the July of 1828 he was appointed Sergeant-Surgeon to the Royal household. Towards the end of that year Sir Astley was involved in perhaps the most sensational libel action ever brought against his former pupil Thomas Wakley, founder and editor of the *Lancet* and a great medical reformer. In its issue of March 29 the *Lancet* described a lithotomy which had been undertaken at Guy's Hospital by Mr. Bransby Cooper. The *Lancet* said in effect that Bransby Cooper had been elected to the staff of Guy's only because he was Sir Astley's nephew, and that he was so unskilful and bungling an operator that he had killed an otherwise healthy patient from whose bladder he was removing a stone. The operation, which took as a rule not more than six minutes, was said to have lasted over an hour. The damages asked for by Bransby Cooper amounted to £2,000. The damages awarded him totalled £100, so that the feeling of the jury was obvious, despite the evidence in Bransby Cooper's favour given by his famous uncle and almost every other hospital surgeon in London.

George IV died in 1830, and though Sir Astley Cooper did not actually attend him in his last illness he directed the embalming of the King's body. His appointment to the Royal household was reaffirmed on the accession of William IV, and about this time learned societies the world over paid tribute to him. Among them were the Royal Society of Göttingen and corresponding bodies in Heidelberg, New Orleans, Palermo, and even Guadalaxara in Mexico. Sundry decorations and orders came from Russia, from France, and from the Netherlands. In June, 1834, the University of Oxford conferred upon him an honorary doctorate in civil law, at the same time that they honoured similarly the Duke of Wellington. That same year he spent some time in Paris and met such men as Dupuytren, Lisfranc, and Dieffenbach. Dieffenbach is still known by the operation he suggested, and performed in several cases, for the cure of stuttering—by cutting out half the tongue. Astley Cooper described France, which a century before had been a centre for surgeons from every country, as being surgically fifty years behind England. He toured Scotland in the following summer and was given the freedom of Edinburgh and an honorary degree from the University. His book *On the Anatomy of the Breast* appeared in 1840 and was the last work he published. It showed the changes that had taken place in surgical thought and practice in the periods before and after John Hunter. When

Astley Cooper amputated a breast he had the whole of it exposed, he knew the exact anatomy of the structures he had to cut through, and his entire procedure was rapid, efficient, and effective. The pre-Hunterian school of surgeons had to work under difficulties almost exactly comparable to those of the man-midwife beneath the blanket. A treatise published in 1678 reveals how amputations were undertaken with the breasts so modestly covered as to make good surgery impossible (*see plate facing* p. 305).

On February 6, 1841, Astley Cooper listened for some time to the physicians and younger surgeons who were in attendance upon him and had been so for some weeks. They had a new plan of treatment for him. The seventy-three-year-old surgeon was not deceived. "My dear sirs," he said, "I am fully convinced of your excellent judgement and of your devotion to me . . . but I shall take no more medicine." He died six days later. In accordance with his own request, his body was carefully dissected thirty-two hours after his death and an account of the necropsy was published in *Guy's Hospital Reports*.

Hunter's teachings had been conveyed by Astley Cooper to some eight thousand pupils, among them Keats, the poet. Astley Cooper had been the first to ligate the abdominal aorta successfully, and the first to amputate a leg at the hip-joint. This operation, which he performed in 1824, took exactly half an hour from the first incision to the application of the last dressing. Astley Cooper was not an original thinker, but he was a great surgeon. His greatest contribution to surgery was in his lecturing. John Hunter's ideas and ideals were like a stone dropped into the still and glassy quiet of the surgery of his time. There was a little disturbance and then ever-widening ripples, which might have had but little effect had not Astley Cooper made a ripple become a flood-tide.

Astley Cooper was the best-known surgeon in London at a time when London was the greatest surgical centre in the world. Paris under Ambroise Paré had had that distinction for a century. London held it for just as long, then Scotland took the lead. In Astley Cooper's lifetime a remarkable school of surgery was growing up in Edinburgh. William Cullen and the Monro family had been among the first to foster it. After them came Benjamin Bell, his two sons, and his grandson, and two brothers of an entirely different family, Charles Bell and John Bell.

Benjamin Bell arrived in Edinburgh in 1766, at the age of seventeen. The first Monro taught him surgery, the second anatomy. William Cullen still held the professorship of medicine, while John Gregory taught the "practice of physic". At the end of four years Benjamin Bell wrote to his father: "Had I been now entering to the world as a physician, I should never have thought of going farther . . . but for a surgeon, I assure you, Edinburgh comes greatly short of either Paris or London". The next two years were spent in these cities, and in London Benjamin found John Hunter "the most agreeable and at the same time the most useful acquaintance I ever met with", and William Hunter "by no means so free or so ready of access as his brother". Then he returned to Edinburgh and took up practice as a surgeon. He was the most successful surgeon in Scotland, and he made a number of minor improvements in technique, notably by using long flaps in amputating and by reducing the instruments employed for different operations to a minimum. Two books were published by him. The first was a *System of Surgery,* which consisted of six unwieldy and diffuse sections. This was important in that it was the first attempt by a British surgeon to bring together in one volume the whole practice of surgery in a loosely systematized form. The second was his *Treatise on Gonorrhœa Virulenta and Lues Venerea,* published in 1793. In this work Benjamin Bell demonstrated clearly that gonorrhœa and syphilis are two entirely different diseases. This ended a centuries-old controversy and finally made clear the error into which even John Hunter had fallen. Benjamin's two sons, George and Joseph, were surgeons of Edinburgh, as was Joseph's son, the second Benjamin, and his son, the second Joseph, who died only in 1911 and was at one time house-surgeon to James Syme.

The brothers John and Charles Bell did not found a dynasty as Benjamin Bell did, but together they contributed much more to the science of surgery than did Benjamin and all his descendants. John was born in Edinburgh on May 12, 1763, Charles in the November of 1774. John was a pupil of the Monros and of Mr. Alexander Wood, better known as "Lang Sandy" and more famous for conviviality than surgical skill. A pet sheep and a tame raven used to accompany "Lang Sandy" on his round of visits. How limited the teaching of anatomy was at that time is indicated by the young man himself: "In Dr. Monro's class, unless there be a fortunate succession of bloody murders, not three subjects are dissected in the year". However, at the age of twenty-three John Bell duly became a Fellow of the College of Surgeons of Edinburgh, which entitled him to act in rotation with other young men of the same status as one of the surgeons to the Edinburgh Royal Infirmary. Before the Medical Faculty was founded in Edinburgh, such surgical instruction as there was centred round the school in Surgeons' Square and was arranged by the Incorporation of Surgeons. Once the university organized its own school of medicine the Surgeons' Square establishment became known as the Extramural School and tended to concentrate its attention on pure anatomy and surgery. John Bell lectured on these two subjects there for ten years and built up a sound reputation. In 1800, at the suggestion of James Gregory, Professor of Medicine in the University, the Royal Infirmary abandoned its old-established method of allowing the younger surgeons to take up duties in the Infirmary according to a rota, and instead elected six men to act as surgeons for two years at a time. This meant the complete exclusion of John Bell and several other men of his age, all of them good surgeons. Edinburgh was split into two camps by this administrative change. Bell and his friends attacked Gregory. Gregory and his supporters attacked Bell and the others. Pamphlets, memorials, letters, even books were written, each side calumniating the other with a wealth of whole-hearted invective. Nothing could disturb John Bell's position as one of the leading surgeons in Edinburgh, but the prolonged feud turned him into a contentious and embittered man.

This may have been a good thing for posterity, for it made John Bell a magnificent champion of any theory or practice which was of a controversial nature. He espoused lost, or almost lost, causes with the zeal of a reforming angel, and, so good was his judgement, the causes were usually worthy ones. Two which he did much to advance were the "doctrine of anastomosing arteries" and the "doctrine of adhesion". The first was one of John Hunter's teachings carried to its logical conclusion—namely, that any artery in the body could be ligatured and that its function would be taken up by the meeting or anastomosing of branches coming from the artery above and below the ligature. Astley Cooper, when he ligated the aorta, dramatized this teaching. John Bell preached it as a gospel, and applied it particularly to saving limbs in which the main artery had been injured by gunshot or other wounds, and which not long before would have been incontinently amputated. The second doctrine was a renewed attack upon the healing by second intention, after suppuration, of operation and other wounds. Bell wrote that suppuration would be prevented in almost every case, if after operation the surgeon saw to the "laying of the wounded parts so cleanly, so neatly, and so evenly in contact with each other that they may adhere". The operative words —in both senses—are "cleanly" and "neatly", and to most surgeons of that time they represented an unnecessary, and almost effeminate, refinement of the orthodox two-fisted butchery. John Bell practised what he preached so successfully that he was emboldened to attempt the first aneurysmorrhaphy—that is, he tried to close the rupture in an aneurysm instead of simply ligating the normal artery above the swelling. He freshened the two lips of the ruptured aneurysm and sewed them together with a thread on a fine glover's needle. Immediately, the artery and aneurysm began pulsating normally. The skin wound was then closed. All went well for fourteen days, when the aneurysm ruptured again at the same place and the ordinary ligation had to be done. This operation was technically successful but failed clinically, probably because thread had been used. Even to-day with modern asepsis and using fine catgut the same reactionary bleeding may occur twelve to fifteen days after an apparently successful operation, so it is not surprising that this happened to Bell's case, though his thread was of "fine cambric".

John Bell died at Rome in 1820 and was buried there. Some seventy years later the Royal College of Surgeons of Edinburgh erected a Celtic cross over his grave. To one side of this cross is a simple stone slab inscribed: "Here lies one whose name was written in water". This is the nameless grave of Astley Cooper's pupil, John Keats. Bell, too, had many pupils, and among them was Ephraim McDowell, who went back to Danville, Kentucky, and performed there the first abdominal operation ever undertaken for removal of the ovaries. Bell was undoubtedly a great teacher. All his teaching rested on his two doctrines and on two other important principles. First, that an operation was not an end in itself but only a means to an end, and secondly, that if surgical intervention was necessary then the operation should be carefully planned, carefully executed, and completed with a dry wound, that is, with all bleeding stopped. Elaborating these points, he insisted that blood-vessels should be deliberately dissected out and ligatured if there was any likelihood of their being endangered. Bell poured scorn upon two types of surgeons: those who were too enthusiastic and those who were too timid. Among the first he classed Heister, who advised in certain cases trephining holes all round the skull as a "hit-or-miss" diagnostic method. The work of the latter group he characterized, inelegantly but forcefully, as "piddling".

Brought up in this tradition many of his pupils became famous, but the most famous of all of them was John Bell's own younger brother, Charles. Charles was born eleven years after John, and had much the same sort of education. While still a student he published in 1798 his *System of Dissections,* with thirty large plates, all his own and all works of art. A year later he was elected a member of the College of Surgeons of Edinburgh, and began to assist his elder brother in lecturing and dissecting at the Extra-mural School. He did some further engravings for a book on anatomy which he and John published, and at the same time made many wax models of normal and diseased organs. Then John started his war with Gregory, and it became obvious that for any member of the Bell family a future in Edinburgh was far from assured. John did not want his young brother to be dragged into the controversy, and so he urged him to go to London. Charles did so and was welcomed, not as an anatomist or surgeon but as the artist responsible for the illustrations in his own book and the one he and John had produced. Within a day of his arrival Astley Cooper asked him to dinner, and wanted him to come and live at St. Mary Axe. Abernethy became a close friend of his, and so did Matthew Baillie, John Hunter's nephew. Young Charles did not accept Astley Cooper's offer, for he preferred to maintain his status as a free lance. He took a house in Leicester Square with the idea of lecturing to artists and medical students.

This was in 1805, and his capital consisted of exactly £12; he had also some paint brushes and some scalpels. The venture prospered. One or two surgical pupils came to him. Seven young artists took lectures from him. A few patients were his, and he had plenty of time for writing, painting, and wax-modelling. He published in 1806 *An Essay on the Anatomy of Expression in Painting,* and became famous almost overnight. Artists and anatomists came to study under him. All sorts of people came to see his paintings and his wax models. Sidney Smith was particularly interested in the latter and wrote: "I saw one to-day which was quite the Apollo Belvedere of Morbid Anatomy". Longman, the founder of the great publishing firm, offered him £300 for two volumes which were to form a text-book of surgery.

Charles forgot about surgery for a while, however, for he was busying himself with the anatomy of the brain. He paused in this study for only those few months he spent in the Naval Hospital at Haslar, which was inundated with the wounded from Corunna. In 1811 he used his wife's marriage dowry to buy a part interest in the then famous Great Windmill Street School of Medicine. It was owned at that time by James Wilson, who was steadily adding to the museum that William Hunter, its creator, had gathered together. Soon Charles Bell's lectures were attracting large audiences, and it was realized that he was as clever a surgeon as he was an artist and an anatomist. The Middlesex Hospital appointed him to its staff in 1814, and in the following year he was in Brussels, operating fifteen hours a day on the wounded from Waterloo. After that his progress was steady. He published his works on the brain and nervous system, acted as Professor of Anatomy and Surgery to the Royal College of Surgeons in London, and was active in the founding of London University and in the creation of the Middlesex Hospital Medical School. He was knighted in 1831, and two years later went over to Göttingen with Sir Astley Cooper, both of them receiving the honorary degree of M.D. Two more years were passed in London, before he returned to Edinburgh as Professor of Surgery to the University. Sir Charles Bell had six pleasant years in Edinburgh, and then at the age of sixty-seven he died suddenly of angina pectoris. He was more blessed than most pioneers, for he had lived to see his work on the nervous system not only accepted but acclaimed the world over.

It was in 1807 that he had had printed just a hundred copies of an essay which he called *Idea of a New Anatomy of the Brain.* At that time the generally accepted views on the nervous system and its structure and function were very much those of Galen. Harvey and Hunter had revolutionized ideas on the physiology of the circulatory and digestive systems. The physiology of the skeletal and muscular systems had also been advanced, but practically the only improvement on Galen's work on the anatomy and physiology of the nervous system was the recognition that

he had, on occasion, confused nerves and ligaments. Woodall
and many surgeons after him had studied the diagnosis and treatment of head injuries. John Bell himself had contributed much
to this subject, but neither he nor anyone else had inquired into
the way in which the nervous system acted. It was accepted
without question that the brain and spinal cord and all the nerves
in the body had simply one function—the conveying of different
sensations into consciousness. The function of the nerves of,
say, the hand and the eye differed only in degree. Both were
concerned solely with sensation, but one had to respond to light,
and therefore was extremely sensitive, while the other only
needed to register crude stimuli, as by touch and heat, and so
was less sensitive. Charles Bell took this popular belief and
destroyed it. He pointed out that if the optic nerve was of the
same type as the skin nerves, only infinitely more sensitive, then
the effect of plunging a needle into the optic nerve—a procedure
disturbing enough to the crude and unrefined nerves of the skin
—should be such that "life could not bear so great a pain".
Actually, if the retina was pierced with a needle the only sensation
produced was that of seeing a spark of fire. Shattering the old
ideas was simple, but Charles Bell proceeded to build upon their
ruins. He investigated the two chief parts of the brain, the large
cerebrum and the smaller hind-brain, the cerebellum, and wrote
that he had "reasons for believing that the cerebrum and
cerebellum are different in function as in form: that the parts
of the cerebrum have different functions; and that the nerves
we trace in the body are not single nerves possessing various
powers, but bundles of different nerves, whose filaments are
united for the convenience of distribution, but which are distinct
in office, as they are in origin from the brain".

Charles Bell could, and did, prove every word of his thesis.
He took up Galen's work where Galen had had to leave off,
though he used the same animals and the same instruments.
He divided nerves in different parts of their courses and studied
the effects of this division. He discovered that the spinal
nerves are "mixed"—that is, half the fibres in the nerve are
concerned with movement and have nothing to do with sensation, which is conveyed by the remaining filaments. He saw
that individual nerve-fibres were continuous with similar fibres
in the spinal cord and brain, and his *Idea* was simply that by
tracing to the brain nerve-fibres concerned with, say, movement,
that part of the brain which initiated muscular motion could be

defined. The function of an individual nerve could be determined, then tracked to their source the fibres in that nerve would indicate clearly the significance of a particular brain area. The *Idea* was elaborated in successive papers. The classical one was on the fifth and seventh cranial nerves. Bell showed the entirely different functions of these nerves. The fifth was responsible for conveying all sensations from the face, though one root of it had a motor function. If it was divided, one side of the face became quite anæsthetic. The seventh nerve was purely motor. Its division left sensation unimpaired but completely paralysed the whole musculature of one side of the face, furthermore, stimulation of the divided end of the nerve caused the facial muscles to contract convulsively. This proof of the different function of two cranial nerves was based on experiments performed on an ass. It was irrefutable so far as the physiology of the ass's nervous system was concerned, and it was probable that the same thing applied to human physiology. Sir Astley Cooper made probability certainty when he brought triumphantly to Bell a lady who was his patient. She had had an enlarged gland in front of the ear. The operation for the removal of this gland was difficult, and in the course of it the seventh nerve had been divided as it emerged on to the face from behind the ear. One side of the lady's face was completely paralysed, but sensation was unaffected. She could feel the effects of a touch or a pinprick just as well on the paralysed as on the normal side of the face. From then onwards paralysis of one side of the face, from whatever cause, was to be known as Bell's palsy.

Bell opened up an entirely new field in physiology, and tilled much of it successfully himself. He pointed out that muscles were supplied with sensory as well as motor nerves, and postulated a definite "muscle sense". He indicated that a motor nerve would convey to the muscle the brain's orders, while a sensory nerve would inform the brain of the demands being made upon that muscle. He showed that when one set of muscles contracts, an opposing set must relax. He described minutely the mode of action of the tiny muscles which control the eyeball. He studied the nerves controlling the muscles of respiration, and one of them will always be "the nerve of Bell".

The brilliance of his discoveries was recognized. It was realized that his work was as important and as revolutionary as that of the Hunters on the lymphatic system. He went to Paris to receive a gold medal. One lecturer, M. Roux, introduced him to the students in a huge lecture theatre and said: "Gentlemen, enough for to-day. You have seen Charles Bell!" Honours showered upon him, but the compliment he would have appreciated most came long after his death when Viggo Christiansen wrote: "He created modern clinical neurology in the same way as his contemporary, Corot, created modern French landscape painting".

In the thirty years that Charles Bell had spent in London great changes had taken place in Edinburgh. John Bell, the Monros, and surgeons and lecturers who succeeded them built up a school of surgery that was second to none. When young Charles went to London he but followed the example of the Hunters and innumerable lesser Scots. London was then a surgical Mecca. When he returned, he found that students in Edinburgh were no longer thinking of going South. Instead they were watching with some amusement the steady trek northwards of keen young southrons. Two young surgeons attracted them—Robert Liston and James Syme. London went on producing great surgeons, and the next after Astley Cooper was James Paget, born just about the time that Charles Bell reached Brussels to see the first fruits of Waterloo, but so far as the immediate advancement of surgery was concerned, Scotland had taken the lead from London, just as surely as London had wrested it from Paris a hundred years previously.

XIX. Scotland Takes the Lead

ROBERT LISTON WAS BORN AT ECCLESMACHEN IN LINLITHGOW-shire in 1794. James Syme was born in Princes Street, Edinburgh, in 1799. At the age of sixteen Liston began his medical studies as a pupil of John Barclay. Barclay was a good anatomist and a diplomat. At the time of the Bell-Gregory warfare he submitted his thesis for graduation and assured its success by a dedication to "Dr. James Gregory and Mr. John Bell". Liston's one aim was to become an operating surgeon, and so he devoted himself wholeheartedly first to the study of anatomy and later to that of surgery. He learnt all he could from Barclay, and then went up to London to attend the lectures given by Blizard at the London Hospital and by Abernethy at St. Bartholomew's. In 1818 he passed successfully the examinations of both the Royal College of Surgeons of Edinburgh and the Royal College of Surgeons in London. Then he became one of Barclay's assistants and demonstrators in anatomy and surgery.

James Syme was not as decided about his future career as Liston. He spent two years at the university, taking classes in Latin, philosophy, and natural science and amusing himself in the chemical laboratories. While he was working there on the distillation of coal-tar he found a solution in which rubber could be dissolved. The resulting solution of india-rubber when painted on to a silk cloak made the material impermeable to water. Syme wrote a short paper on this experiment of "water-proofing", and submitted it to the *Annals of Philosophy*. Publication was delayed for some reason, and before the paper appeared a Glasgow manufacturer, who had been working along the same lines, elaborated the experiment and patented it as a potentially valuable manufacturing process. This gentleman's name was Macintosh, so James Syme missed founding a new industry by only a few weeks.

He began his medical studies at the age of eighteen, going to the anatomy rooms in Surgeons' Square, where the famous Barclay was in charge and his friend Robert Liston was a demonstrator. Liston and he, firm friends before, were soon inseparable, and after only a few years James Syme, too, was one of Barclay's junior demonstrators. The two young men worked together in the dissecting-rooms and at the Royal Infirmary. Liston was a sort of house-surgeon to Mr. George Bell, the son of Benjamin

Bell, while Syme's chief was Mr. William Newbigging. Syme early distinguished himself by giving beefsteak and porter to a feeble and emaciated youth, instead of bleeding him. For this original therapeutic endeavour he was sternly reprimanded. The youth was bled, and died the next day.

Liston launched his own school of anatomy and surgery in the late winter of 1818, and his chief demonstrator and assistant was Syme. Sixty students were soon attracted to the new class, and the only difficulty lay in supplying them with anatomical material. All the resurrectionists had established connexions with Barclay and with the Monros, and were chary of supplying young Mr. Liston with bodies. There seemed no alternative but for Liston and Syme, with a few chosen spirits, to do their own grave-robbing. They did so, and contrived to maintain a supply of recently-buried human material till the resurrectionists decided that supplying the new school would be more profitable than sitting back and seeing enthusiastic amateurs beat up their hire-lings and carry off hard-won bodies without paying anything at all for them. For five years the school prospered, and so did the two young lecturers. Both belonged to the Royal Medical Society of Edinburgh and both attracted no little attention by the papers they read to that body. In 1820, at the age of twenty-six, Liston presented a dissertation on fracture of the neck of the femur or thigh-bone. At that time it was usual to make no attempt at setting such a fracture. The patient was simply propped up in bed with a few pillows or sand-bags to either side of the broken thigh. Liston insisted that a fracture of the femoral neck should be treated like any other fracture. The bones should be properly set, and the limb should be splinted and kept immobile long enough for bony union to take place. He described what he considered the best splint for this purpose, and, though it was devised by a French surgeon, this particular splint is known still as the "long Liston". He concluded his paper by stating quite clearly "that there is no reason why a fracture of the neck of the femur should not unite as well as any other, when put in circumstances favourable to such an occurrence".

Soon after this, while still only twenty-two, Syme created even more of a furore by the way in which he opened his paper to the same society. "Mr. President, the truly deplorable ignorance of many surgical practitioners regarding the diseases of bones is most astonishing. . . ." Then he went on to deal with the pathology of the diseases of bone, dividing them into those in which there was an overgrowth of bone, and those in which there was destruction of bone. This simple grouping established, the surgery of the two different types of disease could be simplified in the same way. Syme advocated strongly the use of simple instruments, and particularly those bone-pliers which Liston had designed, in preference to complicated chain-saws and the like, which he damned as "very pretty mechanical contrivances". It was Liston's turn to take up the running again, and he did so with the publication of a paper on five cases of aneurysm.

The first of these was the most remarkable. The patient, Robert McNair, a lad of sixteen, had been seen by every surgeon in the Edinburgh Royal Infirmary. He had a huge aneurysm of an artery running beneath the shoulder-blade, and the Infirmary surgeons agreed that nothing could be done about it. Liston thought otherwise. In a small, badly-lighted room he proceeded to operate through an incision a foot long. When the swelling was incised, blood gushed forth uncontrollably and the patient collapsed. Liston ripped open the whole aneurysm, and plugged the pulsing artery with the forefinger of his left hand, while with his right hand he excised most of the carious shoulder-blade, leaving only that part of it on which the upper arm pivots. This was perhaps the first time a shoulder-blade had been attacked surgically. Three weeks after operation the lad was well enough to return to his home in the country. Four months later the boy was brought back to Edinburgh. The disease had recurred in that part of the shoulder-blade which was left. Liston wanted to do a fore-quarter amputation—removal of the entire arm and the remaining portion of the scapula—but not a surgeon in Edinburgh would assist him. He needed three assistants, and Syme was too inexperienced at that time for the two of them to dare attempt the operation without additional aid. The boy was sent home to die. After his death the country practitioner who had attended him sent the upper arm and the small portion of the scapula to Liston, and wrote: "We performed in its removal precisely the operation which you proposed to save the unfortunate lad. . . . The disease, you will perceive, had no connexion with any of the vital organs."

This case drew attention to Liston's surgical skill and, though technically he was still only "walking the wards" of the Royal Infirmary and had no official appointment there, he soon had more patients than any of the surgeons on the staff. The school was doing well, too, and for a few months he took all the lectures there himself, while Syme went off to Paris and attended the clinics of the two great masters of French surgery, Dupuytren and Lisfranc. Syme presented Dupuytren with a pair of Liston's bone-cutting forceps. Dupuytren used them the same day and was delighted with them. Syme reached Edinburgh again to find that his gifted friend had just been dismissed from the Infirmary. An agitation had been worked up against him by influential senior surgeons, who saw their practices dwindling away as their patients flocked to young Liston. They complained to the Managers that Liston abused his privileges in the hospital and literally stole patients from them, and that he so criticized the surgical conduct of the hospital as to diminish its reputation in the eyes of the public. This last accusation was certainly true, and both Liston and Syme were equal offenders. They condemned bad surgery when they saw it, and they had seen it often at the Infirmary. The Managers acted promptly and resolved: "That Mr. Liston be prohibited and discharged from entering the wards or operation-room of the Royal Infirmary". Liston appealed in turn to the Managers, to the courts, to the College of Surgeons, and even to the Lord Provost, but he appealed in vain. The vested interests he was up against were powerful.

Grimly, Liston set himself to build up a private practice and overcome the handicap of having no hospital connexion. Syme followed his example, though they kept their school going for another year till they had enough paying patients to assure them of something resembling an income. Each had his own small practice, but they always assisted at each other's operations, and their David and Jonathan friendship was enhanced as much by their temporary adversity as by the realization that they were fourth cousins—a relationship recognized only by Scots and Royal houses. Publicity otherwise denied to them they obtained by publishing paper after paper in the medical press, and two of the operations they recorded, one in which Liston assisted Syme and the other in which Syme assisted Liston, spread their fame far abroad. At much the same time that Astley Cooper was performing amputation at the hip-joint for the first time in England, Syme undertook the same operation in Edinburgh, assisted by Liston and using a technique he had learnt from Lisfranc. The actual removal of the entire lower limb took not more than a minute. The remainder of the operating time was devoted to ligating innumerable vessels. In this same year Liston attracted considerable attention by an operation in the conduct of which "I had the valuable assistance of my friend, Mr. Syme, without which the result might have been less favourable". The case was one of elephantiasis of the scrotum. The swelling was an enormous one. It hung down much lower than the patient's knees, had a circumference of 42 inches, and weighed 44 lb. Liston, as usual in defiance of the expressed opinion of every other surgeon in Edinburgh except Syme, removed the entire scrotum with one sweep of the knife. "The flow of blood was compared by those present to the discharge of water from a shower-bath. . . . Before half the vessels could be tied the patient sank off the table." The patient was quite pulseless and apparently dead. Liston snapped "Cordial!", and went on tying vessels which were no longer bleeding. The patient's mouth was dragged open and a cordial was poured into him. By the time he had taken over a pint of it there were signs of a flickering return to life. This particular cordial—Liston's favourite—was neat Scotch whisky. Three weeks later the patient was quite cured and completely recovered from the effects of both the operation and the cordial.

This was in the year 1823, the year in which the friendly rivalry of the two young surgeons became somehow unfriendly. What they quarrelled about is not known, but from being the greatest friends the two men changed to acrimonious antagonists. They carried their differences into everything they wrote, everything they did, every sphere of private and professional life. Yet the reputation of each of them continued to grow. Liston published his *Observations on Amputation* in 1824. In this he openly exulted in his muscular strength and its application to surgery, perhaps because Syme was relatively so puny. He even went so far as to decry the use of the tourniquet, saying that he could always control the blood-vessels to a limb with one hand and do the amputation with the other. He advocated the formation of flaps by transfixion—that is, by piercing right through the limb, close to the bone, with a thin, sharp knife and then cutting downwards and outwards to leave a wedge-shaped flap of flesh. There is no doubt that in his powerful hands, and in Syme's, this method made amputation easier and quicker, both important considerations for patients who were conscious of every step of the operation. It also gave a good, well-covered

PLATE XVII

Water-divining.

A reproduction of Gerard Dou's *La Femme Hydropique.*

Place this Figure Fol: 166.

PLATE XVIII

An amputation of the breast being performed with great
decorum and no possible affront to a maiden's modesty.

From *A Complete Treatise of Preternatural Tumours* by John Brown, Surgeon-
in-Ordinary to His Majesty, London, 1678.

stump, which could easily be fitted with an artificial limb. Syme's *Remarks on Amputation* was published in the same year. Like Liston, he condemned the circular method of amputation and urged the general adoption of amputation by the flap method, the flaps being cut by transfixion. He admitted frankly his admiration of Liston's work and his indebtedness to him. This might have healed the rupture between the two friends, but Liston was still very heated about the whole business. They went their own ways, and in the next few works from their pens neither mentioned the other. Liston's next two essays were on lithotomy and on amputation of the toes. So far as lithotomy was concerned Liston followed the great master, Cheselden, in the technique he employed, and in insisting that under ordinary circumstances the whole operation "should not occupy more than two or three minutes at most". The Managers of the Edinburgh Royal Infirmary had held out against this remarkable young surgeon for exactly five years. At the end of that time they had no option but to capitulate. Robert Liston was formally appointed to the staff of the Infirmary in 1827.

Syme meanwhile was advancing the principles of a simple conservatism in surgery. In an essay on the treatment of incised wounds he said many students had told him that only once or twice had they seen wounds heal by first intention. Convinced that this state of affairs was due to the complicated plastering and bandaging which Percivall Pott had attacked so many years before, Syme urged free drainage of wounds and the application of the simplest possible dressings. He referred very rudely to that "infallible preventive of adhesion, adhesive plaster", and to the ritual of long bandages "tightly and curiously turned", and, in effect, simplified even further John Bell's simple doctrine of adhesion. He carried the same principle of conservative simplicity into his operative work. He revived the forgotten teaching of Charles White of Manchester that it was often possible to remove diseased or carious bone from a limb without necessarily sacrificing the entire member. This teaching Syme applied in 1826 to a case in which the upper part of the humerus was diseased. He excised the head of the bone and so fixed the upper arm, but left his patient with a perfectly good hand and fore-arm. Any other surgeon would have done a fore-quarter amputation and sacrificed the whole arm.

Then Syme had the sort of luck that young surgeons pray for—the opportunity of performing a really dramatic operation.

Even to-day a single surgical feat, which may be intrinsically unimportant, often gives a man a greater reputation than he would ever have achieved by years of application to some less spectacular, no matter how much more important, surgical problem. Syme's saving of arms and legs by conservative surgery was of both surgical and social importance, but it had no drama, no news value. The case that brought him fame was a rarity. The operation he performed was just surgical juggling of a high order, and his account of the performance was of as much value as Liston's boast that his left hand was muscular enough to improve upon any known tourniquet. Yet this was the case report which established him as second only to Liston in the hierarchy of Edinburgh surgeons. The case was one of a bony malignant growth of the jaw. The very portraits of the patient, in the "before" phase, made the case a marvel. The tumour was the most enormous that had ever been seen in that situation. It had so distorted the man's face that his mouth measured fifteen inches in circumference. Syme excised the entire lower jaw in exactly twenty-four minutes. The patient had "uncommon fortitude", bore the operation well, lost only a few ounces of blood, and was well, if not cosmetically improved, five weeks later.

Soon afterwards there was a vacancy in the Infirmary staff, and there was no doubt that the appointment should have been Syme's. The unhappy Managers went into conference. They wanted to appoint Syme, and the Edinburgh citizens were clamouring for him, but they knew just how Liston would react if they dared take such a step. Weakly, they took refuge behind the belief that Syme's appointment might lead to "disturbing scenes in the presence of the students". It is difficult to see what else they could have done, but Syme was left without a hospital appointment. Little man though he was, Syme, like the six-foot Liston, was constitutionally incapable of sitting back and waiting to see what the gods would send him. He decided to found his own hospital. He rented Minto House, which had fifteen rooms, and made it provide a lecture-theatre, an operating-theatre, an out-patient department, and room for twenty-four beds. In the first year he saw there nearly two thousand out-patients, and nearly three hundred in-patients, and performed ninety-five major operations. Students and patients flocked to the new hospital, and as an outward and visible sign of his prosperity Syme bought a carriage. Then he had to extend the hospital and enlist a board of directors. Two resident house-surgeons were soon each paying him £100, for the privilege of working most of twenty-four hours a day for twelve months. Syme worked just as hard himself. He was practising, teaching, and advancing pure surgery. The principle he had first applied to the shoulder-joint, in excising only part of a bone instead of amputating the limb, he now extended to the elbow and knee, excising both joints completely but leaving still useful, if stiff, limbs. He revived the old quack method of treating wry-neck by simple division of the contracted neck muscle. He saw cases of aneurysm, of hernia, of stone in the bladder, of head injuries, of cancer of the breast and of other organs, and he gained invaluable experience.

It was at this phase of his career that the conflict with Liston flared up again. A professor of surgery was to be appointed to the Royal College of Surgeons of Edinburgh. The two possible men for the post were Syme and John Lizars. Lizars was the first surgeon in this country to perform ovariotomy, or removal of the ovaries, but has no other claim to fame. Nevertheless he was elected to the professorship by one vote, thanks to the frantic campaign waged for him and against Syme by Liston and his supporters. For the moment Liston triumphed, but the tables were soon to be turned. The aged professor of clinical surgery in the University announced in 1833 that he would resign his chair. This time neither Lizars nor anyone else intervened. Robert Liston and James Syme were the only surgeons who could be appointed to the foremost surgical chair north of London. The retiring professor made his resignation contingent upon his appointed successor paying him £300 a year for the rest of his life. At that time this was a common stipulation, for there were no pensions or superannuation schemes for university, or any other, workers. Syme agreed that if appointed he would make the old man this allowance. Liston thought his reputation and standing so much greater than Syme's that he could refuse to pay the £300 a year and still be sure of the appointment. The members of the *Senatus Academicus* of the University begged to differ. They thought that Syme and Liston ranked equal, and if Syme would provide for the retiring professor and Liston would not, what might have been an impossibly difficult choice became easy. Syme was appointed. There followed automatically his appointment to the Royal Infirmary, with three wards for his patients. The need for Minto House was gone, but it filled such a useful place in the Edinburgh scheme of things that it was kept alive, first as a sort of general dispensary and later as part of the Extra-mural School.

For two years Liston and Syme lectured and operated under the same roof. The honours were even. Liston was recognized as by far the more dextrous and competent operator, Syme as the better teacher. What was not realized then was that Syme was easily the wiser, safer, and greater surgeon. The relations between the two men were if anything worse than they ever had been. Everyone in the Infirmary, from the professor of medicine to the ward-maids, had to take one side or the other. The situation was impossible, and it was clear that the newly-appointed professor of surgery could not be displaced. Liston took the first vacancy that offered outside Edinburgh. He went up to London as professor of surgery to University College. Five years went by, and then England's greatest Scotch operator wrote to Scotland's greatest surgeon. Seventeen years of bitter enmity were forgotten and the old friendship was renewed. The two men corresponded regularly, and whenever Syme was in London he stayed with Liston, returning this hospitality each time that Liston revisited Edinburgh.

Liston was soon as busy in London as he had been in Edinburgh. He was a tall, powerfully-built man, and he dressed always in a dark bottle-green coat, with grey trousers and Wellington boots. Soon he was as well known in Berkeley Square as in Lambeth. Students liked him as a man, worshipped his unrivalled surgical dexterity, and delighted in his weekly lectures, perhaps because they did not need to take notes, since the *Lancet* published them all in full. Stories of his imperturbability and his consummate artistry with the knife were legion. He was amputating a leg for chronic disease of the bones. Once the leg was off blood flowed freely. All the obvious blood-vessels were ligated, and only then did it become clear that most of the bleeding came from a large vessel in the substance of the bone. The surgeon's assistants panicked, and his audience leaned forward tensely. Liston seized his straight amputating knife again, sliced a wedge of wood off the operating-table, and with the handle of the knife hammered it into the bone marrow. The bleeding stopped immediately and the patient recovered. On another occasion Liston made an almost historic mistake. A patient had a soft swelling in the neck, which was misdiagnosed as an abscess. Liston plunged a knife into it. Arterial blood spurted forth. In one movement Liston closed the wound with his broad thumb and stopped the bleeding. He sealed the incision temporarily with a metal pin, and said, calmly, that he would tie the carotid artery on the following day.

For twelve years Liston showed those who had eyes to see how to operate. He was the master-craftsman of surgery. People who watched him at work for the first time were bemused. They saw the double flash of a straight knife, heard three strokes of the saw, gazed at a perfectly dismembered limb lying in the sawdust—and did not believe it. He died suddenly from the effects of an aortic aneurysm in the December of 1847, and only long after his death did his contemporaries realize that Liston was not a really great surgeon, whereas Syme was. Liston had brought to technical perfection the oldest and the simplest form of surgery. If a limb was diseased, he cut it off. His doing so was a joy to watch. His friends and assistants knew that pain was measured in seconds, and counted their chief's patients the most fortunate of men. They might have three minutes of blinding agony, but three minutes was infinitely less than six minutes. It was only the patient, and the patient long after his operation at that, who realized that for the rest of his life he would be a legless monument to radical artistry.

Syme in Edinburgh mourned the loss of his friend, and went on with his work. He took twice as long as Liston to make a diagnosis, twice as long to decide on his treatment, twice as long to perform any operation he undertook, but he saved his patients' limbs. The man who had a diseased knee-joint he left with a permanently stiff leg, but the leg was still there, the foot and ankle were normal, and that man needed no crutches. The girl with a tuberculous elbow he left with a stiff arm, but she still had two hands. Syme had published in 1831 his *Principles of Surgery*. The principles were few and simple. The fifth edition, which appeared in 1863, was shorter than the first edition. The principles were fewer and simpler, and by then they were generally accepted. The most important one was the principle underlying all conservative surgery. Its most obvious application was in the substitution of excision of diseased joints for amputation of limbs, but Syme applied it to every operation he undertook, saving and conserving always the maximum of healthy tissue compatible with entire removal of diseased structures. Thus, where amputation was unavoidable he saw no reason for amputating a limb high

[*293*]

up when it could be done as effectively lower down. So he was led to introduce the operation which bears his name—that of amputation at the ankle-joint—at a time when any and every amputation of the lower limb, even if it was for disease of the great toe, was just below the knee-joint. A further triumph for conservatism was removal of the entire shoulder-blade without sacrificing the arm, an elaboration of the operation which Liston had been the first to perform. Another operation that Syme introduced was external urethrotomy, a direct method of attack on obstinate contractions and strictures of the urethra which were impeding the flow of urine from the bladder. This operation provoked a storm of abuse, which was led by Lizars, and culminated in a suit for libel. The last word was with Syme, however. Not quite ten years after his introduction of the operation he reported a hundred and eight cases in which he had performed it; only two of these patients had died. The last advance he made was in the treatment of aneurysms. He was the first to realize that the Hunterian operation was being abused. For half the arteries subject to aneurysmal dilatation high ligation, as practised by John Hunter, was the best operation. For other arteries the old operation of ligature just above and just below the aneurysm was best.

For over thirty-five years Syme was the leader of surgical thought in Scotland and in England. His tenure of the professorial chair at Edinburgh lasted as long, and was interrupted for only six months. After Liston's death Syme was offered the professorship that had been his friend's. He accepted, and after only three months in London realized that "ambition had made him sacrifice happiness". In another three months he was back in Edinburgh, reinstated as professor of clinical surgery and as surgeon to the Infirmary. He resigned these appointments only in 1868, barely two years before his death at the age of seventy-one.

Building on foundations securely laid by Harvey, by Pott and Cheselden, by the Hunters and their many great pupils, Liston, the "Great Northern Anatomist", and Syme, "the Napoleon of Surgery", completed the structure of surgery within the limits of their generation. Syme, in principle, and Liston, in technique, brought the art and the science to a point at which no further advance seemed possible. Liston could not give his patients less pain. It was not humanly possible to perform operations more rapidly. Syme could not extend the operative field further. His patients would have died of pain and shock and hæmorrhage, or of sepsis. Then within their own lifetimes these two masters of the old generation were able to help the new generation to take over. Twelve months before his death Robert Liston performed the first major operation to be undertaken in this country with the patient under the influence of a new-fangled and quite remarkable substance—ether. James Syme, in the last lecture he ever gave, told an audience which did not really believe him that the greatest surgical advance since the discovery of anæsthesia had been made by his son-in-law, Joseph. Joseph was better known as one of Syme's own house-surgeons, Mr. Lister.

XX. Struggle for Corpses

SURGERY HAD BEEN ADVANCING SLOWLY BUT STEADILY THROUGH the long eighteenth century and the early part of the nineteenth century. Difficulties had been gradually overcome. One problem after another was solved. The art was tending to become a science, and a moderately respectable one. More and more young men were attracted to surgery as a career. Their increasing numbers rapidly made more urgent one of the problems which had never been solved. Surgery was based on a knowledge of anatomy. The teaching of anatomy demanded a continual supply of bodies, or subjects, for dissection. Corpses had to be carved that lives might be saved. A few subjects were legally available for dissection, but the legitimate demand was always greater than the legal supply. The need for a supply of anatomical material was recognized in 1540, when the newly incorporated barbers and surgeons were given the right to four bodies a year, the bodies to be those of executed criminals. At much the same time Edinburgh surgeons were granted the "ane condampnit man" they had requested. From then onwards the official supply of bodies was increased by imperceptible degrees, while the demand for them advanced by leaps and bounds. Four gypsies were executed for murder in Edinburgh in 1678 and their bodies were flung into a common grave. Next morning the topmost of the four corpses had disappeared. This is the first record of surgeons having recourse to an unofficial source of supply for anatomical subjects. There must have been many similar instances, for towards the end of that century the authorities in Edinburgh approved two requests; the first from Alexander Monteith, who asked for the bodies of those who died in the workhouse "and have none to bury them", and the second from the Edinburgh Faculty, which sought the bodies of foundlings, suicides, executed criminals, and those dying violent deaths. But however much or however little the supply of anatomical material was increased, the demand outpaced it, and the Edinburgh College of Surgeons in 1711 placed on record the fact that "of late there has been a violation of sepulchres in the Grey Friars Churchyard". Ten years later, as a sop to growing public indignation, all Edinburgh apprentices had a clause in their indentures to the effect that they were not to violate graves.

Meanwhile, the Barber-Surgeons' Company in London was fining its members for conducting dissections in their own homes, and bribing executioners and their assistants to let it have bodies which were the Company's by right. The hangman received a Christmas box from the Company every year, but this did not prevent the Company's beadle from having to fight for his corpses every inch of the way between Newgate and Surgeons' Hall. Criminals generally were horrified by the idea that their bodies might be dissected, and if any of them did fall into the hands of the executioner, their friends were quite capable of provoking large-scale riots if by this means they could ensure that the body did not reach a dissecting-table. "Behold the villain's dire disgrace" is the first line of the rhyme which Hogarth appended to his famous engraving showing the body of a malefactor being dissected (*see plate facing* p. 320). This horror and feeling of disgrace are the more surprising when it is realized that the men and women in question were often guilty of almost unbelievable crimes. There was Nichol Brown, for example, who forcibly held his wife upon an open fire till she was roasted to death; Sarah Metyard and her daughter, who had a millinery shop in Hanover Square, where they literally flogged to death orphan girls who had been apprenticed to them; Joseph Wall, Lieutenant-Governor of Senegambia, who saw one of his soldiers die from his sentence of eight hundred lashes; and many others like them. Yet these sadistic fiends were reduced almost to whimpering imbeciles not at the idea of the death-sentence but at the prospect of having their bodies dissected. It may be that they feared the possibility of being dissected alive. Hanging then was not as invariably effective as it is to-day. There was no drop, and so it was not uncommon for a criminal's friends to range themselves at the foot of the gallows and suspend all their weight from the kicking legs of the hanged man. This quickly stopped his struggling, and made certain that he was killed. In at least three cases, however, the Barber-Surgeons were not a little annoyed to find corpses they had brought from Newgate come to life again. Popular gossip made these three men thirty, and the compilers of the Newgate Calendar did nothing to allay the fears of condemned criminals when they recorded the case of a notorious German criminal. This man was hanged, and his body was laid out before an assembly of surgeons for public dissection. The surgeon in charge realized that the man was still alive. He put the problem to his audience. Should they spend a great deal of time and energy in restoring him completely to life and giving him the opportunity of continuing a murderous career, or should they proceed with the dissection? In effect, the gentlemen of the faculty unanimously turned down their thumbs, and the dissection began. It is just possible that the same sort of thing may have happened in England, though there is no record of it, and certainly English criminals took no chances. They did everything humanly possible to prevent the bodies of their executed colleagues being dissected.

The notorious Dick Turpin was hanged, very properly, at York in 1739. The corpse was allowed to lie in state at the local Blue Boar for twenty-four hours, and was then buried in an unusually deep grave. This did not prevent its being resurrected, but a hue-and-cry was raised and the disinterred Turpin was found in the garden of a surgeon's house. The second interment was successful. The coffin was filled with unslaked lime, buried even more deeply, and relays of watchers guarded the grave. This unsuccessful attempt at resurrection for dissection attracted a great deal of attention, as did more successful sallies, for by this time apprentices and their masters all over the country were going forth in the dead of night to collect the anatomical material that they could obtain in no other way. Soon there was rioting, and every other medical school had its windows smashed and its professors of anatomy and surgery attacked by incensed mobs. The Government grew alarmed, and in 1751 it was enacted that all murderers executed in London and Middlesex should be either publicly dissected or hung in chains on gibbets. The Act came into force the following year, when the Lord Chief Justice passed sentence of death upon a lad of seventeen, who had cut the throat of his prostitute wife:

> Thomas Wilford, you stand convicted of the horrid and unnatural crime of murdering Sarah, your wife. This Court doth adjudge that you be taken back to the place from whence you came; and there to be fed on bread and water till Wednesday next, when you are to be taken to the common place of execution, and there hanged by the neck until you are dead; after which your body is to be publicly dissected and anatomized, agreeably to an Act of Parliament in that case made and provided; and may God Almighty have mercy on your soul.

This Act materially increased the supply of subjects for dissection, but still there were not nearly enough. Apprentices went on raiding the graveyards. Then barely twelve months after Thomas Wilford's body had been duly dissected, there was brought to light the existence of another source of supply. In many districts at that time it was customary to "wake" the dead —that is, the relatives kept vigil over the coffin for the few days that elapsed between death and burial. The rite was losing favour, however, and the bereaved relatives were often very willing to pay the nurse who had attended the dear departed a few pence for continuing to keep an eye on an erstwhile patient. Two women, Helen Torrence and Jean Waldie, made this work their speciality, and as a profitable sideline abstracted from their coffins the bodies they were supposed to watch and sold them to anatomical students. The technique they adopted was body-snatching in its most simple form. There was none of the hard work and danger associated with grave-robbing, and they were paid fairly well for the subjects they procured in this way. Then for some reason or other Helen and Jean were employed less frequently, and their always shaky finances tottered badly. They knew one way of earning a few shillings quickly. They wandered about till they met a woman with whom they were acquainted, and who had her young son with her. The woman was taken to a nearby inn for a drink and one of the nurses took the little boy to her home. He was strangled and his body sold— for two shillings and sixpence and the price of a drink.

Both these women were hanged, and for at least a few months after their execution children were not allowed out by themselves and relatives did their own "waking". For some years afterwards, too, surgeons had to find their own subjects, and soon the graveyards were being despoiled again. Anxious relatives began to tip grave-diggers and sextons to watch over new graves. The surgeons tipped them more heavily to watch with their eyes closed first of all, and later to do the digging for them. For a while all went well, then two grave-diggers of St. George's Church, Bloomsbury, were caught as they were raising the body of a Mrs. Sainsbury. The husband prosecuted them, and each was sentenced to six months' imprisonment and to be flogged publicly from Holborn to St. Giles', a distance of about half a mile.

The underworld of London had begun to realize by this time that grave-robbing could be a profitable pursuit. Unfortunately, after the St. George's affair in 1777, every grave in London was being watched by angry citizens, who had usually a bell-mouthed pistol in one hand and a bottle of grog in the other. London surgeons could not move their dissecting-rooms from the City, but the resurrection men could, and did, widen their sphere of activity. They would make midnight excursions out into the country, and counted themselves unlucky if they could not collect three or four bodies at a time. These would then be taken to some central point for distribution. Certain of the resurrectionists had been doing this even before the sad case of Mrs. Sainsbury, and in 1776 one of them was unlucky enough to lose to the police more than twenty bodies, which he had carefully stored away in a house in Tottenham Court Road.

By the end of the eighteenth century students and their masters no longer went grave-robbing. The amateurs were displaced by professionals. Resurrection men made a good, if dangerous, living in every large city, and their prices were soon as standardized as their methods. The price of a subject at that time was two guineas, and the method of raising it was simple and direct. It was first necessary to learn where and when burials were taking place. Barmaids and barmen, grooms and porters, tramps and down-and-outs, could always be sure of a few coppers for information received. It was then essential to know the lie of the land. *Passé* prostitutes soon became adept in this branch of the business. Dressed in black they would visit new graves soon after the mourners had departed, and while standing by the grave-side, in apparent melancholy, they would make an exact inventory of the way wreaths and flowers were placed, and note the presence or absence of spring guns, trip-wires, and the like devices. They reported back to the resur-rectionist-in-chief, who would reward them suitably and set forth that night with two, or perhaps three, assistants. First the wreaths and other impedimenta were removed, then a hole was dug down to the head of the coffin, the earth being thrown on to a canvas sheet. Once the coffin-head was exposed, broad iron hooks were passed under its lid, sacking was dropped down the hole to muffle any noise, and ropes were tied round the iron hooks. A few stout heaves rived off the upper part of the lid, and the body was extracted. All the winding-cloths and the shrouds were stripped off and thrown back into the coffin, and the body was placed in a sack. Quickly the earth was shovelled back, and smoothed over. Wreaths and other landmarks were carefully replaced, and, once certain that the grave showed no signs of having been tampered with, the body was borne away. The fact that winding-sheets were always removed was due to a misapprehension. Until 1788 there had been no legal property in a body, and, though this was so no longer, all resurrectionists firmly believed that they committed no legal offence in removing a body, but could be held guilty of theft if they took the shroud in which it was wrapped.

For a brief while the conduct of the resurrectionists was as respectable as it could be. There were relatively few of them, and there was enough work for all. Their only difficulties were with the public. Spring-guns they did not mind very much. A little extra time was needed to undo the trip-wires attached to the gun and replace them after the body had been raised, but that was all. They took objection, however, to the cast-iron coffins which certain enterprising undertakers were beginning to sell. The sale of these coffins did not last long, for certain eminent, though hardly disinterested, surgeons pointed out that if iron coffins were generally adopted, every graveyard in the country would soon be full to the brim. Churchyard walls fifteen feet high and covered with broken glass were as harmless as spring guns. The sexton was paid a retaining fee for admitting the grave despoilers by the ordinary gates, and the walls around might have been sky high for all the obstacle they presented. Enormous tombstones of marble and wrought iron did provide impossible barriers, but, fortunately for the anatomists, were too expensive for general adoption. Even the Law, if not on the side of the resurrectionists, was not very much against them. The Government needed surgeons for its armies. It was assured that the supply of surgeons would vary directly with the supply of anatomical material, and so it was made known to those administering the Law that light sentences were the order of the day for those resurrectionists who had to be prosecuted. Sentence of only a few months' imprisonment was used for professional resurrectionists, and if students or surgeons were caught they would be fined £5 or so. The "sack-'em-up man" who went to prison was well treated by his jailer, paid weekly by the surgeon who employed him, and his family received a few shillings a week from the same source.

Only occasionally was the public so incensed that an honest grave-robber had difficulty in pursuing his avocation. When that happened the local resurrectionists would move into the country and send supplies to their employers from some new source. Thus at one time London bodies would be despatched to Edinburgh, at another the fruits of the Edinburgh cemeteries would come to lie on London dissecting-tables. When the inhabitants of both cities were apt to fire at sight on anyone within a hundred yards of a burial-place after dusk, the provinces were explored. Liverpool for a time supplied Edinburgh, London, Glasgow, Manchester, and Birmingham. Then the inhabitants of Liverpool took the bit in their teeth, and their own medical school had to get its supply of anatomical material from as far afield as Exeter. Dublin also was a prolific source of supply, and for years the anatomy school of the Royal College of Surgeons there was used as a warehouse storing bodies for export. Most of them were pickled in brine and shipped to different centres, in England and Scotland, in packing-cases labelled "Agricultural Implements", and so on.

Inevitably, this fairly orderly business expanded till it was well known that there was a great deal of money to be made in it. Then the business became a racket, the like of which Chicago never knew. Rival resurrection kings led a ruthless inter-gang warfare. At different times single individuals had almost a monopoly of supplying material to the twelve anatomical schools in London, which together catered for about seven hundred students. The London resurrectionists were split into two camps, those led by Murphy, and those led by his rivals, Hollis and Vaughan. Murphy discovered a private burial-ground in Holy-well Mount near Finsbury. It was owned by two old ladies and looked after by a grave-digger named Whackett. Whackett responded to financial treatment, and the rest was easy. He gave Murphy a duplicate key to the graveyard, and informed him which graves could be rifled and when. Murphy and his colleagues did their work undisturbed, and often raised as many as six fresh bodies in a night. Bodies which were not fresh were not wasted. The market for skeletons was always good, and that for teeth was even better. False teeth were being worn more and more commonly, and all plates were made of human teeth properly mounted. For a while everything in the graveyard was lovely. Then Hollis and Vaughan became annoyed. They knew Murphy was still maintaining his supply of bodies, though neither he nor his underlings had been seen at any of the well-known burial-grounds for weeks. One night they followed some of Murphy's men and discovered the graveyard at Holywell Mount. The next day they asked Whackett for the same facilities that he had given Murphy, suggesting that they were partners of Murphy's. Whackett, who had been warned by Murphy that some such approach might be made to him, refused first their cajoling and then their bribes. Hollis and Vaughan put their money back in their pockets and began to explain to Whackett how easy it was for a recalcitrant grave-digger to reach a dissecting-room table. Whackett was not unmoved by their threats. In fact, he moved quickly enough to reach the nearest public-house before Hollis and Vaughan realized where he was going. Whackett's breathless announcement to the assembled local worthies that Hollis and Vaughan were resurrectionists trying to bribe him emptied the inn, and the two men had to run for their lives. Unhappily for Whackett, Hollis and Vaughan were older hands at the game than he was. They made straight for the nearest court, where a magistrate was sitting, and in the guise of righteous citizens demanded that officers should be sent at once to the Holywell Mount burial-ground. They assured the court that every grave there had been opened, and that the grave-digger in charge was in the pay of the resurrectionists. In no time the court was as empty as the public-house had been. A huge crowd broke down the gates at Holywell Mount and stormed the graveyard. Hollis and Vaughan stayed long enough to see Whackett rescued from the mob by a few heroic policemen. Finding almost every grave despoiled, the infuriated men and women had flung him into the deepest one available and started to bury him alive. He was dragged out only just in time, and at that point Hollis and Vaughan made a graceful exit. They had Murphy's wrath to reckon with, however. The resurrection king forced them both into hiding, and contrived finally to have Vaughan sentenced to two years' imprisonment.

Another outstanding resurrectionist was Ben Crouch, a famous pugilist in his day, who was almost permanently employed by Robert Liston. Crouch won the right to supply certain schools and teachers, and dealt brutally with those who attempted to undercut him or to trespass on his preserves. If some other resurrectionist did supply a school which Crouch regarded as his own, he was quite capable of ordering a trio of his bullies to raid the school's dissecting-rooms and cut to pieces the subjects which had just been bought from his competitors. Like Murphy, he was in the habit of demanding a retaining fee of perhaps fifty guineas, at the beginning of the winter session, from a series of anatomical teachers, to each of whom he would promise his exclusive services. If the fee was not forthcoming, a series of catastrophes would overtake the stubborn anatomist who had refused to pay it. First, he would have great difficulty in getting any subjects at all. Then subjects that he did get met a variety of fates. They might be cut to pieces, or they might be stolen, for robbing Bart's to supply Guy's was a popular sport. Failing either of these evils, worse would befall. Well-paid agitators would create an appalling disturbance just outside the anatomist's dissecting-room and collect a large crowd. Then, weeping bitterly, they would explain that the exhumed body of a beloved relative was in the hands of the students. The crowd would beat down the doors to the school, break all the windows, and, if it was at all possible, set fire to the entire building.

Surgeons generally soon abandoned the unequal struggle. Over and above the blackmailing retaining fees, bodies which used to cost two guineas each were priced at eight and ten guineas, but whatever was asked was paid. One or two men had a virtual monopoly of the supply of subjects. Undertakers were in their pay and bodies were filched from their coffins before burial. Sextons were their hirelings, and the corpse that did receive decent burial was raised the same night. A few redoubtable anatomists did try to break the ring. When it was found that the police protected them from mobs and prevented their houses from being set afire, new methods were devised to bring them to heel. If one of these men had an interesting case, preferably of some fatal condition, the resurrectionists would have it noised abroad that the intransigent surgeon was attending, say, the child with the enormous head. Soon the child would die and be buried. The rest was simple. The new grave would be ruthlessly opened up and the shattered coffin left lying across it. The child's head, or it might be a girl's deformed arm, was hacked off and taken away. The mutilated body would be left exposed in the graveyard, and, as was expected, a howling mob jumped to the conclusion that the surgeon was responsible. Police might prevent them from burning the surgeon's house down, but could not stop them from booing in the streets and from refusing to attend that surgeon's private or hospital practice.

The situation grew impossible after a time. The surgeons and anatomists had no option but to employ the resurrectionists and body-snatchers, and the uneasy Government had to connive at all their doings. Religious opinion had prevented the Government from introducing legislation to ensure a lawful supply of bodies for dissection. Military and civil needs forced it to maintain teaching standards in anatomy and surgery, and so the Home Office had to see to it that the unlawful supply of anatomical subjects was not interfered with any more than was necessary to prevent rioting. Thus, on one occasion a shipment of bodies from Dublin arrived in London. The police boarded the vessel which had brought them, and seized all the crates and casks in which they were contained. The surgeon who had arrived to claim his property saw what was happening and went immediately to the Home Office. A few hours later the police were helping to load the bodies on to drays, which were to take them to various medical schools. Again, three bodies were being taken one night from Astley Cooper's house to St. Thomas's. Watchmen found the bodies and reported the matter to the Lord Mayor of London. With Astley Cooper by his side the worthy Lord Mayor commended the watchmen for their zeal, and later quietly arranged for the bodies to complete the journey to St. Thomas's.

At length the Government set up a Select Committee on Anatomy to consider the whole question of the supply of anatomical material. The Select Committee, like everyone else in London, knew of the far-famed Baronet's Brigade. The employer of this well-known team of resurrectionists was one of the first witnesses to be called by the Committee. Sir Astley Cooper had always prided himself on having the best of everything, and in his "brigade" he had the best of the resurrectionists. He was asked what effect the Law as it then stood had in preventing exhumations. His reply was simple. The Law did not prevent exhumations, it merely enhanced the price of subjects according to the severity with which it was administered in different districts. Another question provoked a retort categorical: "There is no person, let his situation in life be what it may, whom, if I were disposed to dissect, I could not obtain." This was no exaggeration. General practitioners all over the country informed Astley Cooper as soon as any patient of theirs upon whom he had operated died. It might be twenty or more years after the operation, but Astley Cooper usually contrived to have two of his resurrectionists on the spot soon after he learnt of the patient's death. It was in this way that he accumulated his amazing collection of specimens, showing what happened to amputation stumps, radically cured hernias, and the like, after periods varying from days to decades from the date of operation. Small wonder that Hood's ballad, *Mary's Ghost,* was quoted at one time or another to every surgeon in London. Mary's ghost details to her lover William the sad fate that has befallen her. "Mr. Bell" in the poem became Sir Charles Bell. Bedford Row refers to Abernethy's school, and "Mr. P." was Mr. Partridge, a lecturer in anatomy at King's College Hospital.

> The arm that used to take your arm
>   Is took to Dr. Vyse,
> And both my legs are gone to walk
>   The Hospital at Guy's.
>
> I vowed that you should have my hand,
>   But Fate gives us denial;
> You'll find it there at Mr. Bell's
>   In spirits in a phial.
>
> As for my feet, the little feet
>   You used to call so pretty,
> There's one I know in Bedford **Row**,
>   The t'other's in the City.
>
> I can't tell where my head has gone,
>   But Dr. Carpue can;
> As for my trunk, it's all packed up
>   To go by Pickford's van.
>
> I wish you'd go to Mr. P.
>   And save me such a ride:
> I don't half like the outside place
>   They've took for my inside.
>
> The cock it crows, I must be gone,
>   My William, we must part:
> And I'll be yours in death although
>   Sir Astley has my heart.

After hearing the evidence of Sir Astley and many other surgeons and teachers, one of whom admitted frankly that the extortionate demands of the resurrectionists had forced him to close down his school, the Committee examined a few well-known resurrectionists. From their evidence it appeared that in London alone there were about two hundred men engaged solely in the resurrection business. This rough figure leaves out of account the prostitute mourners who spied out the land, undertakers who gave the "sack-'em-up men" access to their coffins, sextons who left their graveyards unprotected, pseudo-relatives who claimed bodies from the workhouses, and a horde of others on the fringe of the racket. The Committee next elicited some figures as to the number of bodies any one resurrectionist and his assistants could raise in a year. One man had kept exact records of all his transactions. In 1809 he sold the bodies of 305 adults and 44 children to the London medical schools, despatched 37 other corpses to Edinburgh, and had a wastage of 18 bodies that were never used at all. The following year was just as successful; 332 adults and 47 children were sold. The price of these subjects had "improved" steadily. When Astley Cooper was a student the price was two guineas; ten years later four guineas was more usual; another ten years saw the price raised to six guineas; and by about 1820 eight guineas was the least that a good adult subject could be procured for, and on occasion as much as fourteen guineas had to be paid. During the whole of this protracted boom the average price of subjects in France remained stationary at about half a guinea. In fact all the evidence recorded by the Select Committee bore out Astley Cooper's statement that existing legislation served only to make the resurrectionists wealthy.

The knowledge that a Select Committee was sitting soothed the ruffled feelings of the British public. The Government sat back complacently, delighted that for the moment rioting had ceased. But fortunately, or unfortunately, events were taking place in Edinburgh which were to shatter this administrative calm. The spotlight of publicity was focused on the resurrectionists not by their own misdeeds, nor by the Select Committee, but by two clumsy drunken murderers. These two men were never resurrectionists. Their only approach to the business was a single, amateurish body-snatching, so simple that a child could have effected it.

An old army pensioner died in a miserable lodging-house in Edinburgh. The hostel in which he ended his days was owned by William Hare. It was a poor place frequented by vagrants and aged prostitutes. Hare was assisted in the running of it by William Burke, and by Burke's mistress, Helen McDougal. The parish authorities sent a coffin along and the old man's body was duly placed in it. Hare watched this procedure with annoyance. The dead man had owed him £4 and he saw no hope of recovering it. Then came the obvious idea. Burke's help was enlisted, the coffin lid was lifted off, and the body was sold for £7 10s. That was just before Christmas in 1827, and the body was bought by Dr. Robert Knox. Knox was one of the most gifted lecturers in Edinburgh. He had inherited Sir John Barclay's anatomical school, at which Liston and Syme had done their early dissecting, and it was his boast that he always had a "well-kept table".

Burke and Hare had never earned money so easily before. They waited impatiently for other inmates of their hostel to die, but the old men and women remained obstinately alive. The two men discussed the problem. Soon they were wandering about Edinburgh looking for friendless and poverty-stricken strangers. They found several of them. One by one men and women were brought to the lodging-house and made very drunk. When they were quite unconscious Hare would sit on them, while Burke held both his hands over the victim's nose and mouth. Death was fairly rapid, and there was no obvious evidence that it was not from natural causes. The two men knew well that any outward signs of foul play would have been seen by Knox or his assistants, and the police would promptly have been called. For a while the murderers prospered, then they were stupid enough to save themselves the trouble of waiting for strangers to come to their lodging-house. They got Helen McDougal to entice into the house a notorious old drunkard, Abigail Simpson. Her disappearance excited comment, as did that of "Daft Jamie", a well-known imbecile. Their next choice of a victim was even more ill-advised. Mary Paterson was one of the most popular young women in Edinburgh. She graced her chosen profession in a way that made her the gossip of Edinburgh. Rumours that her lovely, if long-commercialized, body was in Dr. Knox's dissecting-room spread like wildfire. Then another woman, named Dougherty, was reported missing. Within a few hours all Edinburgh was roused. Burke and Hare and Helen McDougal were almost torn limb from limb as they were escorted to prison. Dr. Knox had to be restrained by his assistants from going out to tackle single-handed a mob which had broken all the windows in his house and was threatening to set fire to it. On December 24, 1828, at the trial, the craven Hare turned State's evidence and was freed, as was Helen McDougal for lack of evidence against her. On the Christmas Day the jury found Burke guilty. Thousands saw him hanged, and clamoured for the lives of Hare and Dr. Knox. Thousands more saw a public exhibition of Burke's body in the anatomical lecture theatre of the university, and his skeleton was preserved in the anatomical museum, labelled "William Burke, the Murderer".

After this episode, dissecting-rooms all over the country were burnt down, anatomists and lectures were mobbed, and the general agitation only began to show signs of subsiding in the Spring of 1829, when a Bill to regulate the supply of dead bodies for the purpose of dissection was steered successfully through the House of Commons. The Bill would have brought about a state of affairs comparable to that existing in France. It would have allowed hospital governors and workhouse overseers to yield up to recognized schools of anatomy any bodies unclaimed by relatives of persons dying in these institutions. The Commons welcomed this Bill, but the Lords rejected it, as condemning the bodies of the poor to treatment which would not be accorded to the bodies of the wealthy. The resurrectionists breathed again, and for a while business was as usual. Then London itself had a taste of the horrors Edinburgh had known.

One day in the November of 1831 three well-known resurrectionists called at the anatomy department of King's College Hospital. Williams and Bishop were trying to dispose of a body. May was with them simply as a salesman. He had been promised all he could get over and above nine guineas. May told the anatomy steward that the body was that of a boy of fourteen, and asked twelve guineas. The usual bargaining brought this figure down to ten guineas, but Mr. Partridge, the lecturer whom the steward had consulted, was not impressed. He offered nine guineas and no more. May saw his share of the booty disappearing, and was damned if King's or anywhere else was having this exceptionally fine body for less than ten guineas. Bishop cared nothing for May's feelings in the matter. Drunk himself, he assured the steward that May was very drunk, and clinched the deal. About half an hour later the body was brought and toppled carelessly out of its sack. The dissecting-room steward looked at it suspiciously. The mouth was bruised and distorted. That was to be expected, for the subject's teeth were the resurrectionists' rightful perquisites. But there was a gash on the forehead, which had obviously bled a great deal. The eyes were bloodshot and starting. The left arm was bent with the fingers firmly clenched. The steward asked curtly how the boy had died. May was still drunk and very truculent.

"None of your bloody business!"

The steward had a word with Mr. "P." The lecturer in anatomy gave the body a casual glance, and then asked the men to wait while he changed a fifty-pound bank-note. They waited, and had to be fought to a standstill before the police could frog-march them to Bow Street. The three men were tried for the murder of Carlo Ferrari, the boy, and the murder of an unknown man. Another known victim had been Frances Pigburn, a widow, but it seemed that there might have been as many as sixty people all murdered in the same way by Bishop and Williams. They were taken to the house in Novia Scotia Gardens, a slum just off the Hackney Road in Shoreditch, where the two men lived, Williams married to Bishop's half-sister and Bishop to his own widowed stepmother. Rum laced with laudanum was given to the selected victim. Once unconscious, the subject-to-be was stripped. A rope was tied round one ankle, and the body was left hanging head downwards in a deep well in the next garden. Early the next morning one or other of the men would tour the dissecting-rooms till he had arranged a sale. Men, women, and children had all met the same fate. Then the little Italian boy had struggled while being carried to the well, and had to be beaten over the head.

The jury returned a verdict of "Guilty", which was greeted with howls of applause from the crowd tight-packed outside the court. Before sentence was carried out, the confessions of Williams and Bishop absolved May, whose sentence was commuted to transportation for life. At daybreak on the following Monday morning forty thousand people flocked to Newgate to watch a public execution. They cheered themselves hoarse as the two men were hanged. That was on December 5, 1831. Ten days later a Bill to regulate schools of anatomy was read for the first time in the House of Commons. The only amendment proposed to it was that it should apply to Ireland as well as England and Scotland. This Bill received the Royal Assent, and became the Anatomy Act, on August 1, 1832. Two hundred resurrectionists were out of work, and the supply of bodies for the teaching of anatomy was legally assured.

Just a year after the passing of the Anatomy Act a well-known French surgeon died. Alexis Boyer practised in Paris, but his fame was eclipsed by that of two of his countrymen, Jean Dominique Larrey and Guillaume Dupuytren. Towards the end of his life, in 1833, Boyer said: "Surgery seems to have attained the highest degree of perfection of which it is capable". For this summing-up he has been derided. Anyone who delivers an annual oration on the progress of surgery can quote Boyer in the right tone of voice and be sure of a good laugh. Actually, Boyer's estimate was correct. In Britain, in the hands of Liston and Syme, and in France, in the clinics of Dupuytren, Larrey, and

Boyer himself, surgery had attained the highest degree of perfection of which it was capable—failing two major revolutions in thought and practice. That was in the first half of the last century, and neither Boyer nor anyone else could foretell the future. They could not know that chemists and microscopists would throw casually to the surgeons truths which would alter the face of surgery, and break down for ever the two great barriers within which surgical endeavour had been confined since the beginning of time. Boyer spoke within the limits they imposed. He and his fellows, and all their predecessors, had worked within those limits. Pain and sepsis straitly marked the narrow path that surgeons trod.

The pain that patients suffered beneath the knife can hardly be guessed at, but the way in which it affected a few of the men who wielded that knife is known. Their agony of mind may reflect in some small degree their patients' physical sufferings. Cheselden blanched and felt physically sick every time he entered an operating-theatre. Astley Cooper's uncle, William Cooper, did neither of these things, but once only he revealed his feelings. A man who was to have his leg amputated limped into the theatre and was laid upon the operating-table. The usual four porters were standing idly by, waiting to lay hands upon the patient just as soon as the amputation was begun. The man could see an assistant arranging a fearsome array of amputation knives and bone-saws. Sick with horror, he watched until the surgeon had actually taken up his position at the end of the table. Then suddenly he swung himself off the table and hobbled away as quickly as he could. The porters would have seized him, but William Cooper stopped them. He watched the erstwhile patient disappear into the hospital corridor, laid down the instruments he had taken up, and said, "By God, I'm glad he's gone!" William Cooper was not the only surgeon to be relieved when a patient refused to submit to an operation. Cheselden was not the only surgeon who grew pale at the thought of the agony he was about to inflict. John Flint South of St. Thomas's always sought aid by prayer before he operated. Often Abernethy vomited, just before or just after an operation. Astley Paston Cooper, after each operation of the many thousands that he performed, felt that "much had been taken out of him". Every other surgeon shared their distress in greater or less degree, but all they could do about it was to increase their operating speed. This was the only method they knew of attacking the problem, and Liston, who outlived Alexis Boyer by only a few years, brought this method as near to perfection as was humanly possible.

Sepsis was the other angel of death barring the further progress of surgery. After Astley Cooper had operated on George IV— and the operation was a minor one—he and his colleagues were sleepless from anxiety for nearly a fortnight. They feared that the King would develop erysipelas and die of it. Tetanus was another complication that might have followed the operation and proved fatal. A spreading gangrene or a general infection of the blood-stream they dared not think about. A fatal lung condition was less likely as a post-operative sequel, and they would not have minded it so much, for then the King would have died in the hands of his physicians, and his surgeons would have been only indirectly responsible. When the royal patient recovered, Astley Cooper, Everard Home, and Henry Cline breathed again. The chances as to whether the King would or would not survive one of the simplest possible operative procedures had been almost exactly even. About the year 1800, of every two patients subjected to operation one died. If the operation was an amputation, the dice were loaded slightly in the surgeon's favour, for generally only one patient in three succumbed, and, in fact, if Syme or Liston was operating, only one in six or seven might die. On the other hand, if the operation was Cæsarean section, the patient's prospects were grim indeed. In a hundred years, comprising the last half of the eighteenth century and the first half of the nineteenth century, the death-rate was over 80 per cent. In the years intervening between the death of Richard Wiseman and that of Robert Liston, the number of operations, especially amputations, performed each year had increased almost a hundred-fold—and the operative death-rate had increased a thousand-fold. Wiseman's surgery was largely the surgery of war. His patients were young, healthy soldiers, well-fed and lusty. Liston's patients were often old. His amputations were done not for gunshot wounds inflicted on young men but for chronic diseases and tumours of bones, which had been enfeebling his patients for years before they grew desperate enough to submit to operation. After operation they were returned to crowded and ill-ventilated wards, thick with the stench of putrefying wounds. The wonder is that so many survived.

Pain and sepsis worked hand in hand to bring surgery to a full stop. For fear of pain patients delayed operation till such resistance to infection as they might have had was almost gone. For fear of sepsis and the hospital contagion those who might have resisted both delayed operation even longer, till when at length they did submit to the surgeon, the pain and shock of the operation killed them. Surgeons were as conscious of these twin terrors as their patients. Only the well-tried operations would they undertake, for it was unthinkable to submit men to procedures which might mean death if no certainty of relief in the event of recovery from the operation could be promised them. So surgery had resolved itself into a rut of rapid excisions. Cataracts were removed, limbs and breasts were amputated, tumours were cut away, stones were taken from the bladder, aneurysms were ligated, and ruptures cured. Little else could be attempted. The mortality from Cæsarean section made it a desperate last resort, and the same applied to almost every other procedure which involved opening the abdominal cavity, whether it was for removal of diseased ovaries or the reduction of a strangulated rupture. Syme showed the success that attended the conservative excision of joints, but a patient had to be stout-hearted to undergo an operation which might last twenty minutes or more when an amputation could be done in three minutes or less. In his day and his generation Boyer was right. Surgery could advance no further till the two great barriers were overthrown. Both had existed since the history of mankind began. Was it likely then that they would be overthrown?

XXI. Death of Pain

FROM THE DAWN OF CIVILIZATION ATTEMPTS HAD BEEN MADE TO control or at least deaden pain. Magical incantations were used for a thousand years to render patients less conscious of the pain of an operation, and strange deities were invoked on their behalf. For another thousand years, in civilizations less mystical and more crudely practical, the victim was tied down with ropes and instructed to commend himself to God and bear his sufferings beneath the surgeon's knife with such fortitude as he could command. Small wonder that the most famous and most sought-after surgeons were those who handled their knives with the greatest speed and dexterity. Langenbeck, surgeon-general of the Hanoverian army in the time of Napoleon, was said to be able to whip off an arm at the shoulder-joint in no longer than it might take an onlooker to pinch up and inhale a little snuff. Robert Liston worked just as quickly. The measure of a surgeon's skill was recorded in seconds. Few patients ever mentioned the pain they had suffered in crowded, dingy theatres. They never wanted to recall the glimpse of an agonized hell that had been vouchsafed them. Though surgeons never realized it —perhaps because they dared not—fifty-four seconds might have been fifty-four years of operating time for all the patient cared. The merest glimpse of a patient's feelings is given by Professor George Wilson in a letter he wrote. James Syme had amputated his foot at the ankle-joint, performing for only the second time the operation now known as Syme's amputation.

> The operation was a more tedious one than some which involve much greater mutilation. It necessitated cruel cutting through inflamed and morbidly sensitive parts, and could not be despatched by a few strokes of the knife. I do not suppose that it was more painful than the majority of severe surgical operations are, but I am not, I believe, mistaken in thinking it was not less painful, and this is all that I wish to contend for. Of the agony it occasioned, I will say nothing. Suffering so great as I underwent cannot be expressed in words, and thus fortunately cannot be recalled. The particular pangs are now forgotten, but the black whirlwind of emotion, the horror of great darkness, and the sense of desertion by God and man, bordering close on despair, which swept through my mind and overwhelmed my heart, I can never forget however gladly I would do so. During the operation, in spite of the pain it occasioned, my senses were preternaturally acute, as I have been told they generally are in patients in such circumstances. I still recall with

unwelcome vividness the spreading out of the instruments: the twisting of the tourniquet: the first incision: the fingering of the sawed bone: the sponge pressed on the flap: the tying of the blood-vessels: the stitching of the skin: and the bloody dismembered limb lying on the floor. . . .

This letter was written to a man who helped to free surgery from the fetters of pain—James Young Simpson, the seventh son of a village baker.

Queer concoctions to relieve pain were used by the most primitive peoples. Unhappily, they rarely produced complete unconsciousness, except in doses which were lethal. The same literally fatal objection applied also to a method of producing unconsciousness used by the Roman surgeons. The great carotid arteries in the neck, which supply blood to the brain, were forcibly compressed against the bony parts of the spinal column which lie immediately behind them. This diminished the blood-supply to the brain and certainly caused unconsciousness. Unfortunately it also caused irretrievable damage to the brain in many cases, so that if the patient recovered at all, he or she might be paralysed or otherwise disabled for life. Not unnaturally this method was soon abandoned and the surgeons did their best with the few pain-deadening drugs of which they had knowledge. A technique based on the same principle of diminishing the blood-supply to the brain, but with less disastrous results, was that of opening an artery in the wrist and bleeding the patient to unconsciousness. Another Roman practice was to give various drugs in wine to those who were suffering. The Romans crucified thousands of rebels, and while they were on the cross it was customary to give them sour wine which had been drugged with perhaps opium or mandragora, to deaden the pain a little. Vinegar and hyssop were probably given to Christ for this purpose. Opium, prepared from poppy-seeds, was well known, and was probably used by Helen to drug the wine Ulysses drank. Indian hemp, or hashish, was known to the Egyptians, and also to the Arabians; and the Hebrews and Babylonians credited the mandrake plant and the mandragora they prepared from it with magical properties.

The mandrake was for long regarded with fear and wonder, partly because of its definite narcotic action, but also because it bears a decided resemblance to a miniature human form. In the Book of Genesis (Chapter XXX, verse 14) Rachel says to Leah, "Give me, I pray thee, of thy son's mandrakes". But in this instance the mandrakes would be wanted not for their sleep-producing properties but because they were also credited with awakening sexual passion and curing sterility, for "Rachel was barren". The mandrake is found in several parts of the world, in England as bryony, in America as the May apple, and in the East. It is the Eastern variety which is most active and about which various legends were woven.

According to Pliny the mandrake could be male or female, the man mandrake being white and the woman black. Uprooting it was a hazardous business. Three circles had to be drawn round it with the point of the sword and the wind had to be in the west. In the Middle Ages things were even more complicated, for on being torn out of the ground the tiny vegetable-man, or woman, emitted shrieks so frightful and horrible that any human being who heard them promptly went mad. This appalling difficulty was overcome by the more daring and ingenious of the mediæval herbalists. They filled their ears with wax, loosened the earth around the mandrake, attached the mandrake with cord to the tail of a dog, preferably a small and not very valuable dog, and tapped the dog smartly with some appropriate stick. The dog leaped forwards, the mandrake gave its terrifying yell, and though the dog dropped dead, the herbalist had in exchange for it a very valuable mandrake. Paulus Æginata, towards the end of the seventh century, described the narcotic action of man-dragora. Serapion said that the wine of mandragora was given to patients to "dull their sensibilities" before legs or arms were amputated. Even as early as A.D. 77 Dioscorides, an Army surgeon in the service of Nero, recommended that the same wine should be given "before any cutting or burning". Mandrake remained popular up to the sixteenth century, and Shakespeare mentions it in *Romeo and Juliet* (Act IV, Scene 3), "Shrieks like mandrake's torn out of the earth". But in the next two centuries surgeons became less mystically minded. They occasionally intoxicated their patients with alcohol or gave them large doses of opium before operating, but more usually they relied on either stout ropes or two or three strong assistants to keep their victims on the operating-table.

Then came Franz Anton Mesmer, who was born in Ignanz, a small village near Lake Constance, on May 23, 1734. He studied medicine in Vienna, and graduated at the age of thirty-one in 1765. Within ten years his work on animal magnetism was the subject of heated debate in every European capital. His clinic was described by some as a Temple of Divinity and by others as a hot-bed of immorality. Louis XVI set up a commission to investigate animal magnetism. Benjamin Franklin, the Ambassador to the Court of France from the United States, was chairman. Dr. Guillotin—who honestly believed in humane executions and did not invent the guillotine—was a member, as were Lavoisier, the great chemist, and Jean Sylvan Bailly, who before dying on the guillotine was Mayor of Paris. Their official report damned Mesmerism medically, but apart from this a confidential "morality report" was issued, and Mesmer's career ended in disgrace. Bailly was probably largely responsible for the "morality report". Mesmer was too single-minded to realize that his clinics were being used as a meeting-place by all sorts of odd perverts and that his treating hysterical young women in darkened rooms was apt to provoke ribald comment.

After Mesmer had been discredited, all sorts of charlatans, qualified and unqualified, seized on his methods. It was soon claimed that operations of all kinds could be performed under the influence of this magnetism; and in sufficiently hysterical women operations actually were performed with the patient in a somnambulistic state induced by mesmerism. Mesmerism spread to the United States and was practised there by Charles Poyen in Maine. Poyen interested Phineas Parkhurst Quinby in mesmerism, and Quinby influenced Mary Baker Eddy, who founded Christian Science, and indirectly a score of other New Thoughts and New Cults, so that Mesmer has much to answer for.

James Young Simpson was born on June 7, 1811. The mandrake had not long before been removed from the official *Pharmacopœia;* mesmerism was a game played by charlatans; and there was but one ray of light on the surgical horizon. Dr. Thomas Beddoes had founded at Bristol in 1793 the Medical Pneumatic Institute, where diseases were treated by the inhalation of oxygen, hydrogen, and carbon dioxide, then recently discovered. Beddoes himself is forgotten, but his colleague and his assistant are both remembered. James Watt, the engineer, was the colleague, and a young man named Humphry Davy the assistant. This young man published in 1800 the results of his work on nitrous oxide, which soon became known as "laughing gas". He wrote at that time: "As nitrous oxide in its extensive operation appears capable of destroying physical pain it may probably be used with advantage in surgical operations".

Little attention was paid to Davy's work. Laughing gas was too funny to be taken seriously. Even less attention was attracted by a cumbrously titled "Letter on Suspended Animation, containing Experiments showing that it may be Safely Employed during Operations on Animals, with the view of Ascertaining its Probable Utility in Surgical Operations on the Human Subject". This was written in 1824 by Henry Hill Hickman, a general practitioner in Ludlow, who made the animals on which he operated insensible by forcing them to inhale the "laughing gas".

In early boyhood James Simpson was an object of reverent awe, for he was an authentic seventh son. His whole family made sacrifices to allow him to go to Edinburgh University at the age of fourteen. He studied under Robert Liston, and on one occasion, after seeing the agony of a woman who was having her breast amputated, he almost decided to give up medicine, but on second thoughts he returned to his studies, determined if possible to find something to make operations less painful. Four years later he graduated and applied for the position of parish surgeon to a small village on the banks of the Clyde. He was not elected, and felt "a deeper amount of chagrin and disappointment than I have ever experienced since that date". His elder brother came to the rescue, and James went back to the University to qualify for the higher degree of Doctor of Medicine. The thesis he wrote for this degree on "death from inflammation" was given to the Professor of Pathology to examine.

This professor was Dr. John Thompson, who had held in remarkable and rapid succession three professorial chairs—the professorship of surgery at Edinburgh's College of Surgeons, of military surgery at the University, and of pathology, again at the University. Robert Knox promptly christened Thompson "the old Chair-Maker", and the name stuck. Professor Thompson was so impressed by Simpson's thesis that he not only recommended him for the degree but offered him a post as his assistant at a salary of £50 a year. Simpson gladly accepted the position and soon made himself indispensable. He took up the then new method of study by the microscope and composed for his chief a lecture on the subject, which Thompson delivered without having had time to read it previously. As the Professor read the lecture to the class he glared at his assistant more than once, and when the lecture ended he shook his fist in the bland young man's face, and stuttered wrathfully, "I don't believe a damned word of it!" Professor Thompson advised his assistant to try to make a living by practising midwifery. Simpson began to work in real earnest and joined the Royal Medical Society of Edinburgh. He became president of this body three years later, and delivered his inaugural presidential address on "diseases of the placenta". This paper, which was a penetrating study of all the conditions which might affect the afterbirth, was reproduced in German, French, and Italian medical journals and attracted world-wide attention. The baker's seventh son had taken the first step towards fame and fortune.

Professor Hamilton resigned the chair of midwifery at Edinburgh University in 1839. Though only twenty-eight years of age at the time, Simpson announced himself as a candidate. The objection to his youth was not insuperable, for he was a brilliant teacher and had already made several contributions of great scientific value to midwifery. He was unmarried, however, and at that time it was thought that midwifery could never be taught with propriety by a single man. Simpson realized that as a bachelor his chances were small, and so, with characteristic promptness, he disappeared from Edinburgh for a short time and returned triumphantly married to Miss Jessie Grindlay of Liverpool. This delighted his friends and annoyed his opponents intensely. When writing to Mr. Grindlay to ask for his daughter's hand, Simpson was very frank about his pecuniary position:

> I am self-sufficient enough to think that I am as well off as regards station in my profession as any who started here in the race of life with me. They have all, I believe, been aided by friends or private wealth. . . . I have had no such advantages but have worked and stood alone. I have accumulated for myself a library and museum, worth £200 at least, amidst these difficulties. These I have won by my pen and my lancet, and these are my only fortune.

The marriage was a hurried one, and immediately afterwards the young couple hastened back to Edinburgh to take up the election fight in earnest. The professorial appointment was always made by the thirty-three town councillors. The existing professors and surgeons had great influence, and they always openly canvassed for the candidate they favoured. James Syme began a long feud with Simpson by supporting his chief rival, Dr. Kennedy. Political influences were also brought to bear, and at one time Simpson thought ruefully that both Whigs and Tories were opposing him. The election cost Simpson over

£150, which he spent largely in printing and posting testimonials extending to two hundred printed pages to everyone who had even the slightest influence with the Town Council. Excitement grew intense as three of the original five candidates dropped out and left the field clear for Simpson and Kennedy. Finally, on February 4, 1840, at a full council meeting, the Provost himself proposed that Kennedy be appointed. Baillie Ramsay proposed Simpson. When it came to the vote the council appointed— though only just—the man who had boldly said, "Did I not feel I am the best man for the Chair I would not go in for it". That night James Young Simpson was able to write to his father-in-law in Liverpool:

> I was this day elected Professor. My opponent had sixteen and I had seventeen votes. All the political influence of both the leading Whigs and Tories here was employed against me; but never mind, I have got the Chair in despite of them, Professors and all. Jessie's honeymoon and mine is to commence to-morrow.

Simpson's lectures soon attracted students. He was concise, clear, and direct, and very soon the midwifery class was the largest in the University for the first time in its history, despite the fact that Simpson's professorship was still bitterly resented by many of his colleagues, who hated the idea of the youthful son of a village baker being appointed on equal terms with them. One of the best-known professors deliberately arranged to lecture at the same hour as Simpson, with the express intention of attracting students away from Simpson's class. Simpson himself recorded the lack of success of this particular manœuvre when he wrote:

> It is very satisfactory to have beat in the race not only my friends in the Medical Faculty but all the thirty bald and grey-headed Professors. Dr. Alison who changed his hour to lecture at the same one with me has a very small class. Don't he deserve it! He has broken his own head and missed mine.

Simpson did not devote all his time to lecturing. He was building up a large private practice, and at the same time writing innumerable articles, on the treatment of diseases of the womb, on cancer of the neck of the womb, on removal of the ovaries, and other subjects. So prolific was he, and such an influence did he exercise, that in one sense he may be said to have created gynæcology, the study of the diseases of women, as a separate scientific branch of medicine, related to but distinct from the practice of obstetrics. This is all the more remarkable in that

PLATE XIX

The body of a criminal being dissected at Surgeons' Hall.

An engraving by Hogarth.

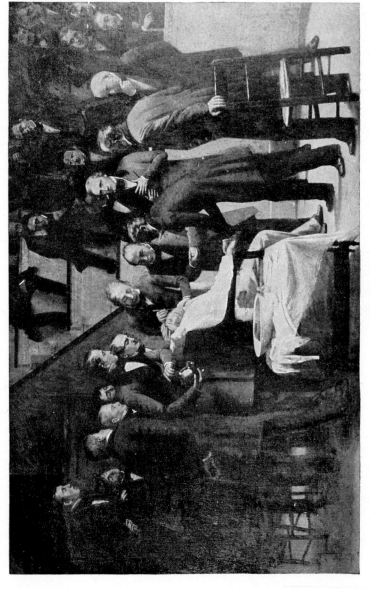

PLATE XX

The first operation performed under ether anæsthesia at the Massachusetts General Hospital.

From the painting by Robert W. Hinckley.

not many years before a heated controversy was still being waged as to whether professional men could, with dignity, attend women in labour at all. Less than a century before Simpson was born the man-midwife was still an object of contempt and ridicule. Simpson's private practice prospered greatly, and when Princess Marie of Baden came to consult him he must have recalled with amusement the words of an old physician and friend of his: "It's all very well to have got the chair. But he can never have such a practice as Professor Hamilton. Why, ladies have been known to come from England to consult him!"

One of the most important of the many papers that Simpson published at this time was on hermaphroditism. He was keenly interested in these unfortunate half-men and half-women, hermaphrodites, whose name is taken from the mythological union into one body of Hermaphroditos, the son of Mercury and the goddess Venus, and the lovely nymph Salmacis. Like all his other writings, this paper shows his keen intellect, his passion for accurate classification, and the tremendous pains he took to collect material for his essays. He described at length the literature relating to Adelaide Preville, who had lived, loved, and married as a woman, but was yet a man. He details, too, the histories of the Corsican Maria Nonya, another half-man who was twice married and lived altogether sixteen years in wedlock with her or his two husbands, and of Maria Duriée, who became Charles Duriée, and many others like them.

Simpson was a man of tireless energy and a born fighter. Hardly two years after taking up his professorial appointment he found time, despite all his lecturing and writing, to lead a campaign against homœopathy, the fantastic medical doctrine laid down by Samuel Hahnemann in his *Organon of Medicine,* first published in 1810. The virulent attack on homœopathy which was made by the Edinburgh school, headed by Simpson and James Syme, arose almost directly from the successful issue of another controversy in which Simpson had engaged. Dr. Thompson, the Professor of Pathology at Edinburgh, "the old Chair-Maker" to whom Simpson had acted as assistant, retired in 1842. Syme and others tried to get this professorship abolished. Simpson thought the chair should be retained, and was soon involved in an argument which was waged with a wealth of invective by both sides. The question was referred by the Crown to the Town Council, which finally decided that the chair of pathology should be retained, and appointed Dr. William

Henderson as professor. Simpson and his friends had hardly had time to congratulate themselves on the success of their campaign before Henderson announced himself a homœopathist. This promptly raised another and even fiercer storm, and Simpson was in the thick of it. Finally, in the course of the year 1851, resolutions prohibiting their fellows and members from meeting homœopathists professionally were passed by the Royal College of Physicians in London, the Royal College of Surgeons of Edinburgh, the Medical Society of London, and the Provincial Medical Association of England, which last has since become the British Medical Association. At the same time, at a meeting of the Medico-Chirurgical Society of Edinburgh, Syme moved, and Simpson seconded, a resolution which was passed unanimously. This was: "That the public profession of homœopathy shall be held to disqualify for being admitted or remaining a member of the Medico-Chirurgical Society of Edinburgh". Simpson in a long and effective speech compared the homœopathists to the Mormons, to the advantage of the latter, be it said. On many other occasions he wrote and spoke on the same subject, and he published *Homœopathy: Its Tenets and Tendencies* in 1853. This is a masterly review of the subject, and is still one of the most blasting attacks ever directed at a medical, or rather pseudo-medical, doctrine. In it Simpson damned Hahnemann's teaching for ever out of Hahnemann's own writings. By so doing the Edinburgh Professor of Midwifery did surgery a great service. In the middle of the nineteenth century homœopathy had an enormous vogue, to the inevitable detriment of surgery and orthodox medicine. Clearheaded always, Simpson recognized homœopathy for what it was. By his speeches and writings he was largely responsible for hounding homœopathy into a disrepute from which, fortunately, it has never really emerged.

While James Young Simpson was building up a tremendous reputation, a young man from Massachusetts was preparing one of the greatest gifts the New World has ever given to the Old. This young man was William Morton of Charlton, Massachusetts. His friend and partner, Horace Wells, had begun to use Humphry Davy's "laughing gas" in dentistry. Unhappily, a death resulted from one administration of the gas, and Wells gave up his practice and, becoming depressed over what he regarded as his own failure, he committed suicide. After this

Morton no longer used nitrous oxide, but still sought anxiously for some means of abolishing pain. While practising dentistry in Boston, Morton was studying medicine at Harvard, and there he met Dr. Charles Jackson, who told Morton of what he had noticed at a party. The party was an ether jag, so called by the medical students who took part in it. At these frolics the students used to inhale small quantities of the vapour of sulphuric ether. This was done for amusement, and as a cheap and effective means of becoming mildly intoxicated fairly rapidly. Jackson, at one of these jags, noticed that students who were "under the influence", though they fell over the furniture and reeled about the room, seemed quite insensible to the pain of any injuries they might sustain. He told Morton about this, and the young dentist went home and literally tried it on the dog. When the dog recovered he tried it on himself, and, as soon as he himself had recovered, on a patient, one Eben Frost. It worked.

The next step was taken a fortnight later when the young dentist, this time as a medical student, obtained permission from Dr. Warren, the senior surgeon of the Massachusetts General Hospital, to try the ether on a painter named George Abbott, who was to have a tumour removed. (*See plate facing* p. 337). A big crowd of students and doctors gathered to watch the operation. The painter was brought into the theatre by two porters. Dr. Warren and the assistant surgeon arrived, and for the first time in history waited for the man who had promised to make the patient insensible. Surgeons all over the world have been doing this ever since. Dr. Warren was sceptical and impatient.

"As Dr. Morton has not arrived, I presume he is otherwise engaged!"

He took up his scalpel. The porters laid hold of the trembling patient, and at that moment Morton came in. He explained that he had been delayed perfecting the apparatus he was going to use. The audience grinned. Dr. Warren waved a not very courteous hand.

"Well, sir, your patient is ready!"

Conscious of the spectators' derision, Morton proceeded to give the ether. A few minutes later he was able to make the remark that was to echo through every theatre in the world.

"Sir, *your* patient is ready!"

The unbelieving audience watched in silent amazement as the quick skin incision was made. The patient remained apparently asleep. The tumour was excised, and the patient went on sleeping. The operation ended, the patient still oblivious of it all, and the surgeon turned to his audience:

"Gentlemen, this is no humbug!"

Later that year the poet physician Oliver Wendell Holmes suggested the name "anæsthetic", and the fame of this new method of "anæsthesia" spread rapidly.

Actually Dr. Long of Athens, in Georgia, was the first man to use ether as an anæsthetic. It was in 1842 that he operated on a patient whom he had rendered insensible by the use of ether. The bill for this procedure is still in existence. Long charged his patient $2 for the operation and 25 cents for the ether. News travelled slowly in those days, however, and so it was that William Morton, the Boston dentist, thanks to his public demonstrations in 1846 received the credit for the discovery, while Dr. Long's claim to priority was for many years overlooked.

On December 21, 1846, in University College Hospital, London, Dr. William Squire, with an apparatus consisting of a reservoir of ether, a flexible tube, and a large sponge, prepared to try this new method of producing unconsciousness on a patient of Robert Liston's. While they were waiting for the surgeon, Squire asked if anybody in the audience would like to try the effects of inhaling ether. There were no volunteers. Then Sheldrake, a huge hospital porter, was pushed bodily forwards by the students, and persuaded to lie down and take deep breaths of the ether vapour from the tube which Squire held in front of his face. In a very short time he was wildly intoxicated, and jumping up he plunged into the mob of students, scattering them in all directions. Fortunately, he soon came round, and the tumult and the shouting had died when Robert Liston arrived.

Liston announced happily:

"Gentlemen, we are going to try a Yankee dodge to make men insensible."

The patient, a butler named Churchill, was quickly anæsthetized, and the amputation was performed with Liston's usual dexterity. The removal of the man's leg took exactly twenty-eight seconds. Then the arteries were ligated and the flaps stitched together. A few moments later Churchill sat up, and said anxiously:

"When are you going to begin?"

He was shown the amputated stump of his thigh, and dropped back, whimpering. Liston turned to the audience, and almost stammering in his excitement said:

"This—this Yankee dodge, gentlemen, beats mesmerism hollow!"

James Young Simpson, Professor of Midwifery at Edinburgh University, thought so too. Early in his career he studied mesmerism in the hope of being able to relieve the pain of operation by it. He tried hypnotism, too, though he did not know that Cloquet in 1829 successfully removed a cancer of the breast from a hypnotized woman. Elliotson in 1843, and two years later Esdaile in India, also used hypnotism successfully to abolish the pain of operations. Simpson, however, was more interested in the pains of childbirth, and he soon found that hypnotism was of little use in these cases. To be successful hypnotism demands the close concentration of the patient's thoughts, and a woman who is having a baby finds it difficult to concentrate on anything else. There is no doubt that Simpson discussed the new anæsthetic with Liston in London, and fired by enthusiasm he returned to Edinburgh determined to try ether in his midwifery practice. On January 19, 1847, he used it successfully for the first time and delivered a woman of her second child. In March he published a paper recording his use of ether in several cases.

Simpson soon observed the disadvantages of ether, notably its persistent and disagreeable smell, the large quantities that were necessary, and its tendency to irritate the lungs and cause coughing during the first inhalations. He tried to find some substance with all the advantages and none of the disadvantages of ether. Despite the tremendous amount of work he was doing, he gave up all his spare time, which usually meant the early hours of the morning, to testing upon himself the effects of numerous drugs and liquids. With the same courage that had inspired Morton, he would seat himself, usually in the big dining-room of his house, either alone or with his assistants, Dr. George Keith and Dr. Matthews Duncan, and proceed to inhale from tumblers or saucers the substance under trial. The results of these experiments often alarmed his household, but Simpson went doggedly on for nearly twelve months, until a Mr. Waldie suggested that he might try chloroform.

Chloroform was a "curious liquid" discovered and described by two chemists independently, Soubeiran of France and Liebig of Germany, in 1831. Its chemical composition was first accurately determined by Professor Dumas, a famous French chemist, four years later. Simpson duly obtained a sample of this liquid from some chemists in Edinburgh, Messrs. Duncan and Flock-hart. It looked a heavy, unpromising sort of mixture, and the bottle was set aside on a lumber table for several days. Then one evening in early November, after a long day's work, Simpson sat down with his two assistants and they continued their rather risky experiments. Several substances had been tried without much effect when Simpson remembered the "curious liquid". A search finally revealed it beneath a heap of waste-paper and empty bottles. The tumblers were filled with chloroform and the three men began inhaling again. Almost immediately three tired men became amazingly talkative. Some ladies of the family were with them, and a naval officer, Simpson's brother-in-law. They were startled and delighted at the change that came over the three doctors, then suddenly horrified as one by one they became rapidly incoherent and then crashed to the floor.

Simpson was the first to come round, to realize in a flash that this substance was better and stronger than ether. Then he heard an appalling noise, and rather dazedly turned round to see Dr. Duncan lying indecorously under a chair, jaw dropped, eyes staring, and snoring stertorously. There were louder noises, and he saw that Dr. Keith who was under the table was making a tremendous attempt to overturn it and destroy every-thing within reach of his violent kicks. Simpson slowly returned to his seat, as did Dr. Duncan. Dr. Keith, defeated by the table, was the last to assume a normal position again. They knew that they had found what they sought, and so more gingerly they tried the chloroform again and again. The ladies were persuaded to join in the festivities which continued hilariously till nearly three in the morning. One of them, Mrs. Simpson's niece, Miss Petrie, as she went under the influence cried out, to the great delight of the others, "I'm an angel! Oh, I'm an angel!"

It was remarkable that none of these innumerable experiments of Simpson's ended in tragedy. He more than once made himself very ill, and on one occasion was insensible for over two hours as a result of trying various mixtures. Simpson was always lucky, however, and he was spared to find chloroform. Messrs. Duncan and Flockhart were pressed into service and arranged to pro-duce the necessary quantities of the "curious liquid". Simpson promptly tried it out in his midwifery cases and found it succeeded just as he had expected. The first patient to whom he administered chloroform was a doctor's wife, who was so delighted at her free-dom from pain that she christened her unfortunate baby girl

Anæsthesia. Anæsthesia seems to have borne this imposition bravely, for on her seventeenth birthday she sent Simpson a signed photograph, which he hung proudly over his desk.

The first public demonstration of the new anæsthetic was on November 15, 1847. Simpson himself acted as anæsthetist for his friend, Professor Miller. A little boy about four years old was the patient, and he whimpered and struggled when Simpson held over his face a handkerchief soaked in chloroform. He was gently restrained and made to breathe the sickly-sweet fumes. Soon he was snoring away in a deep sleep. Almost the whole of one of the long bones in the forearm was removed, and the child was carried back to the ward still fast asleep. Two other severe operations were performed immediately afterwards. All three were watched by a huge crowd of doctors and students, amongst whom was Professor Dumas. After this demonstration Simpson told the onlookers how chloroform compared with ether. It was more agreeable to take, less expensive, more easily portable, and—most important of all—it required no special form of in-haler. A bottle to contain the chloroform and a pocket-hand-kerchief on which to apply it were the only things needed. Hardly a year had passed since Eben Frost had had his tooth extracted by Morton without feeling any pain. A young American had given ether to the world, and Simpson crowned this gift with the recognition of the equally wonderful powers of chloroform. The battle against pain was half over. The war with public opinion promptly started.

There were surgical as well as lay critics, and the first charge levelled against Simpson's discovery was that it would increase the already high death-rate following operations. Amputation of the thigh was the operation most dreaded by surgeons, for of those patients subjected to it two out of every three died.

Characteristically taking the biggest obstacle first, Simpson collected the statistics of this operation and proved that when the operation was done under chloroform only one patient out of every three died. This was still an awesomely high death-rate, but, as Simpson pointed out, it was just twice as good as the death-rate from the same operation without chloroform. He published a long paper on this subject, heading it with a quotation from the *Merchant of Venice*:

> "Why dost thou whet thy knife so earnestly?
> . . . Shylock must be merciful."
> "On what compulsion must I? Tell me that!"

Then in Dublin it was suggested that the use of chloroform in childbirth would increase the incidence of bleeding, convulsions, paralysis, pneumonia, and so on. Simpson collected statistics from the Dublin hospitals, and flourished them indignantly over the heads of his critics. He proved then, and again and again afterwards, that pain itself and the shock and exhaustion it caused were greater dangers than would ever arise from the use of chloroform. The moralists also joined in the fight. One of them—another Dublin man—wrote:

> That he did not think anyone in Dublin had as yet used anæsthetics in midwifery; that the feeling was very strong against its use in ordinary cases, merely to avert the ordinary amount of pain, which the Almighty had seen fit—and most wisely, no doubt—to allot to natural labour; and in this feeling he—the writer—most heartily concurred.

Simpson seized on this joyfully and delivered a magnificent counterblast. He wrote:

> I do not believe that any one in Dublin has as yet used a carriage in locomotion; the feeling is very strong against its use in ordinary progression, merely to avert the ordinary amount of fatigue, which the Almighty has seen fit—and most wisely, no doubt—to allot to natural walking; and in this feeling I most heartily concur.

Next came the religious objections. The fact that as a child he had been made to learn chapters in the Bible off by heart stood Simpson in good stead. His opponents took their stand on a verse in Genesis (Chapter III, verse 16):

> Unto the woman he said, I will greatly multiply thy sorrow and thy conception; in sorrow thou shalt bring forth children.

Simpson countered with the details of the first Biblical operation (Genesis, Chapter II, verse 21):

> And the Lord God caused a deep sleep to fall upon Adam and he slept; and he took one of his ribs and closed up the flesh instead thereof.

Before the clergy had time to work this out, there was published Simpson's famous pamphlet, *Answer to the Religious Objections advanced against the Employment of Anæsthetic Agents in Midwifery and Surgery*, and this was headed with two more telling texts:

> For every creature of God is good, and nothing to be refused if it be received with thanksgiving (1 Timothy, Chapter IV, verse 4),

and

> Therefore to him that knoweth to do good and doeth it not to him it is sin. (James, Chapter IV, verse 17.)

[*328*]

So each opponent of the use of chloroform was defeated on his own ground and with his own weapons. Medical, moral, and religious objections were swept aside and more and more chloroform was used. Six years after the battle had begun, six years after that historic hilarious evening in Queen Street, it ended. Sir James Clark, Physician-in-Ordinary to Her Majesty Queen Victoria, wrote to James Young Simpson:

> The Queen had chloroform exhibited to her during her late confinement. . . . It was not at any time given so strongly as to render the Queen insensible, and an ounce of chloroform was scarcely consumed during the whole time. Her Majesty was greatly pleased with the effect, and she certainly never has had a better recovery.

And so in April, 1853, Prince Leopold was born and the anæsthetic victory was won.

James Young Simpson never seems to have known the art of resting on his laurels. Thanks to Ambroise Paré and John Hunter, boiling oil was no longer regarded as the only possible means of stopping bleeding. Ligatures were used, but were unsatisfactory in many ways, largely because they were made of materials often unsuitable and almost always infected. Prolonged twisting, or torsion, of a bleeding vessel was another method often resorted to, and certain drugs which were supposed to control hæmorrhage were still popular. No one method, however, gave uniformly good results. Simpson plunged into this problem with his usual wholeheartedness. He tried all sorts of drugs and all kinds of ligatures, especially those of fine wire. Finally he worked out an ingenious method which he called acupressure; it consisted in temporary metallic compression. A strong, straight needle was passed through the flesh to either side of the vessel in such a way as to compress the artery on its own natural bed. James Syme did not pause to consider the merits or demerits of the method, but was furious at what he considered an unwarranted trespass by a man-midwife—the term of contempt still lingered—into the sacred domain of pure surgery. He strode into his operating-theatre with a copy of Simpson's original paper on the subject in his hand, called for a scalpel, and before an audience of students cut the pamphlet into shreds, which he threw furiously to the sawdust-covered floor, saying:

"That, gentlemen, is what acupressure is worth!"

Even so, it was an efficient and useful method which had a deserved popularity until ligatures were sufficiently improved for it to be discarded. This was not the only time, however, that Simpson, the now world-famous discoverer of chloroform, strayed into surgical fields. For the last twenty years of his life he argued, wrote, and lectured on the number of deaths that followed operations in hospital. He had given chloroform to the world, and the number of operations performed each year was steadily mounting as a result. But in hospitals the death-rate from operations went on increasing steadily, despite the initial lowering that had followed the introduction of chloroform. Finally, as Simpson himself said, the man who lay on a hospital operating-table to be subjected to the surgeon's knife for any condition at all had less chance of surviving than a soldier on the field of Waterloo. The deaths following amputations were four times as many in hospital practice as amongst private patients. Without knowing why this was so, Simpson was on the right lines when he pleaded for larger and more airy hospitals. He wanted big new hospitals in the country so that the dreadful overcrowding in the town hospitals would be avoided.

His fame had spread far and wide by this time and he became the best-known surgeon in the world. It is said that the King of Denmark, hearing the word Edinburgh, remarked that that was where Simpson lived. Honours were showered on him by British, American, and foreign medical societies. He received a prize of 2,000 francs for "the most important benefit to humanity". He was given the freedom of Edinburgh, and received innumerable honorary degrees. Then in 1866 he accepted from a grateful Queen and her people the baronetcy he had twice before refused. Everybody rejoiced with him in his triumph. His friend Sir Walter Scott, so the story goes, wrote to him one of the first of the congratulatory letters that arrived from all over the world, suggesting the obvious coat-of-arms for him to adopt. It was to typify his work on anæsthesia in childbirth, and was to be simply "a wee naked bairn", with underneath the legend "Does your mither know you're oot?" Since the story is such a pleasant one it is a pity to have to point out that Sir Walter Scott died in 1832. It is therefore unlikely that he would be writing letters of congratulation in 1866. In his last brief illness patients were brought to Sir James Young Simpson even in his sick-room. He died on May 6, 1870. No work was done in Edinburgh on the day of his funeral, and two thousand people followed his hearse through streets lined by thirty thousand other men and women, all come to pay a last tribute to the seventh son of a Bathgate baker.

In his youth James Young Simpson had seen the passing of the Anatomy Act ensure a supply of bodies for the dissecting-rooms. In the prime of his life he had helped to overthrow for ever the barrier of pain in which surgery had been confined. In the last few years of his life he saw the first crumblings of that other great barrier, sepsis.

XXII. Lister

THE VICARAGE OF ST. PETER'S PARISH IN THE LONDON BOROUGH
of West Ham is a large house which was built in the reign of
Queen Anne.   Joseph Lister was born there on April 5, 1827.
At that time the house was known as Upton Lodge, and the
bedroom in which Joseph was born overlooked Ham Park and
the pleasant farmlands of Essex.   Far away in Edinburgh,
James Young Simpson had just enrolled himself as a medical
student, and Robert Liston and James Syme were beginning
to attract the unfavourable attention of their surgical seniors.
In London Henry Cline lay dying, while his favourite pupil,
Astley Paston Cooper, was being elected president of the
College of Surgeons.   Joseph Lister grew up in a prosperous
Quaker household.   His father was a wealthy wine merchant,
with money enough and leisure enough to indulge to the full
his love of science.   The work he had already done in perfecting microscopical lenses had led to his election as a fellow
of the Royal Society.   When his second son announced his
intention of becoming a surgeon, Mr. John Jackson Lister
suggested that Joseph should take the B.A. of London University first, before committing himself to any profession.   Joseph
took the B.A. in 1848, and then went off to Ireland for a long
summer holiday.   He had been working too hard and was just
recovering from a severe illness.   His decision to become a
surgeon was made, however, and already he had seen the opening of a new chapter in the history of surgery.   As an under-
graduate he had strayed into University College Hospital to
see William Squire give ether, for the first time in this country.
He was nineteen then, and had watched Liston operating with
fascinated awe.   He had hoped to become one of the great
surgeon's pupils, but by the time he entered University College
as a medical student, in the autumn of 1848, Liston was dead.

He took the M.B. uneventfully, and went on as successfully
to the F.R.C.S.   During all his medical studies he maintained
his interest in the microscopy his father had taught him.   By
the time he was twenty-five he had published two important
papers in the *Quarterly Journal of Microscopical Science*.   One
was a description of the minute muscles that raise and depress
the hairs of the scalp.   The other was a study of the iris of the
eye.   Kolliker in Germany had just shown that the iris was an

involuntary muscle. Lister confirmed this finding, and also showed that the iris muscles were arranged in two distinct groups, one group dilating the pupil and the other contracting it. After the publication of these two papers, he went off to Killarney for another holiday. On returning to London he saw his friend William Sharpey, the physiologist, and sought advice as to what his next step should be. He had all the qualifications he needed, but he knew that he lacked experience. He had acted as house-surgeon to John Erichsen, who succeeded Liston, but University College was only a small hospital. It had sixty beds, one theatre lit by a single gas-jet, and all the week's operations were usually got through comfortably on a Wednesday afternoon.

Sharpey advised Lister to go to Edinburgh. James Syme, at the age of fifty-four, was acknowledged as the first surgeon in Europe. He knew Sharpey well and would welcome any friend of his to Edinburgh. He was in surgical command of two hundred beds in the Royal Infirmary, which was then the Mecca of all young surgeons. For any young man who took service under Syme there would be surgical experience enough and to spare. Lister waited only long enough to collect a letter of introduction to Syme from Sharpey before leaving London for Edinburgh. Syme at once took a liking to the young Quaker. His daughter, Agnes, agreed with her distinguished father. She liked Mr. Lister's serious eyes, Mr. Lister's good manners, and Mr. Lister's trace of a stammer. That was in the September of 1853, and by July of the following year Lister had established himself. He was betrothed to the lovely Agnes. He had been acting as Syme's house-surgeon for the previous six months, and he had astonished his father by writing enthusiastically of the "high degree of enjoyment I am from day to day experiencing in this bloody and butcherly department of the healing art". He was in charge of twelve dressers in Syme's wards, and as Syme realized that his assistant was always a safe, though rarely a brilliant, operator, he left to young Mr. Lister more and more of the emergency work of the Infirmary. Then a young Edinburgh surgeon named Mackenzie died of cholera in the Crimea. He had been on the staff of the Infirmary and a lecturer at the College of Surgeons. Encouraged by Syme, Lister decided to apply for the vacancy at the Infirmary, and it was arranged that he should give the lectures that Mackenzie should have delivered, starting in the November of 1855. To this end Lister became a fellow of the Edinburgh College of Surgeons, spent a month in Paris learning something of French surgery, and took consulting-rooms in Rutland Street, just opposite Syme's.

He began lecturing to a class of twenty-three students. They were not very impressed by his lectures. For one thing Lister was interested as much in pathology as in pure surgery, and for another students still felt that no real surgeon would spend as much time as Lister did peering down a microscope. The students were not alone in regarding a microscope as an instrument beneath the dignity of a surgeon, for many of Lister's senior colleagues held the same view. Lister was unrepentant. In fact, he made what should have been a secret shame known to all the world when he read before the Royal Society another paper, this time on the changes caused by irritation and inflammation in the minute blood-vessels coursing through the web of a frog's foot.

At the age of twenty-nine he was married in the drawing-room of Syme's house. Then he and Agnes went off for a prolonged honeymoon. They spent long and pleasant weeks in the Lake District, then for three months they wandered desultorily through Germany and Austria. Only a day or so after their return to Edinburgh Lister was unanimously elected to the staff of the Infirmary. Syme had no sons of an age to succeed him, and so he had determined that his daughter's husband should be his successor. Whenever he was away from Edinburgh, Lister did his work. Whenever he operated on private patients, Lister assisted him. When a series of his lectures were published in the *Lancet,* Lister prepared them. Since Liston's death no one in Edinburgh had ever crossed swords with Syme without being completely routed. When Syme let it be understood that Lister was to succeed him, Edinburgh accepted the situation. Yet Lister's lectures were still poorly attended. For at least one lecture only one student arrived, and he was ten minutes late. Seven students attended a summer course, but later there were as many as twenty-four. This pleased Lister greatly, though it disturbed his father-in-law, who at that time never lectured to less than half the medical students in Edinburgh at any one time. Private practice was on much the same scale. Syme was always having to sneak out of his own crowded consulting-room by the back door if he wanted to get away at all, while Agnes was laughing about her "poor Joseph and his one patient".

Patients and students were alike slow to realize Lister's worth, but the contributions he had made to the Royal Society and to the medical journals had not passed unnoticed. The paper on inflammation had attracted attention, and so had later studies on the coagulation of the blood, on the microscopic structure of involuntary muscle-fibres, on spontaneous gangrene, and on certain other subjects. So it was that in the late summer of 1859 Lister was asked, tentatively, if he would care to apply for the professorship of surgery at Glasgow, in the event of the chair becoming vacant. Lister asked Syme's advice. The older man urged him to apply for the chair. Lister agreed that he would do so, and towards the end of that year the chair duly became vacant. Joseph Lister was appointed Regius Professor of Surgery at the University of Glasgow in the January of 1860. The regius professorship had several great advantages. It gave Lister an assured salary of £400 to £450 a year. It ensured almost automatically an appointment to the Glasgow Infirmary. It would lead to a considerable private practice, for there was no outstanding surgeon in Glasgow at the time, and it was a useful stepping-stone to other professorships, if ever Lister decided to leave Glasgow.

The new professor was soon almost as much at home in Glasgow as he had been in Edinburgh. Students attended his lectures and liked them. There were as many as two hundred at his summer course. He got on well with his colleagues, among them being Edmund Lushington, the professor of Greek, who was Tennyson's brother-in-law, and a young professor of physics who was to become Lord Kelvin. Private patients began to attend his consulting-rooms in increasing numbers. His election to a fellowship of the Royal Society delighted his father as much as himself. He had still plenty of time for his purely scientific work, and both he and his wife were very happy. Agnes did not even mind keeping rats and mice, and on occasion calves, in the wash-house, when the impromptu laboratory in the house was overcrowded. Calves were rare experimental animals, however. Most of Lister's work was on frogs, bats, and similar small animals. He took up again with new enthusiasm his work on the early stages of inflammation and on coagulation of the blood. His only difficulties were with the lay board of management of the Glasgow Infirmary. Lister wanted to be appointed to the staff so that he would have the right to take his students into the hospital and teach them at the bedside. He explained this at great length to the lay board. The board replied with some dignity that its institution was a "curative" not an "educative" one, and did not like this "Edinburgh idea". Lister waited patiently for the board to change its mind. At length it did so, and the Regius Professor of Surgery was duly appointed to the hospital staff in August, 1861.

It was only then that Lister realized fully the limitations of his art. All his patients were operated on by himself, or by one of his house-surgeons. The right operations were done at the right time. Chloroform was carefully given, and thanks to this there was no need to rush through an operation. Conservative excisions of joints, such as he had seen Syme perform, could be undertaken and limbs saved without fear of the patient dying from shock. Yet when he took stock of his results after twelve months work he was appalled. It seemed that for every life saved in the theatre one was lost in the wards. Patients might be well for a day or two after operation, then gangrene would set in and kill them. They might escape gangrene and die of blood-poisoning. If they were preserved from both these scourges, they might still die from erysipelas, of which recurrent epidemics swept through ward after ward. The figures could be juggled with and looked at from different angles, but however they were arranged they always told Lister the same thing. Before the discovery of anæsthesia two out of every three patients subjected to operation had died. After the advent of ether and chloroform one out of every three died. Things were better than they had been, but not much better. An East-End woman in London had summed up the situation a few years previously, and her verdict still held good. She was asked if she would consent to a trifling operation being performed on her daughter. "S'orlright," said the clear-sighted parent. "S'easy enough to give consent, but wot I wants to know is 'oo's going to pay for the poor girl's funeral?"

Lister went back to his frogs and his microscope unavailingly. He studied his case-records over and over again, and found little help there. There was just one fact, known to Ambroise Paré and every other surgeon since his time, which seemed significant and might be helpful. If a man broke a leg, his fate depended solely on whether the fracture was simple or compound. If it was a compound fracture, with the bones projecting through the skin, then any procedure short of high amputation would be followed by a fatal gangrene nine times out of ten. If it was a simple fracture and the broken ends of bone had not pierced the skin in any way, the patient would live, whether union of the broken ends of bone took place well, badly, or not at all. The only difference was that in one case the injured bones and tissues were protected by the skin and not exposed to the air, while in the other case the skin was also wounded and all the affected parts were exposed to the air. Lister went on working away at this problem, but he made no headway. Then the professorship of systematic surgery became vacant in Edinburgh. Lister applied for it, but was not elected. It is doubtful whether he or his father-in-law, the Professor of Clinical Surgery, was the more disappointed. Syme vented his spleen on his great contemporary, attacking again the acupressure he had devised. James Young Simpson gave as good as he got, and disappointment was soon forgotten in the joy of a controversy which had already lasted three or four years, and tended to become more friendly as the two great men grew older together. Lister went back to the problem which obsessed him. He knew that in other towns and other countries surgeons like himself were facing the same difficulties. Many of them were content to render thanks to James Young Simpson and Morton, the dentist, and observe with pride mortality rates which had been over 50 per cent. now diminished to perhaps only 30 or 35 per cent. A few of them were trying, or had tried, to solve this problem of which the very nature was unknown to them. One or two of them had almost hit upon the solution even before Lister was born.

There was Theodoric in the thirteenth century, who brought the wrath of Guy de Chauliac upon his sturdy head by insisting that it was not necessary "that pus should be generated in wounds". Henri de Mondeville, in the early fourteenth century, stoutly upheld the teachings of Theodoric, but without avail. Pus was "laudable pus", and if boiling oil alone was not sufficient to promote its formation, there was a variety of pus-promoting salves to hand. Ambroise Paré ended the era of boiling oil, but even his puppy-dog salve would not have affected the progress of inflammations in wards that were heavy with the mingled stench of fever-racked bodies and pus-dripping limbs. Pus was still laudable, and John Hunter himself could not make it otherwise. The whole problem seemed to defy attack. No one could see how the suppuration began, no one could imagine what made it begin. Then two years after Hunter's death a young Scot made an observation, which attracted no attention at all.

Dr. Gordon, of Aberdeen, in the year 1795 wrote a treatise on puerperal or lying-in fever, the fatal infection which seized women soon after childbirth, and which mounted on occasion to a point at which it would kill five or six out of every ten parturient women. Gordon described seventy-seven deaths from this condition, and showed clearly how they had arisen. One woman developed the fever and was attended by a midwife and an obstetrician. The next fifteen or twenty cases attended by this midwife developed the lying-in fever. The same thing happened with the next ten or eleven cases the obstetrician dealt with. Then to one of these cases another obstetrician was called in consultation. The next half-dozen or more cases he attended met the same fate. Gordon said that "every person who had been with a patient in the puerperal fever became charged with an atmosphere of infection, which was communicated to every pregnant woman who happened to come within its sphere". This paper had no immediate effect. It was remembered, however, that even before Gordon's observation attention had been drawn to the same discrepancy in individual results by Charles White of Manchester. White mentioned one town where all the midwifery was done by two men, and "one of them loses several patients every year of the puerperal fever, and the other never so much as meets with the disorder".

Then other practitioners began to tell the same story. Dr. Campbell of Edinburgh examined post-mortem a woman who had died of fever. The affected organs he carried to his classroom, to demonstrate them to his students. The same evening he attended a woman in labour. She died. The following morning he delivered another woman. She died. There were three more deaths in the next week. Mr. Roberton of Manchester took up the tale. One charitable institution in Manchester had twenty-six midwives connected with it. In one month twenty-five of them delivered nearly four hundred women. All did quite well. The twenty-sixth midwife delivered thirty women. Sixteen of them developed puerperal fever and died of it. That was in 1840, by which time enough evidence had accumulated to convince the most obstinate that

Gordon of Aberdeen had been right in his original contention. Unfortunately, the papers and letters that bore upon the subject were scattered through different medical journals. Perhaps because of the vague and illogical theories which he had built up—though on accurately observed facts—Gordon's case had never been presented as it should have been, had never had the publicity it ought to have had. Then in 1842 Oliver Wendell Holmes took up the cudgels. He was not nearly the first to say that puerperal fever was contagious, that it could be conveyed by hands, clothes, or instruments from an infected woman to a healthy one, but he said it so clearly and so often that notice had to be taken of him. The professors of obstetrics at Pennsylvania University and at the Jefferson Medical College attacked him roundly. Holmes did not even reply to them, he simply repeated what he had said and written before.

Holmes was a great writer, but he never wrote anything better than his essays on puerperal fever. He was a man who could not be disregarded. His professional standing was secure. He had been Professor of Anatomy and Physiology in Dartmouth College at Hanover, and he was to hold the same chair at Harvard for thirty-five years. He was not an obstetrician. He had no axe to grind, and his writings had made him better known to the people at large than the most professionally distinguished of his contemporaries. He won his fight, not because he contributed any original knowledge or research to the problem but because he presented the known facts as no other writer could have done. It was realized that for anyone who had just attended a case of puerperal fever to look after a healthy parturient woman was criminal. Holmes established firmly in the minds of men the fact that had been amply demonstrated, though disregarded, fifty years before. Yet it occurred to no one that if infection causing puerperal fever could be conveyed by the accoucheur's hands or instruments from an infected woman to a healthy woman, the infection responsible for all the deaths in a surgical ward might be conveyed in the same way, by the scalpel which had opened an abscess and then amputated a leg, by the surgeon who drained a cavity full of pus then went on to cure a rupture. Oliver Wendell Holmes, the master of polished fiction, won the fight for the recognition of puerperal fever as a contagious disease by telling rhetoric firmly based on demonstrable facts and figures. It was again by startling figures that he ended the long fight he had waged, by showing how the contagion could be prevented.

The Hungarian whose triumph of prevention Holmes flourished in the face of his critics was Ignaz Philipp Semmelweis. Semmelweis was an assistant obstetrician in the Allgemeines Krankenhaus in Vienna. There were two maternity wards there. One was devoted to the teaching of students, who came into the ward direct from the dissecting-room. In that ward many women died of puerperal fever. The other ward was reserved for the teaching of midwives, who were never near the dissecting-room. There very few women contracted puerperal fever, and fewer still died of it. Semmelweis pointed out what his superiors had long known and accepted, that three times as many women died in one ward as in the other. That being so, he suggested that there must be some factor operating in the one ward which did not affect the other. This seemed to dispose of the popular belief that puerperal fever was due to a *genius epidemicus,* a vague atmospheric miasma. Semmelweis poured scorn upon the idea of some cosmic influence attacking one ward and leaving the other unscathed. But as quickly as he demolished one baseless theory another rose up to take its place. Overcrowding was the next suggested cause. Semmelweis pointed out that the Second Ward, which had the low mortality, was always more crowded than the First Ward, which had the high mortality. The next theory was that the mortality in the First Ward was due to the fact that most of the patients were unmarried girls or prostitutes. Semmelweis found that there were more unmarried women and more prostitutes in the Second Ward than in the First. Lack of ventilation, shame at being delivered by men students, fear, the method of washing bedclothes, the tolling of a priest's bell, chilling, diet, long labours, short labours, premature labours, delayed labours, and even the fertilizing semen were among the other skittles set up for Semmelweis to demolish. He did demolish them, disposing of each and every fallacious idea as it arose, but for a long time he had no theory of his own to explain the difference between the two wards.

Then one day the Professor of Medical Jurisprudence in Vienna pricked his finger while making a post-mortem examination, and after a brief illness died of blood-poisoning. Semmelweis was present at the necropsy. The changes in the professor's body were exactly the same as those seen in the bodies of women whom the students had examined, and who had died later of puerperal fever. These students were surprised and a little shocked a few days later, when Semmelweis instructed them all to rinse their hands in a simple solution of chloride of lime before delivering, examining, or in any way touching a patient.

At that time a woman who was to be taken to the Allgemeines Krankenhaus wept bitterly, prayed to be allowed to die at home, and, when at last she was forcibly taken to the wards there, gave herself up for lost. Two years after the first bowl of chloride of lime solution had been placed at the entrance to a maternity ward the mortality rate for the women confined there had sunk to 1.28 per cent. Whereas before one out of every six or seven women was carried from the ward to the mortuary, now only one woman in every hundred died. Semmelweis, who had lacked a theory, now no longer needed one. He had proof positive of the way in which puerperal fever had been caused. Infected material was constantly conveyed by students and professors alike from the corpses they had been dissecting to the women they examined. The chloride of lime cleansed their hands of the cadaveric particles, and so there was no infection to be conveyed to the parturient woman.

The principal cause of the fevers had been rendered non-operative, and their incidence dropped as if by magic. By the autumn of 1847 Semmelweis had formulated clearly his doctrine of the causation of puerperal fever. Any putrid material might be the means of causing it, as, for example, a suppurating knee-joint or an infected cancer, as well as the actual cadaveric material, and if the infection of the knee, or whatever it might be, was sufficiently severe, then the dreaded fever might be conveyed to patients in the same ward without any contact with hands or instruments. The doctrine and the method of prevention were accepted by a few, denounced by many, and disregarded by the great majority. Gradually, however, a mass of figures began to accumulate. An enthusiastic Dublin doctor wrote to Semmelweis after he had conducted over 3,800 deliveries. Exactly six of his patients had died of puerperal fever. In contrast to this a Wurzburg professor wrote that the mortality in his hospital was only 26 per cent., and that only in the Spring when the cosmic influences were most markedly felt. He saw no reason for playing about with chloride of lime in an attempt to alter an atmospheric miasma.

The most powerful of the University professors in Vienna held much the same views. Semmelweis became disgusted with the city of his adoption and went back to his native Pesth. In the Obstetric Hospital there, after twelve months, he reduced the mortality rate from puerperal fever to 0.85 per cent. Then he became Professor of Midwifery at Pesth University, and in the clinic he had charge of then the mortality figures dropped to 0.39 per cent. Semmelweis finally published his *Die Ætiologie, Der Begriff, und Die Prophylaxis des Kindbettfiebers* in 1860. Slowly his teachings gained ground. James Young Simpson, who had at first rejected the doctrine laid down by Semmelweis, was one of the many to announce that he had been in error. Simpson was always honest and enthusiastic. Once he realized that he had misjudged a second-hand version of the doctrine, he became one of the most ardent advocates and powerful supporters of this new advance in midwifery. There was one close friend of Semmelweis's who attached more importance to this work than even Semmelweis himself. This was Karl Haller, senior physician of the Vienna Allgemeines Krankenhaus. As early as 1849 Haller described to the Medical Society of Vienna the work of his young colleague, and concluded his address by saying: "The importance of this experience for lying-in hospitals, and for hospitals generally speaking, especially for the surgical wards, is so immeasurable that it appears worthy of the attention of all men of science."

Lister knew of the work of Semmelweis, and knew of the crusade for its recognition that Oliver Wendell Holmes had led, but even he did not grasp its significance for surgery as Haller had done. He was studying papers by French and German authors at that time, to see if he could find any pointers as to the road he should pursue. The Professor of Chemistry in Glasgow knew of the work he was doing, and in 1865 suggested that he should study the writings of Pasteur. Lister was not able to do so immediately, for he was busy completing a paper on excision of the wrist. The operation he had devised removed all the structures affected by disease of the wrist and yet preserved the movements of the fingers. Syme, himself one of the pioneers of conservative excision of joints, saw the patients Lister had operated on and wrote to his son-in-law just before the paper was published: "I told people yesterday that excision of the wrist had hitherto been found impracticable—and that amputation was the rule of surgery—but that the difficulty had been surmounted by Professor Lister of Glasgow. You should have seen the sensation!" The paper was duly published in the *Lancet* early in 1865. The operation was technically successful, yet the concluding paragraph of the article shows how technical success could never be divorced from the problems which faced every surgeon:

> On comparing these results with those of previous practice, bearing in mind that the cases include all varieties of carious disease, sometimes in the most aggravated form ever likely to be presented, and also that they have been treated under the disadvantages of a hospital atmosphere, so that I have had to contend in no less than six instances with hospital gangrene and in one with pyæmia, it will, I trust, appear that the principles which have guided me are sound, and afford the means of removing one of the greatest opprobria of modern surgery.

Once this article was finished, Lister turned to the work of Pasteur. At this stage his own ideas on inflammation were clear-cut. He knew, and for some years had been teaching, that putrefaction caused the infection of wounds and the formation of pus. He knew that this putrefaction, or decomposition as he sometimes called it, was in some inexplicable way set up by exposure to the air. Most of his contemporaries would have agreed with him thus far, but only the more advanced among them accepted an additional teaching of his—that the air alone did not give rise to decomposition. This last point was based on fairly obvious clinical grounds. If certain wounds were exposed to the air, not all of them became infected. If his private and hospital patients were considered in different groups, though all their wounds were exposed to air the effects of that air differed. The majority of wounds in hospital patients suppurated. The majority of wounds in private patients healed well, only a relatively small proportion becoming infected. The gaseous make-up of the air was constant and unvarying, so obviously this difference had to be accounted for by some other factor. Certain surgeons maintained that the variation was due to the differing constitutions of the patients themselves. Lister realized that this was true to a certain extent, but knew that it was not the whole truth. He was insistent that there was something else, something associated with the air, in it but not of it, though he knew not what what this "something" was. Pasteur told him what it was.

Louis Pasteur was already well known in this country. The

Royal Society had awarded him a medal in 1856 for his paper on crystallography, and he was already famous for his work on this and on other subjects when he began to study the problem of fermentation. Gay-Lussac had done some of the earliest experiments on this subject in 1810. Cagniard-Latour continued his work, and in 1837 announced his belief that yeast consisted of a small mass of globules, vegetable in nature. Schwann showed that these vegetable cells would cause fermentation in certain circumstances. Then Liebig, the famous chemist, insisted that the process was a purely chemical one, and the views of Schwann and Cagniard-Latour were lost sight of. That was in 1839, and there the problem remained till Pasteur took it up again. He began this work in 1856, and in the space of a few years had demolished the teaching of Liebig and confirmed that of Schwann. He studied every known type of fermentation, and particularly that of lactic acid. He showed that the fermentation of this acid was due to the presence of a microscopic organism, and that the fermentation of butyric acid was due to another micro-organism which could not live in air. Then he went on to a study of putrefaction, and found that this too was caused by minute organisms.

This was the experiment that Lister seized upon. He read avidly everything that Pasteur wrote on the subject. He learnt that the micro-organisms causing putrefaction could be carried on particles of dust floating in the atmosphere. They could be destroyed by heat, or filtered from the air by tightly packed cotton-wool. From Pasteur he also learned how on a mountain top, or in an undisturbed cellar, there were few, if any, organisms in the air, while in a dusty room they were legion. It was not only in the air that the microscopic living things were found. They clung to clothes, to the hands, even to metals and glass. Lister's own problem was solved. Pasteur had shown him the "something" which was in the air and which caused open wounds to putrefy and suppurate. The problem of causation seemed to be solved. The question of the treatment of infected wounds could be left aside, for the major problem now was to prevent these air-borne organisms gaining access to wounds, or to destroy them if the wound had already been exposed to air. Lister decided first to try to destroy the organisms in the broken skin about compound fractures of bones. Two methods of achieving this end presented themselves. The organisms could be destroyed by heat or by chemicals. Heating an injured limb to a point at which invading micro-organisms would be destroyed was obviously impracticable. Lister began to look round for some suitable chemical agent. He decided to use carbolic acid.

Frederick Calvert of Manchester was the first English chemist to make carbolic acid, and Lister had seen it being used as a deodorant and disinfectant of sewage at Carlisle. One of his colleagues at the University supplied him with a sample of carbolic acid in its crudest form. It was a dark, tarry, malodorous fluid, usually referred to as German creosote. Lister next had to select the cases on which he would use it. He chose cases of compound fracture, because the wounds in these cases had always been exposed to air and so infected with micro-organisms, and because he would have an ideal yardstick by which to measure his results—namely, the results of treatment of simple fractures in which the skin was intact and the broken bones and wounded tissues had not, therefore, been exposed to the air.

He tried the carbolic-acid treatment for the first time in March, 1865. He and his house-surgeon, young Hector Cameron, worked together on a case of compound fracture of the leg, which had been brought into the Glasgow Infirmary; they cleaned the limb carefully, squeezed out all the obvious clots of blood, then with a piece of lint soaked in the undiluted carbolic acid they probed up and down the wound, making sure that every exposed surface had its meed of carbolic. A large piece of lint soaked in carbolic was then placed so as to cover the wound completely. Over this they fixed with adhesive plaster a piece of tin slightly larger than the lint. This was intended to prevent the disinfectant evaporating. Finally, the limb was splinted. Soon a thick crust of blood and carbolic formed beneath the tin. This was left undisturbed, except that fresh applications of carbolic acid were made to its surface.

Eagerly, the Regius Professor and his houseman watched this case, and soon they realized the disadvantages of the method. Crude carbolic acid destroyed micro-organisms, but it also destroyed human flesh. It would have to be diluted in some way. This was difficult, because carbolic acid was almost insoluble in water. A purer sample of the acid was prepared in crystalline form. This was much less offensive in odour, and one part of it could be dissolved in twenty parts of water. The watery lotion was not very stable, however. Oil was tried. They found that almost any strength of an oily solution could be made up, and the oil retained the carbolic acid well— so well that the disinfectant action of carbolized oil persisted for much longer than that of the watery solution. Lint soaked in carbolized oil was the next dressing to be tried. It was much more successful than the original German creosote, but still far from ideal. Many experiments followed—and as many disappointments—in the next twelve months. At last Lister found a vehicle for the carbolic acid which seemed better than any he had tried previously. The acid was dissolved in linseed oil, to a strength of perhaps 1 in 4 or 1 in 6, then the oil was mixed with common whitening to form a sort of putty. This was easy to make, simple to apply, had a good and prolonged disinfectant action, and did not injure healthy tissues or skin.

Satisfied that he had the preparation he wanted, Lister grew tired of waiting for cases of compound fracture. For no obvious reason people in Glasgow were suddenly sustaining any kind of injury other than a compound fracture. So, in the October of 1866, Lister began to apply the carbolized putty poultice in the treatment of abscesses. Further modifications in technique were laboriously worked out, till in these cases, too, a satisfactory routine was found. Lint soaked in carbolized oil was placed over the area to be incised and left for some hours in order to purify the skin. A knife dipped in carbolized oil was used to make the incision, and immediately fresh carbolized lint was reapplied. The theory was that the pus in the abscess could drain off beneath the lint, but any air sucked back into the abscess cavity had to pass through the lint—and so be freed of micro-organisms. Once the pus was evacuated, the carbolized putty was substituted for the lint, and then changed every day or every other day. The abscesses treated were usually chronic ones, arising in connexion with disease of the spine or other bones. Previously patients suffering from such abscesses presented an impossible problem to the surgeon. If he did not open the abscess, the patient died slowly. If he did plunge a knife into it, then almost certainly within two days the abscess cavity would be pouring out thick, putrid, evil-smelling pus and the patient would die quickly. Lister's patients recovered from their abscesses, and every recovery provided just so much more evidence that Pasteur was right, and that Lister's application of Pasteur's principles to surgery was right.

Lister began to collate his case-records and prepare a paper for publication. The paper was entitled "On a New Method of Treating Compound Fracture, Abscess, Etc., with Observations on the Conditions of Suppuration", and appeared in the *Lancet* in 1867. In this paper Lister paid full tribute to the "flood of light that has been thrown upon this most important subject by the philosophic researches of M. Pasteur", then went on to describe in detail eleven consecutive cases of compound fracture. If these cases had been treated by the ordinary methods, the results would have been easy to forecast. Any surgeon would have counted himself fortunate to have saved the limbs of three and the lives of six out of eleven patients. Of Lister's eleven patients, one had died four months after sustaining his original injury, one had lost his injured limb, and nine patients had both their lives and their limbs. This paper, which was published in several parts, excited wide interest. Surgeons all over the country wanted to know more about this new antiseptic treatment. Syme urged his son-in-law to go to Dublin for the annual meeting of the British Medical Association and read a paper there. Lister did so, and his address "On the Antiseptic Principle in the Practice of Surgery", though criticized by some surgeons, among them James Young Simpson, was well received by most of them, and soon afterwards appeared in the columns of the *British Medical Journal*. It was the concluding paragraph in this paper that gave the first casual reference to a surgical miracle. Lister wrote:

There is, however, one point more that I cannot but advert to—namely, the influence of this mode of treatment upon the general healthiness of a hospital. Previous to its introduction, the two large wards in which most of my cases of accident and of operation are treated were amongst the unhealthiest in the whole surgical division of the Glasgow Royal Infirmary, in consequence, apparently, of those wards being unfavourably placed with reference to the supply of fresh air; and I have often felt ashamed, when recording the results of my practice, to have so often to allude to hospital gangrene or pyæmia. It was interesting, though melancholy, to observe that, whenever all, or nearly all, the beds contained cases with open sores, these grievous complications were pretty sure to show themselves; so that I came to welcome simple fractures, though in themselves of little interest either for myself or the students, because their presence diminished the proportion of open sores among the patients. But since the antiseptic treatment has been brought into full operation, and wounds and abscesses no longer poison the atmosphere with putrid exhalations, my wards, though in other respects under precisely the same circumstances as before, have completely changed their character; so that during the last nine months not a single instance of pyæmia, hospital gangrene, or erysipelas has occurred in them.

As there appears to be no doubt regarding the cause of this change, the importance of the fact can hardly be exaggerated.

Came the deluge. After the publication of this paper, Lister, who hated controversy and could not have written a polemic to save his life, was drawn into a wordy battle with that master controversialist, James Young Simpson. Simpson was still annoyed at the non-acceptance of his method of acupressure, and he saw in Lister's work not a fundamental principle, but just a carbolic putty, which to his fierce eye compared very unfavourably with his acupressure needles. He flung at Lister the accusation that Jules Lemaire, a French general practitioner, had been using carbolic acid in his surgical practice for some years past. So he had, but Lemaire's use of carbolic was neither here nor there. What Simpson and his supporters either would not, or could not, see was that carbolic acid was adopted simply because it was one of the strongest antiseptics known. As Lister himself said, he might just as easily have used chloride of zinc or any other antiseptic. It was the method of application and the principle underlying it that were new. But though there were many detractors, there were many more enthusiastic converts. Young men travelled from St. Petersburg, Edinburgh, New York, London, Leipzig, Paris, and Vienna to see the work that was going on in grimy Glasgow. Most enthusiastic of all were Lister's students and those few young graduates who became his house-surgeons. They watched successive experiments bring the method slowly nearer perfection, though the principle remained always the same. A 5 per cent. watery solution of carbolic acid was soon to be found all that was necessary for a first dressing. Attempts were also being made to find a method of mechanically excluding invading organisms from a wound, so that the wound might be left undisturbed once the first application of carbolic had disinfected it. Lister had realized that, while a first application of carbolic acid might be well borne, repeated applications tended to set up a chemical inflammation almost as disastrous as the inflammation caused by infecting organisms. The problem was to find a substance which when packed around with lint would provide an air-tight cover for a healing wound. Among the "protectives" tried were rubber, block tin, tinfoil, gold-leaf, oiled and varnished silk, and even cotton gilded on one side and coated with rubber on the other. At the same time Lister was trying to improve upon the carbolic putty itself. A mixture of carbolic acid, olive oil, paraffin, and wax, was tried, but proved too brittle. Shell-lac and carbolic acid was more flexible but too sticky. Lead oxide mixed with the lac plaster reduced the stickiness, and for some time this preparation was constantly used in Lister's wards.

Lister himself was satisfied with this preparation for the moment, and so he was able to turn his attention to another closely related problem. In one sense his problem was an old one, for he was searching for the ideal ligature material, just as other surgeons had been since the time of Ambroise Paré. In another sense it was new, for Lister wanted ligatures that were free from micro-organisms. The usual practice at that time, in Glasgow and most other hospitals, was to use long strands of waxed silk. After the artery had been tied, the two ends of silk would be left hanging out of the amputation stump, or whatever wound it might be, until in the course of perhaps ten or fourteen days the entire ligature sloughed out. The method presupposed infection, and infection invariably resulted. Apart from infection, which if it did not arise in the ordinary way was implanted in the tissues by the micro-organisms in the interstices of the silk itself, secondary hæmorrhage was not uncommon. As the silk sloughed out the end of the artery would also slough away, bleeding would be profuse, and the whole process of ligature would have to be gone through all over again.

Lister approached this problem just as he had approached the major problem of preventing infection in the wounds associated with compound fractures. He steeped his silk ligatures in carbolic acid, with the idea of disinfecting them completely. Simpson had the same idea, though he knew not why or how it worked, when he introduced his acupressure. Ligatures of silk were infected. Metal needles were much less likely to be infected, and yet controlled bleeding just as effectively as ligatures when properly applied. Lister's first theories on this subject were put to the test in December, 1867. He used a piece of unwaxed purse-silk which had been steeped for some time in a watery solution of carbolic acid to ligature the carotid artery in an old horse. The animal was quite unaffected by the operation, but died of old age and exhaustion not quite two months later. Lister dissected out the carotid artery and found all that he had hoped for. The silk was recovered unchanged from healthy fibrous tissue, and there were no signs of infection. Encouraged by this success, Lister used silk which had been soaked in carbolic acid for two hours in treating an aneurysm of the femoral artery in a female patient. The artery was tied above the aneurysm, and to the horror of Lister's colleagues the knot was cut short and the wound closed completely. The patient did well in the immediate post-operative period, but died of another aneurysm in the abdomen some ten months later. A necropsy was arranged, and, to his disappointment, Lister found a minute abscess at the point where the knot of the ligature had been.

It became obvious that some material which could be more easily and thoroughly disinfected than silk was needed. Catgut had been tried often by other surgeons, and as often abandoned. Lister began work on it with his usual untiring perseverance. He found the subject complex. The disinfection alone seemed fairly simple, but the resulting product had to be thin yet strong, thoroughly disinfected yet not slippery from carbolic, tough and seasoned with age yet not so tough that it lost elasticity or so aged that it became friable. It had to be such that the tissues could absorb it but the absorption had not to take place until the artery had been completely sealed off, a process which took at least ten days. One by one Lister encountered these difficulties, and tried innumerable methods of overcoming them. His first major experiment on this problem was undertaken in the Christmas week of 1868, when he ligated the carotid of a calf with catgut. Other experiments followed, and by the end of the next year a carbolized catgut ligature was on the market and being extensively used. It was not a perfect ligature, but it was better than any previously produced, and again Lister was satisfied for the moment. He was to take up new experiments on catgut, however, in later years, and his work was no longer to be done in Glasgow.

James Syme had the paralytic stroke from which he never fully recovered in the April of 1869, and in the summer he announced his resignation of the Edinburgh chair of surgery. As soon as it was known that applications for the professorship were being invited, one hundred and twenty-seven Edinburgh medical students presented an address to the Regius Professor of Surgery in Glasgow, begging him to apply for the vacant chair of clinical surgery. By August 18 James Syme had the satisfaction of seeing his son-in-law elected his successor. Lister was entering into a great inheritance. Soon he had a large private practice of his own, and in 1870, within a few months of each other, Syme and Simpson died. They were the only two men in the country who had even approached Lister's stature. From then onwards Lister was the first surgeon in Europe, a fact which was recognized in country after country. Norway was the first to honour him, making him a foreign associate of the Norwegian Society of Medicine almost as soon as he took up his appointment in Edinburgh.

Characteristically, Lister barely noticed the fame that was rapidly becoming his. At Edinburgh he had fewer lectures to deliver than he had had in Glasgow, and altogether far more time to devote to research work. He turned to his microscope again, and began a study of the life-history of fungi and bacteria and their relation to fermentation and putrefaction. He was exchanging letters with Pasteur on the subject, and his work on bacteria was dove-tailing into his extension of the antiseptic method, just as his experiments on catgut had done. He introduced in Edinburgh a further elaboration of the antiseptic system of prevention, the carbolic spray. It was known by that time that there were minute micro-organisms and fungi always present in the air. What was not known was which, or how many, of them were harmful or pathogenic. It was generally assumed that most, if not all, of them were dangerous. This being so, Lister endeavoured to kill these tiny germs in the air itself, so that they could not possibly gain access to operation wounds. First a small hand-spray filled with a dilute carbolic-acid solution was used, then a spray worked by the foot, then a cumbrous, long-handled affair, which was soon known as the donkey-engine. At length a steam apparatus projecting a spray which consisted of one part of carbolic acid to forty of water was elaborated. It made every operation a physical ordeal, for the hands became white and numb and the vapour was constantly inhaled. Lister and his innumerable followers, however, used it for a long ten years or more, until they realized that surgeons who were literally physically incapable of using the spray, so much did it affect their health, were obtaining just as good results without it. Finally, in 1887 Lister abandoned the spray, which, though short-lived, had served several useful purposes. When it was first used other parts of the antiseptic ritual had been abandoned for a brief while. They had soon to be taken up again, and with new modifications based on this experience of doing without them. Thus the lac preparation was discarded in favour of a gauze dressing, so simple that even the most inexperienced could not fall into error with it. The gauze consisted of eight layers of thin muslin, smelling faintly of carbolic acid. Between the seventh and eighth layers was thin mackintosh, dyed pink—as it is to this day—so that there should be no doubt as to which side of the dressing was to be applied to the wound. This gauze was introduced after it was realized that too much confidence could not be placed in the spray alone, and was used all over the country till about 1889. It was then replaced by gauze impregnated with the double cyanide of mercury and zinc, the best for that purpose of an ever-growing series of antiseptics with which Lister had been experimenting since ever he heard of Pasteur.

A minor surgical advance which Lister did much to popularize during this same period was in connexion with the drainage of wounds. As early as 1859 Chassaignac had used india-rubber tubes for draining abscesses. Lister used one for the first time in 1871. He opened a deep-seated abscess in a lady's armpit, and used a strip of lint for drainage, as had been the usual practice in this country for many years. When he dressed the narrow wound the next day a large quantity of pus flowed out of the abscess just as soon as he removed the strip of lint. He realized then that unless the pus to be drained away was very thin and serous the lint might act as a plug rather than a drain. There was some india-rubber tubing on the carbolic acid hand-spray he had used at the operation. He took a suitable length of it, cut several holes in the wall of the tube, and attached knotted silk thread to the end, so that the tube could be pulled out of the wound easily after it had been inserted. Insertion was simple, and the improvised method of drainage allowed the abscess to clear up in less than a week. Lister spent the whole of this week with his patient, who was in residence at Balmoral at that time and was none other than Queen Victoria.

Lister began to use rubber drainage tubes regularly, and soon they were to be found in every hospital in the country. Many tubes were placed in each wound when strong and irritating solutions of carbolic acid were still being used and there was a certain amount of exudation produced by the acid itself. Later, as weaker solutions were employed, and the irritation

PLATE XXI

The meeting of Pasteur and Lister at the Sorbonne, during the celebration, on December 27, 1892, of Pasteur's seventieth birthday.

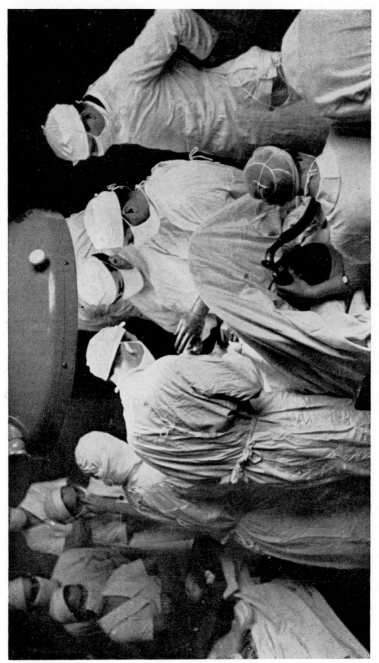

PLATE XXII

A modern surgeon and his assistants and nurses.

was consequently lessened, fewer tubes were necessary. Lister himself looked forward to the time when "we could dispense with drainage altogether". The search for milder and milder antiseptics continued. Pasteur suggested boric acid, and Lister began using boric lint. Charles Darwin drew Lister's attention to the properties of benzoic acid. Many other suggestions were made, and patient Mrs. Lister was still writing constantly "2.55 a.m. Bacteria in full activity . . ." and the like entries, in what she and her husband called the "Commonplace Book".

There were still occasional attacks on the antiseptic method, but they were becoming few and far between. Only in London, where the older and more conservative surgeons still held sway, were the germ theory and the antiseptic treatment which was based on it still disregarded, as much from apathy as from ignorance. Many of the London surgeons had heard Lister's address on antiseptic treatment at the annual meeting of the British Medical Association at Plymouth in 1871. They had all seen the successive papers published in the *British Medical Journal* and the *Lancet*. Yet at the 1879 annual meeting of the British Medical Association, this time in Cork, a well-known London surgeon, Mr. Savory, took up again the attack on the antiseptic system. His address was the swan-song of surgeons who did not practise antisepsis. Savory referred to his own favourite dressing, the bread poultice, and he thought his results at St. Bartholomew's were as good as it was "reasonably possible to expect". Certain general infections followed some of his operations, but that was inevitable. In twelve months there had been only seventeen cases of pyæmia, sixteen fatal; only sixty of erysipelas, of which twelve had proved fatal; and only seventy-seven patients had developed blood-poisoning, and of these no more than twenty-eight had died.

In the provinces, and particularly in Manchester, men whom Lister had trained himself were carrying on his work enthusiastically. Abroad, one surgeon after another took up the antiseptic treatment. Professor Karl Thiersch of Munich, and later of Leipzig, adopted the method soon after Lister introduced it. Because of this, he was enabled in 1874 successfully to introduce a method of skin-grafting which is used to this day and still bears his name. So thoroughly did he follow Lister's principles, that he was able to boast that he had had no cases of hospital gangrene and only one of pyæmia in twelve months.   These figures from a hospital of three hundred beds compare strangely with those which satisfied Mr. Savory.

Richard von Volkmann first tried the antiseptic method in his clinics in 1872, and from then on was one of Lister's most devoted adherents.   Stromeyer of Hanover, Esmarch of Kiel, Trendelenburg of Bonn, and Nussbaum of Munich were others who reduced the mortality in their surgical wards to an unheard-of degree, simply by adopting the antiseptic technique.   Nussbaum's book on the method ran through four editions in six years, and was translated into Greek, French, and Italian.   In other parts of Germany, however, the method was not studied properly, the details of its application were neglected, and as a result antisepsis was either forgotten or derided in many centres.   The same thing happened the world over, but in each country there were one or two surgeons who practised the method with complete success.   In St. Petersburg there was Reyher, in Copenhagen Saxtorph, and in Amsterdam Tilanus. At Berne there was the renowned Kocher, in Paris Lucas-Championnière, at Pavia Bottini.   American surgeons were chary of accepting the germ theory at first, but by 1877 Robert F. Weir and others in New York were accepting the ritual if not the dogma.   So it was that in both the Old World and the New the teachings of Lister were slowly spread.   There was often opposition due to ignorance, often difficulty in obtaining· the complicated sprays and expensive gauze, but gradually, as knowledge of the technique was disseminated, difficulties were faced and overcome.

The spread of the antiseptic system was greatly helped by Lister's own personal contacts.   Early in 1875 he made a holiday tour of the German university towns, which became a sort of triumphal march.   In the same year he was able to meet scores of provincial practitioners who attended the annual meeting of the British Medical Association at Edinburgh.   He was appointed to the General Medical Council, which had been set up by the Medical Registration Act of 1858, and for the first time began to meet regularly some of his London colleagues. In 1876 Lister presided over the surgical section of an International Congress held in Philadelphia.   After the congress he visited Chicago and San Francisco, and spent some days with Bigelow in Boston.   By the time Lister was fifty, which was in 1877, London was almost alone in the outer darkness.

On February 10 of that year Sir William Fergusson, Professor of Clinical Surgery at King's College, died. It was expected that John Wood, who had succeeded Fergusson in the chair of systematic surgery at King's, would take up the clinical professorship. The authorities responsible for the two professorial appointments were anxious to elect someone who might retrieve the waning prestige of the school. Lister was approached, and agreed that he would accept the chair in clinical surgery provided that certain conditions, involving a radical reform of the methods of teaching at King's, were complied with. From the outset Lister made his position quite clear. He was prepared to leave a university which was attracting nearly two hundred new medical students each year for a school that rarely boasted an annual enrolment of more than twenty-five students. He was ready to throw up the finest surgical practice in Scotland and start all over again in London. He knew that his reception in London might be hostile, but he was certain that by his presence he could assist the few but faithful followers he had there to imbue London with the antiseptic fervour which already possessed every other capital city in the world. For this reason, and for this reason only, he agreed to make considerable personal sacrifices. The approach made to him had been entirely unofficial, but soon the rumour spread that he was leaving Edinburgh for King's. Seven hundred medical students promptly drew up an address, begging him to remain in Edinburgh. Lister thanked the students and made a short impromptu speech, contrasting the clinical professorships of King's and of Edinburgh, and explaining how in London "the magnificent opportunities of demonstrative teaching presented by clinical surgery are, to a great extent, neglected". Neither he nor anyone else knew that a reporter was present, till they saw the report of his speech in the *Times* the next day. London surgeons were annoyed, and the *Lancet* was very bitter about Mr. Lister's "arrogating to himself the right to sit in judgement on his fellows". Mr. John Wood was thereupon appointed Professor of Clinical Surgery at King's College, London, and for a while the shouting and the tumult died. It arose again when, on June 18, Mr. Joseph Lister was elected to an additional chair in clinical surgery at King's College. Though Wood had been appointed, the negotiations with Lister had continued. It was arranged that attendance on a course of lectures in clinical surgery should become obligatory for the students at King's, and the number of beds in the hospital was increased from one hundred and seventy-two to two hundred and five, so that Lister should have a ward of his own.

Mr. and Mrs. Lister made their London home at No. 12, Park Crescent. This was near the Park Square Garden and the Botanical Garden, and sufficiently remote from Harley Street and Wimpole Street to provide a gentle indication that Mr. Lister did not intend to compete in any way with the established surgical consultants. His first battle, however, was with the ward sisters in the hospital. Lister had brought with him from Edinburgh four young men, two graduates, who acted as senior and junior house-surgeons to him, and two students, who were his dressers. It was the junior house-surgeon who first came up against the sisters' hostility. As Lister left the hospital one afternoon, a colleague asked him to see a boy in the medical wards. The case was one of acute osteomyelitis—a severe infection of the bone-marrow—and immediate operation was necessary. Lister and his senior assistant went off to the theatre. Since no porters could be found to transfer the patient from the ward, the junior house-surgeon, with the assistance of the students, took a stretcher to the ward. The sister told him that the lad could not be moved without a permit from the secretary to the hospital, who had gone home and would not return till the following day. There was a brief argument. Then when the young men attempted to lift the boy, the sister and one of the nurses took hold of the stretcher, and it looked for a moment as if a most undignified tug-of-war was to be started. The junior house-surgeon took up the patient in his arms and carried him bodily out of the ward, while one of the students fended off the sister and her nurses. There were other similar instances, which created a most unpleasant atmosphere and led to a situation in which Lister could not trust the sisters of his wards to carry out his instructions. In time, however, the nurses, who had never been very hostile to the Edinburgh group, were won over, and the sisters were gradually either retired or converted.

The students of King's College were not hostile like the ward sisters. They were simply apathetic. They knew that they would not be examined by Lister when their course was completed. They found that if they quoted Lister's teachings to the surgeons who did examine them, they were likely to be failed. The result was that Lister's class, even including the faithful four from Edinburgh, dwindled to a dozen or so.

Wood, Lister's associate professor, became convinced that there was something in Lister's work, though he was never an enthusiast about it, after Lister had supervised the antiseptic arrangements for two major operations, the removal of a goitre and the excision of diseased ovaries. Both patients did well, yet previously the mortality from the last operation had been such that the governors of King's forbade the surgeons to undertake it. Then Lister performed an open operation on a broken knee-cap, wiring the two fragments together, in October, 1877. The general feeling about operating on joints was well expressed by one London surgeon, who trusted that when the patient died after this dangerous and unjustifiable operation the relatives would proceed against Lister for malpraxis. The patient made the usual uninterrupted recovery, and had normal knee movement as a result. This case was talked about, and so were many others.

Gradually it was realized that Lister was performing successfully every day operations which had long been known as theoretically possible, but which had never been undertaken by contemporary London surgeons, because the chances of the patient dying of some general hospital infection were so great. It was an old story. What years of patient writing and lecturing had failed to achieve was effected by the accounts spread from one surgeon to another of occasional dramatic operations, which no one else would have dared tackle. Liston and Syme had had the same experience, but whereas comment always centred about the speed with which they operated, in the case of Lister's operations it was the speed with which his patients recovered that excited discussion. Lister's lecturing and writing continued, and, thanks to the relatively unimportant operative triumphs that everybody was talking about, lectures to medical societies were delivered before huge audiences, and articles in the *British Medical Journal* were widely read. A visit to the Universal Exhibition at Paris in 1878 made even Lister himself realize that he was a celebrity. The Sixth International Medical Congress in the following year gave him embarrassing proof of it. The *British Medical Journal* gave an account of this function:

The public meeting of Tuesday was principally devoted to an address by Professor Lister in reply to various objections that have been made to the antiseptic system. Professor Lister was received by the whole Congress with an enthusiasm which knew no bounds. When he stepped for-ward to the desk to open his address (which was delivered, with but few notes, in improvised French), the whole assembly rose to their feet; and, with deafening and repeated rounds of cheers, waving of hats and hand-kerchiefs, hailed the distinguished Professor of King's College with accla-mations renewed minute after minute, and time after time, as his name was again shouted forth by some grateful and enthusiastic acolyte. This remarkable scene—unprecedented, we imagine, in the history of medical science—continued for some minutes, until Professor Donders, the Presi-dent, advancing with the distinctive grace and dignity for which he is remarkable, and taking Professor Lister by the hand, as he stood over-whelmed with this magnificent ovation, obtained a moment's silence, and addressing him said: "Professor Lister, it is not only our admiration which we offer you; it is our gratitude, and that of the nations to which we belong."

Other honours followed in rapid succession. Soon after he came to London, Lister was appointed Surgeon-in-Ordinary to Her Majesty. Both Oxford and Cambridge conferred honorary degrees upon him, and a baronetcy was bestowed on him in 1883. The Prussian Order of Merit and the Boudet Prize of 6,000 francs, for "his application of M. Pasteur's researches to the art of healing", were among the innumerable tributes from abroad. He was elected to the Council of the Royal College of Surgeons, and served on the Committee of Manage-ment controlling the Conjoint Board examinations, which were begun after a long-desired association between the Royal Colleges of Medicine and Surgery had been brought about in 1884.

It was in the following year that Pasteur first applied to a little Alsatian boy, Joseph Meister, the preventive treatment for hydrophobia on which he had worked for five years. The first dogs made mad by rabies which Pasteur had investigated were brought to his laboratory in 1880. After seven years it was known that Pasteur had triumphed again. The *Institut Pasteur* was inaugurated in 1888, its object being to study the nature and means of prevention of infective diseases. The life-saving preventive work on hydrophobia was still carried on there, but only as one among a score of varying activities. Similar institutes were soon being set up in Russia, Italy, Spain, and Austria. Chicago was early in the field, as were Bucharest, Buenos Aires, and Havannah. England lagged behind, despite the efforts of Lister, Sir James Paget, and others. Gradually, however, more and more influential persons were won over, and in 1891 the British Institute of Preventive Medicine was incorporated, with Lister as its first chairman. Its declared objects were to study the prevention and treatment of infective diseases, to promote the spread of knowledge of these subjects, to prepare and supply protective and curative materials, and to treat persons suffering from, or threatened with, infective diseases. The Institute really began work two years later. Klebs and Löffler had discovered the organism causing diphtheria in 1883. Roux and Yersin by 1890 had shown how the toxin or poison elaborated by the organism could be separated off, and in the same year Behring and Kitasato had immunized animals against diphtheria. The first human patients were treated in 1893, and so in that year the British Institute secured a farm at Sudbury and began the manufacture of antitoxin. This was some few months after Lister's retirement, at the age of sixty-five, from his professorship at King's College. In December, 1896, just a few months before the centenary of Jenner's discovery of vaccination, Sir Joseph Lister appealed for a subscription for a national memorial to Jenner. He suggested that the money raised should be devoted to research at the British Institute, the name of which would be changed to the Jenner Institute. This was done, but difficulties were created because there was in existence a firm trading under the name of the Jenner Institute for Calf-Lymph. So in 1903 the short-lived Jenner Institute became the Lister Institute.

The year in which Lister ceased lecturing to the students at King's was the year of Pasteur's seventieth birthday. The occasion was marked on December 27 by a great ceremony at the Sorbonne. Lister gave a brief address, according to Pasteur the tribute that was due to him from medicine and surgery, the twin sciences which he had done so much to advance. (*See plate facing* p. 352.) In the following·year Lister's wife died, and for a while he was inconsolate. Soon, however, he picked up again the threads of his research work, and in 1895, the year of Pasteur's death, he succeeded Lord Kelvin as President of the Royal Society, an office which he held for the usual period of five years.

He was President of the British Association in 1896, and in his address he reviewed the advances that had been made in medicine and surgery since the discovery of anæsthesia, fifty years previously. There was Pasteur's work, and his own, and there were all the recent discoveries in connexion with the tubercle bacillus, and the cholera vibrio. Serums and vaccines were being elaborated for treatment and prevention. Metchnikoff had shown how the white cells of the blood were the advance guard of the body's defences against bacterial invasion. There were many other things to be mentioned, among them the discovery, less than twelve months before, of the Roentgen rays.

Queen Victoria's Diamond Jubilee was in 1897, and with the appearance of the New Year Honours list Sir Joseph became Lord Lister—and the first member of the medical profession to be elevated to the peerage. Then came another shower of academic honours, addresses, and receptions: the freedom of Edinburgh; more honorary degrees from Toronto and Liverpool; and later the Order of Merit, which was an order newly created by King Edward VII, and membership of the Privy Council. The Copley Medal of the Royal Society was awarded him in November, 1902. December 9 was the fiftieth anniversary of Lister's admission to the fellowship of the Royal College of Surgeons. The *British Medical Journal* produced a special Lister number, there were many laudatory articles in the lay press, and the King of Denmark conferred on Lister the Grand Cross of the Order of the Dannebrog. Six months later there began a long illness, which precluded almost any active work for some three years. Then his eightieth birthday approached, and the Royal College of Surgeons set up a small committee to gather together all the papers Lister had ever published and present them in the form of a commemorative volume. Members of the committee were Sir Hector Cameron, who had been Lister's first private assistant; Sir Watson Cheyne, who came from Edinburgh to London with Lister; Lister's nephew, Rickman John Godlee; and Dawson Williams, the editor of the *British Medical Journal*. The *Collected Papers* appeared finally in 1909.

Lister died on the morning of February 10, 1912. He had made surgery safe for patients. He had banished sepsis from hospital wards. Long before he died he had opened up new fields of surgical endeavour. Since his death surgery has advanced steadily, but it may be truly said that every advance has been dependent in more or less degree upon his genius— genius which enabled him to link the work of a French chemist with an experiment in sewage control to effect a revolution in every department of the surgical art.

XXIII. After Lister

IT HAS BEEN SAID THAT THERE ARE ONLY TWO PERIODS IN THE history of surgery—before Lister and after Lister. The first of these periods began when the world was very young, the second not thirty years ago. Yet in the last thirty years more has been achieved than in the thirty thousand years before them. The merest list of the advances that have been made in this century would fill several volumes, and would be out of date before it was off the press. From day to day and week to week the face of surgery changes. New facts are brought to light. New theories are proved or old ones abandoned. But through all the conflicting changes and counter-changes the trends of advancement are clear. They date from, and depend on, the discoveries of anæsthesia and antisepsis.

The first changes to take place after the general acceptance of antisepsis can be measured very roughly. A simple yard-stick—perhaps too simple—is provided by the proportion of deaths following amputations, at different hospitals, before and after the introduction of the full antiseptic ritual. At Pennsylvania, for thirty years before 1860, the mortality rate after amputation averaged 24.3 per cent. The Massachusetts General Hospital at Boston boasted of a 26 per cent. mortality— that is, there were only 180 deaths in a consecutive series of 692 amputations. Boston might well boast when it knew the corresponding figures from other hospitals. From 1836 to 1863 the patients subjected to amputation in Paris numbered 682; of these patients 397 died, giving a mortality rate of 58.8 per cent. At Zürich the mortality rate was 46 per cent.— that is, seventy-five patients out of 163 operated on died. It was the same everywhere. The hospital with a mortality rate among its amputation cases of not more than 30 per cent. had something to brag about. If only one out of three of his patients died, a surgeon could point with pride to his results. Sir John Erichsen, the professor of clinical surgery at University College Hospital, whose house-surgeon Lister had been, recorded on one occasion the results of 307 amputations he had performed over a period of years. Sir John was justly proud of the fact that only seventy-nine of these patients had died after operation. He wrote:

Now a general mortality for many years of from 24 to 26 per cent., in all major amputations of the limbs for all cases, may be considered a very satisfactory result, although there can be no question that it is one that admits, and that ought to be susceptible, of improvement. If we compare it with the results that have been obtained elsewhere, it is one of which we need not be ashamed.

Sir John Erichsen's results were good. In fact at that time only the American surgeons could produce comparable figures. Surgeons in Paris envied him, yet even they could look down upon the military hospitals, where death-rates after amputation mounted often to 70 per cent., and they could pity, too, their colleagues in Munich, for at the Krankenhaus there, for one short period, "80 per cent. of the wounds became affected with gangrene, and filled the surgical wards with horror".

All this was only a few years before the introduction of antisepsis. To learn what happened after the development of Listerism it is sufficient to turn to Lister's own hospital. The total number of operations performed in the Edinburgh Infirmary in 1897 was 2,666, and the death-rate was 6.2 per cent. At this point the operation of amputation, on which all surgical reputations rested before the advent of Lister, becomes too simple a yardstick for further effective measurement. Great changes had been quickly brought about in the number and nature of operations performed. In the twelve years preceding the introduction of anæsthesia only 11 per cent. of the patients in surgical wards were thought fit for operation—and the operation was a two-minute amputation in five cases out of ten. In the twelve years after the introduction of antisepsis 34 per cent. of the patients in surgical wards were operated on—and the operation was amputation in only two out of ten cases. The rise in the number of operations performed is seen clearly at Lister's other hospital, the Glasgow Royal Infirmary. Even in 1873 less than four hundred operations were performed there in twelve months. Twenty-five years later, during the same length of time, over two thousand patients were operated on. There was the same change in surgical records everywhere. St. Bartholomew's Hospital had 397 beds for surgical patients as long ago as 1848, yet there, too, no more than four hundred operations were performed each year, and between eighty and a hundred of these operations were amputations. In the year in which Lister died St. Bartholomew's had still much the same number of surgical beds, but 3,561 operations were undertaken, and exactly twenty-five of them—or 0.7 per cent.—were amputations. Every hospital had the same story to tell. Fewer and fewer patients were being subjected to the old operations, but more and more patients were being treated by new operations, which antisepsis had made possible. Previously surgery had saved a proportion of lives at the expense of innumerable limbs. Now it was saving innumerable lives at the cost of only an occasional limb. It was Sir John Erichsen again who sign-posted the advances to be made when he said that no advances could be made.

In the course of an address at University College Hospital in 1873 he said:

> That there must be a final limit to development in this department of our profession there can be no doubt. The art of surgery is but the appli-cation of manipulative methods to the relief and cure of injury and disease. Like every other art, be it manipulative, plastic, or imitative, it can only be carried to a certain definite point of excellence. An art may be modified, it may be varied, but it cannot be perfected beyond certain attainable limits. And so it is, and indeed must be, with surgery. There cannot always be fresh fields for conquest by the knife: there must be portions of the human frame that will ever remain sacred from its intrusion, at least in the sur-geon's hands. That we have nearly, if not quite, reached these final limits, there can be little question.

Twelve months later he defined those "portions of the human frame that will ever remain sacred", when he said that "the abdomen, the chest, and the brain would be for ever shut from the intrusion of the wise and humane surgeon". Erichsen was not alone in holding these views. He was expressing the feeling of the majority of surgeons. There was a famous French surgeon, Denonvilliers, for example, who always told his pupils: "When an operation is necessary think ten times about it, for too often when we decide upon an operation we sign the death-warrant of the patient". There was a colleague of Erichsen's, too, who said quite firmly: "An abdominal operation should be classed amongst the methods of the executioner".

Sir John Erichsen was ranking high among the false prophets in less than quarter of a century. Lister's laborious but certain proof of the correctness of Pasteur's germ theory, and his slow evolution of a preventive antisepsis based on that theory formed a key which would unlock each and all of the body cavities. The need for unlocking them was shown clearly by the pathologists.

Giovanni Battista Morgagni had introduced into late eighteenth-century medical practice an "anatomical concept". Patients he had watched in life Morgagni dissected after death, and on a grand scale he correlated the signs and symptoms of disease with affections of particular organs. At the beginning of the nineteenth century Marie François Xavier Bichat went one shaky step further, when he divided individual organs into different tissues. Then the great Rudolf Virchow, Lister's most distinguished contemporary, established solidly the conception of cellular pathology. The cell is the biological unit. Groups of similar cells form tissues. Interdependent tissues make up the various organs which form the individual animal or man. Virchow showed that the cell was the important unit, that cells arose only out of other cells, and that any sickness or illness was simply the reaction of the cell to altered conditions. Disease processes began in a cell, spread through a tissue, and only in the relatively late stages affected an entire organ.

Advances in pathology led to advances in diagnosis and in treatment. Aneurysms, which had for so long been a major surgical problem, ceased to appear except as clinical curiosities, when it was shown that the great majority of them were syphilitic in origin and would never arise if syphilis was diagnosed moderately early and treated adequately. Amputation was a lost art from the moment Lister laid the spectre of hospital gangrene. The science of bleeding fell into disrepute when the physiologists and pathologists made clear how rarely it was needed. The three chief props of the old surgery crumbled and disappeared, shattered by the weight of pathology and physiology on which a new surgery was being based. This new surgery became possible when Listerism was carried to its logical conclusion and antisepsis became asepsis, a change which took place in Lister's own lifetime.

Neuber, at Kiel, made the first deliberate attempt to obtain Lister's results by different and simpler methods, which were based, however, on the same Listerian principle of excluding micro-organisms from wounds. Everything that might come into contact with the operation wound he had boiled. Dressings, bandages, instruments, overalls, even the patient's clothes were all boiled, as was the salt solution with which wounds were irrigated. From 1885 onwards Neuber used this method with such excellent results that other surgeons soon adopted the same technique.

Ernst von Bergmann, who succeeded Langenbeck at Berlin in 1882, was another of the leaders in the evolution of asepsis. He and his assistant, Schimmelbusch, by the end of the last century had developed steam-pressure sterilizers, in which all the cloths, towels, bandages, and dressings to be used at operation could be freed completely from bacteria, and they elaborated a ritual use of antiseptics to ensure that no organisms could gain access to an operating wound. William Stewart Halsted, professor of surgery in the Johns Hopkins University, added one of the final touches when in 1890 he had bronze casts made of his own hands. On these casts the first surgical rubber gloves were moulded. Being made of rubber, they could be completely sterilized, being thin, they did not interfere with his delicacy of touch. Masks of gauze, which were first used at Charing Cross Hospital in 1900 by Dr. William Hunter, completed the equipment for asepsis. Since then there have been refinements of technique and a slow standardization of aseptic procedures, but the fundamental principles, which Lister laid down, remain unaltered.

The ritual of asepsis to-day is the same the world over. It is Listerism perfected. The patient has all the protection afforded by the old technique of antisepsis with none of the irritation which was inevitable when solutions of carbolic acid, however dilute, were applied directly to skin and wound edges. The whole field of operation is sterilized before operation, usually by repeated applications of iodine or some other mild antiseptic. All the blunt instruments are sterilized by boiling. Cutting instruments are kept in an antiseptic, and as often as not this is some preparation of carbolic acid. Ligatures and sutures have all been subjected to prolonged antiseptic procedures. Then everything except the actual operative field is covered with towels, which have come from a high-pressure steam sterilizer. The surgeon and his assistant and nurses are the only people to come in contact with this carefully prepared skin area. They wear all-enveloping, long-sleeved gowns extending from their necks to their feet, white caps, gauze masks, and rubber gloves drawn well up over the sleeves of their gowns. Everything they wear is free externally from bacteria. Contact with the surgical incision is made by only one thing which has not been specially treated—the air. The air does contain innumerable organisms, as Lister and Pasteur knew, but if it is still and at a fairly constant temperature, very few of the organisms will enter a wound. Those that do enter are for the most part harmless. Stray organisms which are virulent are dealt with rapidly by the tissues, provided those tissues are reasonably healthy and have been cut cleanly and handled gently. The patient who is subjected to operation under these circumstances is in far less danger of death than the individual who has to travel a few miles to work.

Asepsis was never defined more succinctly than by an old Yorkshire veterinary surgeon. This old man was the most successful veterinary surgeon in the north of England. Before every operation he performed he insisted on being left alone in the farm kitchen for half an hour. What he did in that time no one knew. When at last he was on his death-bed his son begged him to tell the secret of his success. The old man looked round the room to make sure that no one else was in earshot, then he leaned forward and whispered to his son, "I boils me tools".

When Lister made surgery safe for patients he accelerated unbelievably the pace of diagnostic achievement. Before Lister, if a man had a lump in his abdomen, the question as to what the lump consisted of was largely of academic interest. It might be a blood-clot, a stone, an abscess, a cyst, a simple tumour, or a cancer. But whatever it was, nothing could be done about it unless the patient would accept a two-to-one chance of never recovering from the opening of his abdomen. Since the patient was rarely rash enough to take these odds, there was nothing much to be done, and the necropsy would allow a final diagnosis to be made. With the development of antisepsis, and later asepsis, exploring an abdomen became less dangerous than the amputation of a little finger had been. Academic problems in diagnosis were suddenly of urgent practical importance. If the abdominal mass was a blood-clot it would resolve without interference, if a stone it could be removed, if an abscess it should be drained, if a cyst it ought to be excised, if a cancer it might still be amenable to surgical treatment. Some of these distinctions might be made clinically, but it was important that the diagnosis should be as nearly positive as possible. In pre-Listerian days surgeons had one constant fear—that they might subject to the horrors and risks of operation a patient who did not need an operation. Now the surgeon's fear is that through a misdiagnosis he may not operate at all on a patient whose life might be saved by operation, or he may not operate early enough to achieve a cure which would have been possible had his first diagnosis been certain. Listerism and all that followed it made early and accurate diagnosis of vital importance.

[*366*]

Carl August Wunderlich in 1868 showed the importance of the thermometer in diagnosis. Surgeons and physicians began to compile temperature charts, but the compiling was difficult. Thermometers were massive instruments, ten inches long, and took five or more minutes to register the patient's temperature with any degree of accuracy. Sir Clifford Allbutt improved upon these primitive instruments, and finally devised the accurate pocket clinical thermometer which is in universal use to-day.

Galileo used a pendulum to count the pulse rate. Graphic records of the pulse rate and blood pressure were first made at the end of the last century. Sir James Mackenzie was perhaps the greatest exponent of the value of these pressure-recording instruments. Einthoven developed the electrocardiograph, which gives an accurate representation of the changes in electric potential taking place with every contraction of the human heart.

Réné Laennec invented the stethoscope in 1819, when he used a cylinder of paper to conduct the heart-sounds from a patient's chest-wall to his ear. This first experiment was prompted by a shy young lady, who was deeply embarrassed when Laennec applied his ear directly to her charming chest. Soon stethoscopes were used everywhere, and the diagnosis of conditions affecting the heart and lungs became increasingly certain.

Electrical engineers, when they perfected lamps so small that they could be passed through the narrowest orifices of the human body and yet give full illumination, made it possible to see directly into the bladder, the rectum, the gullet, the windpipe, the lungs, and—most recently of all—the stomach and the abdominal cavity. But of all the new diagnostic aids the most unexpected and the most valuable was the one to which Lister referred in his presidential address to the British Association in 1896—the Roentgen ray.

Professor Wilhelm Conrad Roentgen of Wurzburg was working in his darkened laboratory on November 8, 1895. He was experimenting with the so-called cathode rays, which Hertz and Lenard had described. These rays came from the negative electrode of a Crookes glass tube, which contained gas at a very low pressure. Roentgen noticed that a small piece of paper covered with barium platinocyanide shone brightly while the electrical discharge was taking place in the Crookes tube. He had no idea of the nature of this unusual phenomenon, so he began a thorough and patient investigation of it. In less than two months he was sufficiently certain of the results he had obtained to present a paper on "A New Kind of Ray" to the Physical Medical Society of Wurzburg. He admitted that he still did not know much about the nature of the rays, and therefore referred to them as X rays. He had certain and convincing evidence of what these rays could do, however. They travelled in straight lines and could not be polarized or magnetically deflected. They penetrated with ease a surprising variety of objects, books and clothes, for example. They would affect a photographic plate, but could barely be seen by the human eye. They would pass through a human hand, yet show on a photographic plate the outline of the bones and of the flesh in very different densities.

Roentgen was a famous physicist before ever he discovered X rays, but the discovery was of such general interest that his name became a household word within the space of weeks. The lay Press found that science had a news value, and devoted much space to the "invisible light", which could penetrate the stoutest clothing. The public response was magnificent. Morality brigades were formed overnight to resist to the death the destruction of all decency and privacy. A London firm rose to the occasion, and made a small fortune from the sale of X-ray-proof underwear. New York was also in the van, with a determined attempt to obtain legislation against "the use of X rays in opera-glasses in theatres". Slowly—and with some disappointment—the general public realized that an X-ray picture was not pornographic nor ever likely to be. New York and London grinned a little shamefacedly, and thereafter left the X rays to physicians and surgeons, who seemed to find an unaccountable delight in the disappointingly moral shadow-pictures. The bogey of X-ray immorality became very pale and unsubstantial when the German Emperor had a radiograph taken of his crippled left arm in January, 1896. It vanished for ever when Queen Amelia of Portugal had X-ray photographs taken of several of her maids-in-waiting, to show them just what their sixteen-inch corsets did to their livers.

Roentgen was awarded a Nobel prize in 1901. Even in the five years that had elapsed since he discovered X rays their usefulness in medicine and surgery had been amply demonstrated. Their value in showing up fractures and tumours of bone was self-evident. They showed stones in the kidneys, metallic foreign bodies in the tissues, displaced teeth, and the like. Even the heart and lungs had their own shadows, though at that time these shadows revealed little of the processes taking place in these organs. As early as 1896 W. Becher filled the stomach of a guinea-pig with a solution containing lead, and X-rayed this organ effectively. Then bismuth and barium solutions were found to be just as opaque to X rays and, since they were much less poisonous than lead, could be introduced into human stomachs. Solutions of iodine in different forms were the next liquids found to be opaque to X rays. Elaboration of the technique of radiology, and improvement of the materials and apparatus used have continued steadily. It is now possible to visualize more or less completely the entire alimentary tract from the mouth to the rectum. An oily compound of iodine in poppy-seed oil—lipiodol—injected through the glottis allowed the windpipe and the bronchi, which branch off it, to be seen clearly in radiographs for the first time in 1922. The heart can be visualized directly and various abnormalities detected. The radiography of bones has reached a stage at which it is now possible not merely to say that a bony swelling exists but to state in most cases the exact nature of the swelling. The changes in the brain caused by tumours can often be shown by the injection of air or gas into the ventricles, the natural cavities inside the brain. Structural and even functional alterations in the kidneys can be observed radiologically. The presence of inflammation of the gall-bladder can be detected with certainty, and even the bile-ducts themselves, with all their ramifications through the liver, have been outlined. Arteries show clearly on an X-ray film if they have been injected with thorotrast. The patency or lack of patency of the Fallopian tubes, which connect the ovaries with the womb, can be demonstrated. The bladder, like every other hollow organ, can be filled with an opaque solution and X-rayed. In fact, only the muscles, the spleen, the pancreas, and the ductless glands remain more or less invisible to X rays.

The ever-widening application of X rays in diagnosis has been made possible by the improvements effected in technical details. Stereoscopic X-ray pictures now give a three-dimensional visualization which was previously only approximated to by the study of radiographs taken in three different planes. Tomography allows of the detailed study of one-inch sections of the living body. The X-ray tube is simply focused on the desired section—say that part of the lungs three inches in front of the spine—and then swung through a mathematically calculated arc, so that the wanted section stands out boldly in the finished film, while the structures in front of and behind it, which are not in focus, are "blurred" out of existence. Cine-radiography and kymography, both made possible simply by the labours of persevering technicians, show precisely the pathology of the living. The old pathologists saw certain changes post-mortem, correlated the pathological appearances with the clinical history of the patient during life, and deduced the causation of the symptoms from which the patient had suffered. Now it is possible to see, for example, the spasm due to irritation of the gut, and to study it minutely in the earliest stages of disease.

Antisepsis freed surgery from the last of its shackles. Roentgen rays and other aids to diagnosis showed what scope there was for this new-found freedom. One by one the forbidden organs came within reach of the surgeon's knife. Surgery, like medicine, began to embrace so wide a field that the individual could till but a small corner of it. Specialism began. Specialists in the past were all general surgeons with particular interests. Tagliacozzi was a general surgeon who liked creating new lips and noses just as the old Hindoo surgeons had done. Cheselden made lithotomy his speciality, but still did only one lateral lithotomy to half a dozen amputations. Specialism as we know it to-day only became necessary or even possible towards the end of the last century. With the specialists there came also the consultants, men who did but little operating themselves, yet had a vast experience of diagnosis, based usually on a long training in pathology. The consultant was generally a man who had become a surgeon after being a pathologist, but who was far better fitted to advise his colleagues what operations to perform than he was to perform them himself. In this sense the first surgical consultant proper in this country was Sir James Paget.

James Paget was born in 1814, one of seventeen children. One of his elder brothers became Regius Professor of Medicine at Cambridge. Another, named Arthur, was the model for Arthur Pendennis, a character created by a friend of his, William Thackeray. James served a surgical apprenticeship of four-and-a-half years. He dissected the limbs he had helped to amputate, and made wonderful drawings of his own dissections.

One such drawing of an ulcerated bowel was so beautifully executed that the patient's widow begged for a copy of it. His apprenticeship ended, he studied at St. Bartholomew's for two years, in which he made his first original observation. Hard little specks were often seen at that time in the muscles of dissected subjects. James wanted to know what these specks looked like under a microscope. There was no microscope in St. Bartholomew's. He went to the head of the natural history section of the British Museum. This gentleman was in the same state as St. Bartholomew's, but referred the young man to a colleague of his, who was able to produce this rare instrument. James Paget was delighted to find that the tiny specks were not, as had been tacitly assumed, "bony spicules", but were little worms curled up and surrounded by a hard capsule. Having discovered the *trichina spiralis*—which is usually conveyed to the human body by infected pork—James Paget turned again to more orthodox medical studies. In 1836 he duly qualified and was asked to a celebration breakfast by one of his examiners —Sir Astley Cooper. After qualifying he tried coaching backward students without much success. Then he became a sub-editor of the *Medical Gazette,* at a salary of £50 a year rising to £70, and curator of the museum at St. Bartholomew's at £40 a year.

Some dreary years followed, till in 1842 he began to assist in the cataloguing of the College of Surgeons' Museum, and in the next year he was given the lectureship in physiology at St. Bartholomew's, and appointed Warden of the new residential college for the medical students of that hospital. His lectures attracted students to the hospital, and inevitably he was made an assistant surgeon in the course of a few years. The professorship of anatomy and surgery of the College of Surgeons came next, and the course of lectures Paget delivered was on general pathology. In 1849 the *Pathological Catalogue* of the College of Surgeons' Museum was completed, and formed an exact description of over 3,500 specimens. From 1850 onwards the rise of James Paget to eminence was slow but steady. The number of students at St. Bartholomew's doubled during his long wardenship. His private practice, which about 1840 was bringing him sums varying from £3 to £14 a year, by 1878 was worth over £10,000 a year.

It was at this stage that Paget ceased to operate himself, and became a surgical consultant. He was perhaps the foremost pathologist of his time, and because of his pathological knowledge one of the greatest diagnosticians of all time. When Sir William Fergusson, the star pupil of Robert Knox, was at the height of his fame as a practical surgeon, it used to be said to any Londoner who was ill, "You ought to go to Paget to find out what is the matter with you, and then go to Fergusson to have it removed". Often Paget was asked to be present at operations performed by other surgeons, simply in order that he might be consulted if things went wrong. Appointment to the Royal household had long before then become inevitable. For forty-one years James Paget was a surgeon to Her Majesty Queen Victoria, and for thirty-six years to the then Prince of Wales. A baronetcy was conferred upon him in 1871. He was president of the Royal College of Surgeons, and of the Medico-Chirurgical Society, and a member of the General Medical Council, but the greatest honour that fell to his lot was the presidency of the International Medical Council Congress in London in 1881. On the opening day he addressed an audience of three thousand, which included the Prince of Wales, the Crown Prince of Germany and other Royalties, with Pasteur, Virchow, Koch, Charcot, Darwin, Huxley, Tyndall, and a host of lesser celebrities. Thirty learned bodies had conferred distinctions upon him in his lifetime. He had been the first to describe a disease of the nipple which precedes the appearance of cancer of the breast and which is now known as Paget's disease. He was not the first to describe Paget's disease of bones, or osteitis deformans, although it bears his name because he described it so accurately and separated it so clearly from other bony conditions. He died in 1899 at the age of eighty-five. Lister's methods he had tried late in life and with no success. Lister's own work in London he watched carefully. Then typically, once he was convinced that his previous lack of success was due to his own faulty application of the method, and not to anything in the method itself or the principles upon which it was founded, he paid public tribute to Lister. Referring in a speech to anti-sepsis and the results Lister had obtained, he said, "His success has been so great in contrast with my failures that I cannot for a moment doubt its value".

Sir James Paget lived long enough to see Lister taking his place as the leading London surgeon of the day, and to observe also the early growth of different specialities, for one of which he was, at least by example, in some measure responsible.

The old specialities were given a new lease of life by Listerism, and new specialities arose as if by magic.

Ophthalmology is one of the oldest specialities. Hammurabi, laying down his code in 2250 B.C., legislated specifically for operations on the eye—ten shekels for a successful operation, amputation of both the surgeon's hands in the event of failure. Celsus gave detailed descriptions of couching for cataract and several other ophthalmic operations. During the long Arabian period the surgery of the eye fell into the hands of itinerant practitioners, and was forgotten. Even in the Middle Ages the contributions made to ophthalmology were few and far between. A true knowledge of the anatomy of the eye was gained slowly in the sixteenth and seventeenth centuries. Preparations in which the arteries and veins had been injected were studied. The hand-lens was used increasingly often, then the microscope was brought into play, and the minute anatomy of the eye was worked out in the late eighteenth and early nineteenth centuries. Old theories of vision were overthrown, and it was realized that fundamentally the eye was a simple optical apparatus, with, however, the unique property of focusing objects both near and far. The ophthalmoscope was invented by Helmholtz in 1850, and allowed the surgeon to see the fundus of the living eye. Within a decade all ophthalmology was revolutionized. There was no longer any excuse for leaving the surgery of the eye in the hands of the strolling mountebanks, of whom one of the most famous had been Henry Blackbourne:

> Who travelled contynuouslye from one market towne to another, who could couche ye Cataracke welle, cure yt, Laye a scar Lipe, set a crockt necke strayght & helpe deafness. Though he could doe good in these cures yet he was soe wickedlye gyven that he would cousen & deceave men of great som of moneys by taken incurable diseases in hand. He was lusty amorously gyven to several women so that his coseninge made him fearfully to flee from place to place and often changed his name and habits in divers places & was often imprisoned for women. His skille was excelente, but his vices . . . *longus,* his practeste was this, yf he made a blinde man see; after he had couched ye Cataracke . . . yf he herde they did welle he woulde see ym agayne, yf not he would neuer come at ym.

Henry's innumerable descendants and all their fellows lost interest in ophthalmology when it became, almost overnight, one of the most exact of the many inexact sciences which make up medicine and surgery. Accurate diagnosis made feasible the planning of new operations. Listerism made it possible to carry out with safety procedures which had barely been dreamt of. Since that time every decade has seen firmly established some new advance in the surgery of the eye. Not much more than a hundred years ago ophthalmology was in much the same state as it was in the time of Galen. Of practitioners generally it was true to say that they could do only one of two things to their patients' eyes. They could instil drops or couch cataracts (*see plate facing* p. 385). If anything more was needed, the patient was unfortunate. Now even the age-old dream of new eyes for old is partially realized. The transplantation of a perfect cornea from an eye removed for some condition not affecting that part of it is possible. The procedure whereby such a cornea is grafted on to another eye to replace a cornea opaque from birth, or by accident, is now a standardized operation. It is literally possible to restore sight to at least a small proportion of the blind.

A speciality as old as ophthalmology is that of plastic surgery. It was practised by the ancient Hindoo surgeons, then forgotten except by a few itinerant families till Tagliacozzi revived one branch of it in the late sixteenth century. After his death the reconstruction of noses was again forgotten, until 1816 when Joseph Carpue—of *Mary's Ghost* fame—took it up once more. But Carpue's revival was even briefer than Tagliacozzi's. At a time when surgeons hesitated to perform even life-saving operations, because they feared hospital sepsis, no one in his senses would have embarked upon a long and complicated procedure for mere cosmetic reasons. It was again Listerism which made plastic surgery possible, but at the end of the last century and the beginning of this surgeons were too busy elaborating operations which were curative to worry about cosmetics. It was the war of 1914 to 1918 which made plastic surgery a pure speciality, by giving constant opportunities for its practice.

Men who were injured in the wars of the last century died from their wounds in many cases. Sometimes the injuries they received were themselves severe enough to cause death, and those less severely injured succumbed to gangrene, hospital sepsis, pyæmia, and other general infections. Listerism abolished these things. Men might live though they had limbs shot away, men might survive even the loss of a lower jaw. It became necessary to restore such men to some semblance of

humanity. A few surgeons began to treat these cases by building new jaws out of living bone and cartilage and flesh. Portions
of ribs could be built into jaw-bones, or bone could be taken
from the hip or shin. Sliding muscle flaps could mimic in
some degree the normal musculature, flaps of skin could be
brought up on long pedicles from the neck and shoulders.
First attempts at this new branch of surgery made passable
caricatures of men who had lost the semblance of man, but by
the end of the war plastic surgeons had cosmetic miracles by
the hundred to their credit. For years after the war they
were still repairing human wreckage. Innumerable patients
passed through their hands, and were given new noses, new
lips, and new cheeks, but at last all the flotsam of the "war to end
war" seemed to have been dealt with. Plastic surgery had ful-
filled the need which brought it into being, but plastic surgeons
still had work to do. Every modern means of transport, every
industrial mechanism, is potentially as apt to disfigure as a Mills
bomb—and disfigurement needs plastic surgery for its correction.
Plastic operations are still needed for such deformities as hare-
lip and cleft palate, for the facial scars left by burns or tuberculosis
of the skin, and even for birth-marks, like port-wine stains, which
may so disfigure as to make life miserable.

Older than either of these ophthalmic and plastic specialities is
that of midwifery. The surgical branch of pure midwifery
had no real existence, however, till antisepsis changed Cæsarean
section from a last-minute attempt to extract a live child from a
dying mother to an operation which would almost always save
the lives of both mother and child. In Paris in the century
between 1787 and 1876 not a single successful Cæsarean section
was performed. In England during the same period the
mortality from the operation was 86 per cent.—or about 100 per
cent. up to 1846 and not much more than 30 per cent. after
the discovery of anæsthesia. The Allgemeines Krankenhaus in
Vienna had its first successful Cæsarean section in 1877. After
antisepsis made the operation safe it was attempted more and
more often—so often that the wisdom of performing the operation
was never in doubt in the appropriate cases. Discussion began to
centre round the technique of operation. There were a dozen
different ways of performing the operation, now there are only two.
Even with full antisepsis, and the early form of asepsis, mortality
rates were often between 10 and 20 per cent. In the last quarter
of a century the mortality rates for both the mothers operated on

and the infants thus brought into the world have become steadily lower and lower. At Boston City Hospital, for example, over a period of ten recent years, 703 Cæsarean sections were done with a death-rate of 4.3 per cent. With the more modern operation, in which the womb is opened transversely low down in the pelvis, even this figure is bettered. A recent collected series of 3,700 such operations showed a death-rate of only 1.78 per cent. The operative risk is still there, but it is becoming less and less. As a result attention has now shifted from the question of technique and is concentrated on a clearer definition of those cases in which Cæsarean section is really necessary. There is no doubt that in the immediate past—and in the present—the operation has been performed sometimes on women who did not really need it.

It was in the last half of the nineteenth century that the men-midwives divided their art into the twin specialities of obstetrics and gynæcology, the one concerned with pregnancy, delivery, and the puerperium, and the other with diseases peculiar to women but not necessarily connected with pregnancy and parturition.

James Young Simpson and Lawson Tait were largely responsible for much of the earlier work which made gynæcology merit a place as a separate speciality, and Marion Sims was its greatest exponent. Ephraim McDowell of Virginia, a pupil of John Bell of Edinburgh, in 1809 removed a diseased ovary successfully for the first time. He performed the operation thirteen times altogether with eight recoveries. In this country the operation was undertaken by Lizars, by Charles Clay of Manchester, and by Spencer Wells in London. A few years later C. J. M. Langenbeck removed the entire womb in a case of cancer. Then it was found possible to remove fibroid tumours from the womb. But these operations were all isolated endeavours in different parts of the world. Gynæcology proper was established by James Marion Sims of South Carolina when in 1852 he successfully repaired a vesico-vaginal fistula—an abnormal communication between the urinary and genital passages in women—a condition which had defied all surgery for hundreds of years. He described, too, a method of amputating the neck of the womb. In England Robert Lawson Tait did more than anyone else to make gynæcology a speciality. He performed literally thousands of gynæcological operations, and he was a most truculent opponent of Lister and all his works. He never practised antisepsis, yet rarely lost a patient. This was because he insisted on strict cleanliness and always flushed out his operation wounds, and even the abdominal cavity, with boiled water. He was, in fact, though he refused to see any relation between bacteria and disease or between soap and water and the results he obtained, practising asepsis before the word was thought of. Tait was one of the first gynæcologists to operate successfully on a woman dying from the internal bleeding which follows the rupture of a pregnancy taking place inside the abdomen but not in the womb. He saw such a case in 1881 and was urged to operate by the patient's general practitioner. Not unnaturally Tait refused. The operation was theoretically possible, but had never been performed so far as he knew, and the patient was in a dying condition. She did die, but at the next opportunity Tait attempted operation. This patient also died, but in March of 1884 a third case was operated on successfully. After that, though the operation was always an emergency one, it became as standardized as it could be, and to-day it is performed regularly with complete success in the majority of cases.

Since Tait's death in 1899 gynæcology has grown up. The last twenty years or so of the last century was a period of rather hysterical adolescence. One procedure after another became fashionable as the guaranteed cure of most, if not all, of the ills to which women are prone. There was a long pessary phase, in which every other womb was perched on a long-stemmed cup and lifted as near the umbilicus as possible. Pelvic cellulitis held the field for a while, and the internal organs of every other woman were believed to be in a state of spreading inflammation, for the relief of which a variety of odd procedures was recommended. Excision of the clitoris was an acutely fashionable relapse to barbarism for some years. Even recently in certain centres Cæsarean section has been more often fashionable than necessary, as has dilatation and curettage. These growing-pains are not quite over, but to-day gynæcology embraces as wide and as valuable a sphere of operative and non-operative treatment as any other department of surgery, and is as closely related to obstetrics as it should be, despite attempts even in recent times to divorce the two.

Many other young specialities grew up side by side with gynæcology. Diseases of the ear, nose, and throat were conditions treated by quacks till the late nineteenth century. John of Gaddesden discussed vaguely certain diseases of the ear, but his only contribution to their treatment was in cases in which there was a discharge. He recommended that all the morbid material in the ear should be sucked out through a tube, which unhappy duty was, of course, to be delegated to one of the lower orders. Small wonder that surgeons of succeeding centuries, tough-stomached though they were, left their patients' ears to the quacks. Then about 1770 J. L. Petit opened the mastoid cavity behind the ear for the first time. Some thirty years later Astley Cooper perforated the ear-drum for the relief of inflammation. Gradually the anatomy of the ear, which had long been known, was properly related to its pathology. The indications for different operations were clearly defined. The operations themselves were carried out more often after the discovery of anæsthesia, more often still after the establishment of antisepsis.

The same progress was seen in laryngology. Laryngology, unlike other specialities which "just growed", was created one September day in 1854 by a singing-master, strolling in the Palais Royal in Paris. Señor Manuel Garcia wanted to see how his larynx worked. Since Galen first watched this organ in his long-suffering pigs many other men had had the same wish. Garcia saw how it could be realized. The idea came to him out of a very blue sky. With two mirrors it is possible to see round a corner, and the larynx is so far round a corner as to be normally invisible. Garcia bought his two mirrors, a little dental mirror with a long handle, which cost 6 francs, and a hand mirror. The dental mirror he placed firmly against his uvula, and what appeared there he saw in the hand mirror, which reflected a ray of light on to the dental mirror. The rest was almost as simple. The larynx could be, and was, studied in life. Departures from the normal were detected ever earlier and earlier. Simple operations, such as removing polypi, were attempted with success. More difficult procedures followed, and by the time Garcia died in 1906, at the ripe age of 102, a distinct department of the surgical art had been firmly based upon the laryngoscope he invented. Otology, the speciality concerned with diseases of the ear, and laryngology were soon linked together, and watched with interest the rise of rhinology, the study of diseases of the nose, the youngest branch of the triple speciality of otorhinolaryngology. The nose and the air sinuses opening off it were studied by anatomists, then by pathologists and bacteriologists. Then the surgeons took a hand, and sinuses were drained of pus, curetted, syringed out, and sometimes excised. Now there are accepted operations for a variety of nasal and near-nasal conditions, as well as operations not generally accepted for an even greater variety of conditions about which relatively little is known.

Otorhinolaryngology, like ophthalmology, is now an accepted and valuable speciality. Yet barely a hundred years ago neither of these departments of surgery existed in the sense in which they are known to-day, and in fact they were not even respectable. The London Eye and Ear Infirmary was in need of an honorary president at a time when the redoubtable Abernethy was at the height of his fame. Abernethy was approached by the governors of the newly-founded institution, and asked to act in this capacity. He replied to the invitation with his usual forcefulness.

"I can see no good that can arise from this to the public; it may be of use to the surgeons, but I candidly tell you I consider it quackery; I will never lend my name to sanction it; every surgeon should be acquainted with the diseases of the organs of sight and hearing; and to detach them from regular surgery would be not less injurious to the science than oppressive to the public."

In one sense Abernethy was right. Specialization has inevitable disadvantages, but the many specialities into which surgery has been divided would not be surviving, and indeed flourishing, to-day if they had not justified themselves by their accomplishments. The great empires of more than a thousand years ago saw their surgery decay not because their surgeons specialized but because their specialists achieved nothing.

XXIV.   Today and Tomorrow

LISTER'S WORK NOT ONLY GAVE NEW LIFE TO ALL THE OLDER specialities but created entirely new specialities, by giving the lie direct to the age-old doctrine of the forbidden cavities.   Antisepsis allowed surgeons to explore with impunity the regions which Sir John Erichsen, and wiser and greater men than he, had called taboo—the abdomen, the chest, the skull, and the joints.

Before the time of Lister there had been no abdominal surgery other than that described by the Elizabethan surgeons and an occasional successful Cæsarean section.   If by accident the abdomen was slit open, the protruding contents would be pushed back again and the wound hastily sutured.   The next step was taken by Ephraim McDowell and his followers when they deliberately opened the lower abdomen to excise diseased ovaries. Then came the era of antisepsis, and the slow realization that there was no more danger in opening an abdominal cavity than there was in amputating a limb.   A German contemporary of Lister's led the way in exploring this new field—the surgery of the abdomen.

Theodor Billroth became professor of surgery at Zürich in 1860, and at Vienna seven years later.   This latter chair he held till his death in 1894 at the age of sixty-five.   He was the first surgeon to treat cancer of the stomach by excising the affected portion of that organ.   He was the first to resect the œsophagus, or gullet, and the first to excise completely the larynx.   These were his outstanding and dramatic contributions to surgery. They were important, but not as important as his less sensational achievements.   He showed on hundreds of occasions that "internal amputations" could be undertaken as successfully as the amputation of limbs.   Diseased segments of the intestine were resected by him, and the two remaining ends of the gastro-intestinal tube joined together again.   Other affected parts of the gut he treated by short-circuiting operations, joining up parts of the bowel above and below the diseased area so that it would be left at rest, no longer irritated by the passage of the intestinal contents.   A great deal of work on the pathology and surgery of the alimentary tract Billroth undertook.   The innumerable problems he could not himself elucidate he left to his distinguished pupils.   There was Johann von Mikulicz-

Radecki, a Pole who was Billroth's assistant up to 1881, then professor of surgery at Königsberg and later at Breslau. Billroth had excised the gullet. Mikulicz took the operation to its logical conclusion and combined excision with a plastic replacement, so that after operation the patient could take his food in the ordinary way instead of having to rely on fluids poured through a valvular opening direct into his stomach. Mikulicz extended his great teacher's work in other directions, advancing still further the surgery of the stomach and the large intestine. He was also one of the first surgeons to wear gloves while operating. But the white cotton gloves he introduced were soon superseded by Halsted's rubber gloves. Anton Wolfler was another pupil of Billroth's. He perfected the operation of gastro-enterostomy in which the stomach is made to open into the upper part of the small intestine. This again was simply a technical advance based on the work Billroth himself had done in joining together parts of the small intestine. Other schools took up the same work. Richard von Volkmann of Leipzig, for example, was the first to excise the rectum for cancer.

By the end of the last century there were very few organs left in the abdomen which had not been attacked by different surgeons. A gall-bladder was removed for the first time in 1882, and at much the same time a floating kidney was neatly anchored. In 1888 it was found possible to make a section of the large intestine open and discharge its contents through the abdominal wall. Twelve months later Charles McBurney of Roxbury, Massachusetts, showed that pain and tenderness localized at a point on the abdomen which has since been known as McBurney's point indicated the need for operation. Operation was necessary to deal with inflammation of the appendix by removing this vestigial organ. Appendicitis was not a new condition. Mestivier described a case in 1759 and even attempted operation; the patient died, however. James Parkinson, one of John Hunter's pupils, in 1812 recognized the perforation of an acutely inflamed appendix as being the cause of death in one of his patients. Hancock of Charing Cross opened an abscess arising from an inflamed appendix in 1848. Kronlein in 1886 did the first appendectomy for a perforated appendix. His patient died, but in the following year Morton operated on a similar case successfully. The appendix was a neglected organ till the latter part of the nineteenth century. Then once McBurney had clarified the question of diagnosis, appendicitis became successively common, more common, and fashionable. Perhaps the greatest early exponent of the operation in England was Sir Frederick Treves, who, incidentally, operated upon King Edward VII in 1902. The incidence of appendicitis is still rising, and will probably continue to do so unless a revolution in the dietetic habits of civilized man is brought about. It was also in 1889 that a first attack was made on the chest wall. A small portion of a rib was removed so that an abscess between the lung and the ribs might be properly drained. In the year 1893 a new peak of achievement was reached when Fedor Krause opened a patient's skull and excised the ganglionic enlargement of the fifth cranial nerve, which lies on the base of the skull beneath the frontal lobe of the brain, to cure a case of facial neuralgia. At much the same time Heusner was successful in sewing up a perforation of the stomach due to gastric ulceration. In successive years this operation was performed more often, until in 1901 Moynihan elaborated further the actual technique of operation. Certain of these cases had some degree of obstruction of the terminal part of the stomach—the pylorus—at the point where it opens into the small intestine. Moynihan overcame this by supplementing the actual repair of the perforation with a short-circuiting operation to overcome the partial pyloric obstruction.

All these early operations were for the most part excisions—removal of the appendix, or of part of a rib, part of a nerve within the skull, part of the intestine or stomach, part of the ligaments or bones making up a joint. Reconstructive surgery was to come later, but already four new specialities were being rapidly defined. The many followers of Billroth were devoting themselves to the surgical treatment of conditions affecting abdominal organs. Another school of surgeons was concentrating upon diseases of bones and joints. A smaller group were tentatively exploring the surgery of the brain and spinal cord and the nervous system generally. By the beginning of this century there were specialists in each of these three fields, and one or two men in different parts of the world were laying the foundations of the newest speciality—thoracic surgery, the surgery of the heart and lungs and other structures in the chest.

The French surgeons of this period were among the first to realize that so far as the surgery of the abdominal organs was concerned further specialization was necessary. Felix Guyon and others took up the cystoscope, which had been introduced in 1877, and were able to see clearly the changes taking place in the urinary bladders of their patients. They began to develop the surgery of the genito-urinary tract, taking within its compass the treatment of surgical diseases of the urinary passages, the bladder, prostate, ureters, and kidneys. Henry Jacob Bigelow of Boston advanced the same speciality, reviving, for example, the treatment of stones in the bladder by a crushing operation. Then came other advances which have led to the perfection of two operative triumphs. One is the operation in which the whole bladder is removed. The secret lies in a trick of plastic surgery whereby the ureters, which drain the kidney, are moved from the points at which they enter the bladder and made to open instead into the rectum. The drainage of urine from the kidneys having been safeguarded in this way, it is possible to remove the entire bladder—a procedure which was long thought incompatible with life. The second advance has been made possible by electrical technicians. Enlargement of the prostate could only be treated effectively—by removal of the gland—after the development of antisepsis. Several operations were elaborated, and each had its exponents. As with cases of stone in the bladder, two approaches were possible— through the abdomen or through the perineum. Now there is a third route. An electric resectoscope can be passed down the ordinary urinary channel of the male, and by means of an electrically cutting loop of fine wire all the obstructing part of the gland can be removed under direct vision. This approximates as nearly as anything can to bloodless surgery. The success that may be achieved by this method is well shown by the latest figures from the Mayo Clinic. There 1,200 patients, all over the age of seventy, had transurethral prostatectomies performed by means of the electric resectoscope. The mortality rate was 1.6 per cent.

Victor Horsley was the greatest early exponent in this country of neurosurgery. He and Macewen of Glasgow and Rickman Godlee were among the first surgeons to operate on the brain. In 1887 Horsley removed a tumour from the spinal cord for the first time. This was at the National Hospital for the Paralysed and Epileptic at Queen's Square, London, and throughout the operation the carbolic spray was used. He also mapped out different areas of the brain controlling different functions, and tracts of nerve fibres leading from the brain to the spinal cord, and he standardized the operative approaches to the central nervous system. The experimental mapping out of the functions of different parts of the brain had been begun by Broca as early as 1861. Knowledge of cerebral function led to greater certainty in clinical diagnosis. It became possible to say with increasing accuracy that if certain functions were disturbed the corresponding parts of the brain must be affected. Later developments in pathology and in roentgenology were to make diagnosis even more exact. Not only the site of a lesion but the nature of that lesion—whether a blood-clot, a cyst, a tumour, or an inflammatory process—could be foretold in an increasing number of cases. Exact diagnosis has made cerebral surgery more of a science than an art. The surgeon who opens a skull today is almost always certain where he will find the seat of pressure or destruction, usually certain as to the nature of the pathological process concerned, and in many cases certain of its extent and operability. The surgery of the skull, which began when primitive man made the first trepan hole, is now but a part of the approach to the brain within the skull. The freshly flaked flint has been displaced by an electrically driven saw. The opening in the skull is no longer an end in itself but only a means to an end.

Neurosurgeons did not long confine their activities to the brain and spinal cord. They began to deal with the nerves arising from these organs. One of the nerves taking origin from the brain, the trigeminal, may be affected in such a way as to produce a neuralgia which causes almost unbearable facial pain. Obviously if this nerve could be cut through, the pain would be relieved. To be effective the division had to be made at the point where the nerve enlarged into a ganglion on the floor of the skull. Krause cut across this ganglion in 1892, as did Hartley, and a year later he excised the entire ganglion.

Thus in 1919 Hutchison was able to report seventy such operations with only three deaths. Slowly the operation has been perfected to give the maximal relief and the minimal interference with the functions of the nerve other than the conduction of pain stimuli. Charles Frazier, who died only in 1937, performed this perfected operation over a thousand times, with a mortality rate below 1 per cent. Now Sjöqvist of Sweden has gone one step further. He divides the pain fibres—and the pain fibres only—in the descending trigeminal tract in the medulla oblongata.

Neurosurgeons also found it possible to unite successfully

divided nerves. Then in cases in which nerves had been extensively injured, portions of other nerves were used to link the divided ends, or a severed nerve might be linked with an intact one which could be trained to take up a new function. The first operation of this type was performed in 1898, when the nerve which controls the movement of shrugging the shoulders was linked to a divided facial nerve.

The modern surgery of bones and joints is compounded of parts of the old and the new surgery. Since prehistoric times fractures have been sustained and have had to be repaired. In this sense manipulative orthopædics is as old as it can be. Operative orthopædics, however, is a development which Lister made possible and to which he made several personal contributions, as for instance when he wired together the fragments of a fractured knee-cap. From then onwards it became more and more common for surgeons to operate on fractures of the knee-cap and the tip of the elbow. In either case the procedure was the same. The fragments were replaced in exact position and held there by fine wire. The same principle was further applied by Arbuthnot Lane in the ten years preceding the war, when he fixed fractures of long bones by means of metal plates. Lane's success was due to his remarkable "no-touch" technique, every step in the operation being done with instruments, so that even the surgeon's gloved fingers never touched the damaged bone. Meanwhile in Liverpool Robert Jones was continuing the work of Hugh Owen Thomas. Thomas had insisted upon the importance in the treatment of fractures of prolonged rest, with the injured limb in properly devised and carefully applied splints. He insisted, too, on the importance of the functional rather than the anatomical result. The patient wanted a full range of movement in his limb rather than meticulously exact union of the broken bones. Robert Jones followed his teaching and deprecated the too-frequent recourse to open operation. The war of 1914 to 1918 provided the acid test of different methods of fracture treatment. The metal extension splints, accurately fitting, that Thomas had devised replaced only slowly the old, clumsy, flat, wooden splints, but in 1917 Thomas's splint for lower limb fractures was literally brought to the battlefield. The splint was applied on the field to all cases of compound fracture of the thigh before any attempt was made at moving the man to a casualty station. The American orthopædists who were working with Robert Jones at that time almost took as their motto the briefest possible description of this method—"Splint 'em where they lie". This simple measure, combined with more adequate methods of treating shock, reduced the mortality from this injury from 80 per cent. to 15 per cent.

Robert Jones, as Director of Military Orthopædics, thus brilliantly demonstrated the soundness of the principles he had learnt from Hugh Owen Thomas. The period after the war saw reconstructive orthopædics coming into its own. There were a multitude of disabled men who had to be fitted for civil life again. As in the case of plastic surgery, the need for special hospitals was obvious, and was met. Units were created which dealt only with orthopædic cases. Surgeons worked in teams, assisted by highly trained nurses and technicians. Their results were admirable, but it took ten years' propaganda before it was generally realized that the same degree of specialization would be attended by the same excellent results if applied to dealing with fractures sustained in civil life. In this country the first fracture unit was established at Ancoats Hospital, Manchester, in the early part of 1914. Now there are similar units associated with almost every large hospital, but few of them are of more than three or four years' standing. Two powerful stimuli led to their creation. The establishment in 1926 of the Vienna Accident Hospital, under the direction of Lorenz Bohler, was the first, and the second was the publication in 1935 of a report on the organized treatment of fractures by the British Medical Association. Bohler showed what excellent results could be achieved if one unit was dealing with all fracture cases, if there was absolute continuity of treatment from the moment the fracture was sustained to the day the patient returned to work, and if there was unity of surgical control throughout this period. The B.M.A. report showed how badly the results of fracture treatment generally compared with the results achieved in the few organized fracture clinics then in existence in this country. Bohler's results were largely due to his application of moulded plaster-of-paris splints directly to the skin, so that, once reduced, the fractured ends of a bone were kept in as perfect fixation as possible. For many fractures this is now standard treatment, but in one or two special instances other methods of fixation are being tried. Fracture of the neck of the femur, for example, has always been notoriously difficult to treat. Still on trial is the Smith-Petersen operation, in which the two fragments of bone are fixed by driving through them under radiological control a three-flanged nail. The Smith-Petersen operation—and all its innumerable minor modifications—has been on trial almost long enough. It is probably correct to say that it is a method which has come to stay. The same cannot be said of a recent revolutionary operation for the treatment of severe fractures of the knee-cap. In about twenty cases this accident has been treated by removal of the entire knee-cap—and it is claimed that the patient has a more powerful leg after than before operation. This may be a major step forwards—or it may not.

The treatment of fractures, and fractures only, made up the orthopædics of the early nineteenth century, till in 1835 W. J. Little, an English physician, allowed Stromeyer of Hanover to operate on his deformed foot. The operation was the simple division of a contracted muscle tendon—in principle exactly the same operation that the quacks had long been performing in cases of wryneck. Little was so impressed with the improvement of his own deformity that he mastered the technique of the operation, and soon was performing it on his own patients in the treatment of clubfoot and other deformities. Then he founded in Bloomsbury the Orthopædic Infirmary, which was to become the Royal National Orthopædic Hospital. For thirty odd years deformities of different types were treated with varying degrees of success by dividing tendons, manipulating, and fixing in a splint or other appliance. Anæsthesia and antisepsis allowed the orthopædists to correct surgically bony as well as muscular and tendinous deformities, and in 1880 William Macewen of Glasgow did the first deliberately planned bone-grafting operation. Now it may be said that the scope of orthopædics has widened to include the treatment not only of accidents, but also of any disease which may directly affect the locomotor system of the body. Bone and muscle are the twin raw materials of the orthopædist's art, and the emphasis now is always on the prevention rather than on the correction of deformity and crippling. Bone grafts and tendon transplants are of more interest to-day than the most cunning mechanical contrivance for the support of deformity, which, unless congenital, always represents an orthopædic failure.

The surgery of the chest and of the heart and lungs is a twentieth-century development. Ernst Ferdinand Sauerbruch made the first advances in this new department of surgery while acting as assistant to Mikulicz at Breslau. Now as a result of his work, and that of a handful of enthusiastic contemporaries of his, almost unbelievable advances have been made. Lungs which are diseased can be collapsed and put at rest for long periods, then expanded again. Individual lobes of the lung can be removed, or even an entire lung. The technique of operations on the lung and the membranes surrounding it has been steadily improved. It is now possible, for example, to divide fibrous adhesions which are connecting the lung to the chest wall under direct vision. This is done through an instrument resembling closely the operating cystoscope, which is passed into the space between the lungs and the chest wall, just as a cystoscope is passed into the bladder. The excision of an entire lobe of a lung, which used always to be done in two stages, is now carried out as often and as successfully with only one operation. When a foreign body, perhaps a small coin or a tooth, is inhaled into the lungs it is now routine practice to localize it exactly by X-ray examination and remove it through a bronchoscope—a long, tubular instrument, electrically lit, which can be passed down the entire trachea and into the bronchi, the smaller respiratory tubes into which the wind-pipe divides. In recent years attempts have been made to excise cancers of the lung. Cancer of the lung is a condition which is being recognized more often, and which seems to be on the increase. Successful operations are still relatively few, but will obviously become more common with earlier diagnosis. Another condition in which the thoracic surgeons are scoring occasional remarkable successes is bronchial asthma. Asthma is for the most part a medical condition, which can be cured, or at least alleviated, by medical treatment. There are a proportion of cases, however, which resist every method of treatment from psychotherapy to Plombières douches. Asthma is due to a nervous spasm of the small tubules in the lungs. The nervous spasm may be set up by emotion, in which case a psychiatrist is called in, or by sensitivity to pollen, feathers, or some other agent, in which case a physician may be able to desensitize the patient, and so on. In the few resistant cases the original exciting cause is either not known or incapable of correction. The ultimate pathology of the asthmatic condition is the same, however, whatever the cause may be. There is an over-action of the nerves controlling the bronchioles which sets up spasm. Surgical attack is directed at these nerves. They are dissected out from the root of the lung, which lies deeply in the chest, and once these over-acting nerves are removed, the patient simply cannot have asthma again.

Surgeons who found they could remove entire lungs with impunity were not likely to regard the heart and its coverings as untouchable for very long. For centuries the heart was ranked with the brain as an organ the slightest injury to which would prove fatal. Ambroise Paré, with his usual temerity, suggested that wounds of the heart might occasionally heal spontaneously. Since Paré said so, his contemporaries had to agree, though none of them really believed it, and his immediate successors tolerantly placed this remark with the more apocalyptical of Paré's monsters, certain of which were the undoubted products of his lively imagination. After the publication of Harvey's *De Motu Cordis* it was possible to take a rational view of the problem, but, even so, it was only in the latter part of the nineteenth century that Paré's suggestion was considered seriously. Then Block showed by animal experiments that successful repair of a wound of the heart was possible. He and others promptly suggested that this experimental finding should be applied to human cases as and when they arose. Even the great Billroth condemned this revolutionary proposal, and for a while it was forgotten. Then on June 8, 1896, Guido Farina attempted the operation. This valiant endeavour failed and the patient died, but shortly afterwards Rehn successfully sutured an injured heart. To-day there are records of many similar successful cases. The next step was to drain from between the heart and its coverings pus which had accumulated in certain cases of pericarditis. Tuffier in 1898 published the first account of direct heart massage. Since then the procedure has been attempted on scores of occasions, and at least a proportion of patients whose hearts stopped suddenly in the course of operation have been literally brought back to life by the hand of a quick-witted surgeon.

Trendelenburg in 1907 astonished the surgical world by his impossibly daring suggestion that pulmonary embolism should be treated by operation. This condition is almost always fatal. It occurs when a blood-clot which has formed in a vein, perhaps after some simple operation, such as the repair of a hernia, becomes freed and is carried by the circulating blood to the artery conveying blood from the heart to the lungs. Here the solid clot is held up, obstructing the whole circulation and causing death, usually within the space of a few minutes. Trendelenburg found that it was possible in a calf to expose this pulmonary artery, incise it, and repair the incision by suture without killing the animal. On theoretical and experimental grounds the same operation should be possible in man and clots could be removed from the artery. Practically the difficulties were immense. Rarely was there any warning of the fact that a clot had suddenly entered the general circulation, and once this had happened, life remained in the patient for not more than ten minutes after the clot had been firmly lodged in the pulmonary artery. The difficulties were overcome. The operation was practised on dissecting-room subjects till its essentials could be completed in three or four minutes. In this period of time a T-shaped incision was made through skin and muscle; the inner ends of the second and third ribs were removed; the artery which supplies the breast was ligatured; the membrane surrounding the left lung was pulled gently aside; the thick membrane around the heart itself was opened; a rubber tube was passed round the pulmonary artery so that it could be lifted up and incised; the incision was made into the artery itself; the clot was lifted out with forceps; then a clamp applied to the incision in the artery allowed the blood to circulate freely again. This was surgery which would have delighted Robert Liston. The surgeon and his assistant and theatre nurses went into training till all these things could be done like clockwork. In sewing up the artery and the chest wall again speed was necessary, but no great speed, for by that time the patient would be alive again, and the operation could be completed peacefully. If the patient was not alive, the operation just became a post-mortem exercise and speed was even less necessary. The team being trained, all that remained was the necessity for keeping a theatre and the appropriate instruments always ready. Trendelenburg did this, and in 1908 operated on two cases. The first patient died during the operation, and the second lived for thirty-seven hours. A few enthusiasts in different centres began to follow in the footsteps of Trendelenburg. One patient lived for five days after operation. Then another, and finally in 1924 a patient of Kirschner's made a complete and lasting recovery.

The most remarkable achievement of the thoracic surgeons, however, is the most recent. The heart, like every other organ, has to be supplied with blood, which is conveyed into the substance of the heart muscle by the coronary arteries. These arteries are subject to the same diseases as other arteries, but with infinitely more disastrous results, for the heart which is not receiving an adequate blood-supply will not long support life. Leriche and Fontaine in 1932 implanted a chest muscle on to the heart of a dog, which had previously had one branch of its coronary artery ligatured. The chest muscle—the pectoral— brought a new blood-supply to the failing heart, and the dog survived. Then Beck tried the same operation in man, and now six of his patients are still living and well. Laurence O'Shaughnessy described the operations he had performed on racing greyhounds in 1936. Instead of grafting the pectoral muscle on to the heart, he brought up from the abdomen a graft of the omentum—the fatty apron, well supplied with blood-vessels, which covers the intestines. What these greyhounds did to the electric hare after recovery from the operation is racing history. Since then a series of patients has been operated on, and even at this early stage it seems that another advance has been made in the surgery of the heart. Patients who were cardiac cripples, unable to drive a car, walk farther than a few hundred yards, or live other than in ground-floor rooms, have been enabled to live almost normal lives. These patients have not been given new hearts for old, but they have received a literal new lease of life, for at least a few years.

The way in which this operation has been devised, perfected, and applied to human patients epitomizes the whole trend of modern surgery. In the first place the problem is approached in the experimental laboratory. It is found that the disease in man can be mimicked in animals. Cutting off part of the blood-supply to the heart by ligating a branch of the coronary artery gives rapidly the effects brought about slowly in the human heart by arterial disease. Then one by one different procedures are tried. Many are unsuccessful. Some succeed technically, but involve too great operative risks. At length a procedure is found which is successful and as free from risk as may be. It is perfected so far as possible and applied to a series of animals. After operation they are watched carefully for long periods. When fully recovered, their tolerance for exercise is estimated and compared with their pre-operative performance. Then the surgeon leaves the laboratory and goes to the hospital wards. Suitable cases are brought together. They are in the care of distinguished physicians, who select those suitable for operation. There is a final consultation between three men. The physician is satisfied that this suggested operation offers the only hope the patient has, is satisfied that the operation can do no harm and may do good. The anæsthetist is as certain as he can be that the patient will stand the anæsthetic. The surgeon has weighed the risks of operation; the technical difficulties have been assessed. A decision is made, and a freely consenting patient is prepared for operation. This preparation is undertaken jointly by the surgeon and the physician. By every medical aid the patient is made as fit as he can be for operation. A carefully planned anæsthetic is given one day, and the operation is begun and ended. There is nothing very dramatic about it. Perfect teamwork and a practised craftsmanship do not make for drama. The patient is returned to the wards. He recovers fully from the anæsthetic, and passes from the hands of the anæsthetist into those of his two colleagues, the physician leading and the surgeon in attendance. The first few days are anxious ones. Then it is clear that the post-operative danger period is ended. Convalescence is slow and quiet. Three months later the patient is examined again. Simple tests and exercises are gone through. Six months after operation this process is repeated, and again at the end of twelve months. Preliminary communications to the medical press on the results of the animal experiments are now supplemented by reports of the first few human cases—ordinary individuals going about their work, unconscious of the fact that they are integral parts of the living mosaic of surgical history. In ten years' time a reasonable assessment of the operation may be fairly made. After twenty years it should be possible to define the limitations of the operation quite clearly, and to answer the recurrent question—has this procedure contributed to surgical progress or not?

It is not only in thoracic surgery that laboratory workers, physicians, and surgeons are showing what can be achieved by close team-work. There has been exactly the same approach to the surgery of the endocrines and the surgery of the sympathetic nervous system, both of which specialities are still in their infancy.

The sympathetic nervous system controls all the involuntary muscles in the body, whether in the heart, the lungs, the intestines or blood-vessels. In the case of any group of these muscles it may be that an impulse from the sympathetic nerves causes spasm or constriction. Normally this is balanced or prevented by the opposing action of the parasympathetic nerves, which will cause lengthening of the involuntary muscle-fibre and so dilatation. In other muscle groups the parasympathetic may cause contraction and the sympathetic relaxation. If these two actions are perfectly balanced, as they are in health, the organs controlled by these autonomic nerves will function normally. But where the balance is upset there will be an over-action of one or the other group of nerves. This may be shown, for example, by persistent contraction of the blood-vessels in the hands or feet, or both. This condition is known as Raynaud's disease, after Maurice Raynaud, who described it first in 1862. The early symptoms are slight. The hands are white, cold, rather insensitive, and liable to chilblains. Later, the fingers become blue and icy cold. Last of all a dry gangrene may set in. The surgery of this condition, and of a corresponding state of affairs affecting the lower limbs, is only effective in the early stages. At a late phase the small arteries have become permanently constricted and are quite unable to expand again to their normal size. But if the over-acting sympathetic nerves can be literally cut out before this happens, then the unopposed parasympathetic will take control and the vessels will dilate and become even slightly larger than normal. The condition has been over-corrected, but the onset of gangrene has been prevented. The various operations devised for the correction of this lack of autonomic nerve balance are all more or less severe, and the results are often not permanent. But with improved technique, earlier diagnosis, and closer co-operation between general practitioners and surgeons and physicians the results are steadily becoming better. The conditions in which the operation of sympathectomy may have some value are innumerable, and range from dysmenorrhœa to disseminated sclerosis, but the conditions in which the value of sympathectomy has been proved are inevitably few, since it is only in the last ten years that this operation has been practised at all extensively. As early as 1899 Jaboulay contrived to relieve severe pain in the legs by simply removing from around the affected arteries the fine network of sympathetic nerves. Réné Leriche continued this work, and Royle and Hunter extended it by dividing sympathetic nerves at the point where they left the spinal cord, but it was not till May 20 of 1924 that A. W. Adson of the Mayo Clinic removed the sympathetic ganglia which lie deep in the abdomen and achieved the same results as Jaboulay and Leriche, but much more permanently. Since then the operation has become an established method of treatment. Eighty-seven of a recent group of one hundred cases of thrombo-angiitis obliterans, a vascular disease of the lower limbs, were markedly improved by the operation, which is known as lumbar sympathectomy. In Raynaud's disease the same operation may be called for, or an equivalent procedure directed at the sympathetic nerves in the neck, according to whether the arms or legs are most affected. Now the operation of sympathectomy has been applied to a variety of conditions, often with success, occasionally with no more good than harm done, and slowly the surgery of the autonomic nervous system is advancing.

The endocrine or glandular system has only in recent years been the subject of planned surgical attacks. The foundations of this department of modern surgery were laid in 1878 when Theodor Kocher of Switzerland, a pupil of Billroth, removed the enlarged thyroid gland of a patient suffering from goitre. This ductless gland in the neck may enlarge without causing anything other than local disfigurement. But if it enlarges and at the same time becomes over-active, a series of typical symptoms arise. The patient becomes nervous, loses weight, and has palpitations and a fine tremor of the hands, and his eyes seem to be starting from his head. Kocher cured this condition by surgical removal of the gland, but in thirty of his first hundred cases he left his patients without sufficient thyroid tissue for the normal needs of the body. They became fat, dull, dry-skinned, and lethargic. For a long time every surgeon had his own ideas about how much of the thyroid should be excised and how much left. Now it is generally accepted that about seven-eighths of the over-active gland should be removed. If by chance too much is removed, the patient can be maintained in normal health by the administration of thyroid extract, a second line of surgical defence provided by the physiologists.

Physiologists the world over began studying the other ductless glands—the parathyroids which lie beneath the thyroid, the pituitary in the skull, the adrenals which lie above the kidneys, and the male and female genital glands. Harvey Cushing in his monograph on the pituitary, published in 1912, showed to perfection the interdependence of physiology, pathology, clinical medicine, and surgery in the study of glandular disturbances. From each point of view he and his colleagues studied this tiny gland lying beneath the brain. They laid down the indications for its removal in certain disorders such as giantism, infantilism, or great obesity, changes brought about by disorders of the gland. Cushing in his first series of forty-three cases in which operation on the pituitary was undertaken had an operative death-rate of just over 10 per cent. Previously, perhaps a dozen surgeons in different parts of the world had operated altogether on fifty-three cases, the mortality rate for this collected series being 40 per cent. The functions of the pituitary are still being unravelled, as are those of the parathyroids, which are concerned with the laying down of calcium in bone, and of the adrenals.

It is in connexion with the adrenals that the most recent advances in surgical endocrinology have been made. It has been known for some years that changes in the adrenals in females may lead to masculinization, with the most unfortunate physical and psychological results. The bearded woman of the fair-ground is an extreme example of this kind of case. Usually in these cases the girl is quite normal till the age of fifteen or sixteen. Then hair begins to appear on her face, arms, legs, and abdomen. The texture and distribution of the hair correspond exactly to those of the male. The general structure of the body tends more and more to the masculine. The girl becomes broad-shouldered, deep-chested, and narrow-hipped. Her breasts are either infantile or quite undeveloped. Her voice deepens. Menstruation may never occur, and the genitalia approximate to those of the male. In a few years an adrenal tumour may convert a normal girl into an abnormal half-man. The mental state of these unhappy creatures can barely be imagined, yet until recently nothing could be done for them, and they could but choose between a fair-ground and a nunnery.

In 1933 H. W. C. Vines showed that part of the adrenal gland in these patients differed microscopically from that of normal women. An operation was devised for the removal of one of the two glands. The excision of both glands is fatal, but it was thought that if the two were over-active and one was removed, the over-activity of the remaining gland might simply represent the joint activity of two normal glands. A special clinic was set up at Charing Cross Hospital. Cases were sent there by physicians and neurologists. A psychiatrist saw them, and weeded out those cases in which the sexual disturbances were purely psychological, or more psychological than endocrine, in origin. The remaining cases were subjected to a long series of laboratory tests. Then the abdomen was explored and the two adrenal glands examined. After this first diagnostic operation some cases were left alone, but the suitable cases were kept in the clinic and operated on again a few weeks later, the larger of the two adrenal glands being removed. In almost every one of the thirty cases operated on successfully it has been possible to remove all the masculine hair painlessly the day after operation. Soon after operation menstruation has returned, or begun for the first time, and gradually the bodily contour has changed back again to the female type. Hairy half-men have become normal women again. It is clear that the number of patients requiring this operation is few, and the number who will be thought good operative risks fewer still, but the gain in human happiness from this procedure is already considerable.

This is but one of several instances in which results have been achieved by surgeons, physicians, and laboratory workers, co-operating with specialists in such an apparently unrelated department of medicine as psychiatry. Much the same kind of team in the last few years has been delving into almost unexplored regions, and gathering material on which may be based the surgery of the intellect and emotions. Many parts of the brain have known functions—largely utilitarian in character. Thus, certain parts of the cerebral cortex control the movements of the limbs, while others record sensations of heat, cold, pain, and so on. Others still register the senses of sight, smell, taste, hearing, and so forth. But though knowledge of cerebral function is accumulating fast, there remain relatively large parts of the human brain about which little or nothing is known. Occasionally some such part of the cerebral cortex is destroyed, perhaps by accident or disease, perhaps in removing surgically a difficult cyst or tumour. Patients thus affected have been studied carefully, and particularly those in whom the frontal parts of the brain have been removed at operation. For many years this brain area has been vaguely accepted as the seat of intellect and memory. Recently, in a number of patients, one of the two lobes of the frontal area of the brain has been successfully removed. Those patients who had no mental symptoms remain exactly as they were. Those who had symptoms, perhaps severe headaches, depression, and a general irritability, have been greatly improved. Slowly it is becoming clear that there is no one point in the brain which is exclusively concerned with intellectual functions. The brain functions emotionally and intellectually as a whole, and not as a telephone exchange with one cell for this and another for that. Only when both frontal lobes of the brain are removed, as happened in one case, are these character changes for the worse. More usually such changes are brought about by localized disease processes, and then it may be said that a well-planned operation will often convert the "bear-with-a-sore-head" individual back to normality and sweet reasonableness.

Whether there ever will develop from the joint activities of surgeons and psychiatrists a pure surgery of the intellect and emotions it is impossible to tell. The prospects for the surgical conversion of bad gangsters into good citizens are very remote. Probably it will never happen, and if it did the world might be a very dull place. One thing is certain, neurosurgery is advancing fast enough to defy all prophecy, and, however unlikely it may seem, there is a bare possibility that the surgeons of a hundred years hence may make supermen of us all, unless they fall beneath a dictator's spell and are given to solve the much simpler problem of making morons of the most of us.

XXV.   The Future

SURGERY HAS HAD AS MANY FALSE PROPHETS AS ANY OTHER human activity.   The most recent of them was one of the greatest British surgeons of this century—the late Lord Moynihan. Only five years ago Moynihan said: "The craft of surgery has in truth nearly reached its limit in respect both of range and of safety."   Five brief years have seen surgery extend its range without impairing its safety, and the limits of surgical endeavour are still far from being reached.   Even the immediate future cannot be forecast with any certainty, but it is perhaps possible to discern some sort of a pattern in prospect into which all the innumerable surgical specialities can be roughly fitted.

Modern anæsthesia has been advancing steadily since the last decade of the last century.   Cocaine was first isolated in 1859 by Nieman, but it was 1880 before Van Anrep demonstrated its anæsthetic properties on dogs and rabbits.   Three years later it was used to abolish pain in operations upon the eye. Then in 1894 the technique of infiltration anæsthesia was elaborated, and in 1899 August Bier of Berlin injected a cocaine solution into the fluid which surrounds the spinal cord.   Both these methods have been improved to near perfection.   It is possible now to anæsthetize a finger, a limb, or even the lower two-thirds of the body with the patient still quite conscious. Even the brain surgeons have found that much of their work can be done with local anæsthesia, brought about by injecting a solution of some cocaine product into the site of operation. From the patient's point of view these advances are important. After an operation under local anæsthesia the patient has no sickness or nausea, and can often return to work immediately. A spinal anæsthetic presupposes that the patient is in hospital, but again has the advantage of having few after-effects.

Complete anæsthesia by inhalation is still largely achieved by the use of ether, chloroform, or Humphry Davy's "laughing gas", but such new inhalants as cyclopropane and divinyl ether are being tried increasingly often.   There are other recent methods which Morton and Simpson never dreamt of.   Avertin is a substance which can be injected into the rectum and produces a profound narcosis.   It is employed most often by surgeons operating on nervous and excitable patients—for example, cases of goitre.   Each morning the patient is given an ordinary enema, then on the day of operation avertin is substituted for the enema solution, and it is only long after operation that the patient realizes that he has been having anything other than normal sleep.

A similar effect may be achieved by drugs of the barbiturate series, taken in tablet form or injected hypodermically. Sometimes they are given to supplement avertin anæsthesia, or are themselves supplemented, just as avertin may be, by the administration of a light ether, or gas and oxygen, inhalational anæsthetic. Another recently elaborated anæsthetic is injected into a vein and produces full anæsthesia almost instantaneously.

All these anæsthetics are constantly being improved. Each has advantages and disadvantages, which must be assessed from the point of view of the individual patient and the operation he is to undergo. Each causes one, two, or perhaps three, deaths in every thousand administrations. For this reason alone advance along any of the accepted lines is bound to be slow. The death-rate for any one anæsthetic is so nearly infinitesimal that attempts to bring it ever nearer to a hypothetically possible vanishing point become more and more difficult. Minor advances in several directions are still possible, and are gradually being made. The drugs used are becoming more potent yet less dangerous. The apparatus involved in their administration is approximating ever more nearly to the fool-proof. These changes will be recorded from time to time in the medical press, but they will excite no general interest. What will reach the headlines will be the next major advance in anæsthesia. This may not happen for many years, but when it does come anæsthetists may be the first members of the medical profession to boast a death-rate of exactly nil per thousand. As to its nature, one guess is as good as another, but the ichthyologists may unearth the secret first. They know already that the electric eel can, and does, render smaller fish unconscious for several hours simply by flinging at them the 500-volt charge it carries in its tail.

Aseptic methods have been improving gradually ever since they were introduced. In recent years weaknesses in three links of the chain of asepsis have become evident. Attention has been concentrated on them simply because all the other integral parts of the ritual have been perfected, and so by comparison these three defects have been relatively magnified. The problem of the sterilization of catgut, which engaged

Lister's attention for so long, is still not completely solved.
Perhaps a dozen or more deaths are caused every year from
tetanus conveyed by catgut. The problem is not one for the
bacteriologists. They have shown that catgut can be completely sterilized. The difficulty has lain in the occasional use
of catgut sterilized apparently efficiently but actually not quite
completely. Such catgut might be used in hundreds of cases
with never a death. Then one strand may cause a solitary
death from tetanus. The sterilization of catgut was regulated
by the Therapeutic Substances Act of 1925, and by Regulations
laid down in 1931. Even since then there have been occasional
deaths. Surgeons who thought they were using catgut manu-
factured under licence from the Ministry of Health have, in
a few isolated cases, discovered too late their mistake. It is
possible that such mistakes may still occur, but unlikely, for in
October, 1937, there came into force amendments to the
Therapeutic Substances Regulations which should make it almost
impossible for this confusion to arise again.

The second problem lies in protecting the patient from
organisms in the surgeon's nose and throat. Masks of all
shapes and varieties have been in use since the early part of this
century. A recent investigation of no less than sixty different
masks from hospitals throughout the United States showed
that none of them were completely efficient under all circumstances. In each experiment undertaken a few stray organisms
penetrated the gauze mesh of the mask. Now, however, masks
in which cellophane is incorporated are being tried out. Some
of them are shaped absurdly like dogs' muzzles, but being
impervious to the passage of even the most minute micro-
organism, they are as effective as they are comic.

The third difficulty is presented by the air itself. Lister
stopped using carbolic sprays because the pathogenic organisms
in the air were so relatively few, and because this method of
dealing with them was so disproportionately distressing alike
to patient and surgeon. Nowadays these few organisms have
become important again, since they are the only ones which have
an uninterrupted access to the operative field. A first step in
dealing with them was by the process of air-conditioning and
air-filtration. Then one surgeon took up a purely Listerian
method but used formaldehyde vapour instead of a carbolic
spray. The next and most recent advance is one that may
be generally adopted in the next ten years or so. It consists

in irradiating the theatre by means of a battery of ultra-violet lamps suspended directly over the operating-table. The surgeon and his theatre staff have to protect their eyes and skin from the rays—the patient, too, has to be protected in some measure— but the effects of this method have been remarkable. In the first place almost complete sterility of the air in the operating-theatre is ensured, for the ultra-violet light is lethal to most micro-organisms. In the second place this artificial sunshine has the same effect upon wounds that real sunshine has always had. Healing is more rapid and the general health of the patient is more quickly restored than was the case before the introduction of this technique.

It seems, then, that the risks associated with anæsthesia and with the possibility of infection at operation may perhaps disappear in the future. There must always be some operative shock, but this too has been appreciably lessened by improvements in anæsthesia and in operative technique. Only yesterday surgeons were still being praised for their showmanship and operative speed. Today—and it will be even more so in the future—except in a few highly specialized procedures, such as pulmonary embolectomy, speed is at a discount. Surgery is one of the few modern activities in which speed is neither necessary nor desirable. Careful and gentle handling of all tissues, ligature step by step of even the smallest blood-vessels, careful and accurate excision or correction, and exact apposition and suture of divided structures are the ideals aimed at—and their achievement is not compatible with operative speed and surgical showmanship.

When shock does arise, as it must in a proportion of cases, it is treated more successfully now than ever before. Blood transfusions, which were exciting novelties, are now routine procedures. In the future it should be possible to assess the different methods at present in use and standardize the more successful techniques for general adoption. It is likely, too, that more and more use will be made of stored blood. The bodies of healthy individuals who have died suddenly as the result of some accident would provide an ideal source for large quantities of blood. This method has been used extensively and with great success in Russia for some years. The surgical advance has in fact been made, but some education of public opinion and of the legislature will be necessary before its general application in the Western world can be undertaken.

Pre-operative and post-operative treatment is changing to-day, and will continue to change in the future. In the eighteenth century a surgeon was in many cases a high-grade plumber. He was called in to see the patient, he operated, and he left. If the patient was still alive when the last skin suture was tied, the operation was a success. In the early part of last century much the same attitude was maintained. Particularly in cases of abdominal disease the physician in charge called in a surgeon when he thought fit, saw the operation performed, and took the patient back to the medical wards immediately it was over. What the physicians did to emergency cases in those days forms a dark chapter in the history of surgery, just as what the surgeons have been doing to cases of duodenal ulcer in the last twenty years forms a grim chapter in the history of medicine. The supremacy of the physicians continued right up to this century, then surgeons won the right to have these abdominal emergencies admitted directly to their own wards and kept there. The period of surgical care extended from the immediate pre-operative stage to the day of discharge from hospital. Imperceptibly this period has widened. Cases of exophthalmic goitre are brought into hospital a fortnight or more before operation is contemplated, so that they may be made as fit as possible for it. Obscure cases may be investigated for months before operation is decided upon. Even the simplest cases—of hernia, for example—are admitted a few days before operation, so that the patient may become accustomed to the hospital regime and have at least two or three days' rest and pre-operative preparation.

The pre-operative extension of surgical care has been increasing continuously for several years and will continue to do so. Its natural development and extension have already been seen in what have been termed "follow-down" systems—as contrasted with the better-known "follow-up" systems. It was found, for example, in 1936, by tracing back the medical and surgical histories of a group of women with cancer of the mouth and gullet, that no less than 65 per cent. had had a simple anæmia, an absence of the hydrochloric acid normally present in the gastric juice, soft and spoon-shaped nails, early loss of the teeth, and a paleness and dryness of the mouth and tongue. This is a recognizable and easily curable condition. Its early recognition and its cure will not be dramatic—but it will prevent cancer. Of equal importance to another group of women is the recognition—after long "follow-down" studies—that though cancer itself is not inherited in the strict sense of the word, there is inherited an "organ susceptibility". Thus the female relatives of a woman with cancer of the breast are several times more likely to develop cancer of the breast—though not of any other organ—than other women of the same age and circumstances. Therefore, when a history of breast cancer in female relatives is obtained from a woman who has no symptoms or signs of cancer, but who has a thickening of part of a breast or perhaps a small lump in one breast, then the appropriate operation is a surgical method of preventing cancer. In the case of such a woman the necessary operation, for preventive reasons, is amputation of the entire breast, whereas in the ordinary case removal of only the lump itself is probably all that is needed. *X* rays and radium are being applied in the same way whenever possible, to prevent the appearance of cancer if ever its development seems likely. *X* rays and radium, however, are the chosen weapons of the physicist-physicians, who call for a surgeon only when their radium needles are to be implanted in some particularly inaccessible spot. Already the remote causes of different varieties of cancer affecting different groups of the population are preventible, and there is no doubt that the future of all cancer research lies in prevention. Surgery, *X* rays, and radium, either alone or in combination, are achieving an increasing proportion of cures in cancer cases, but all are forms of attack on an established condition. To prevent the condition becoming established, so that surgery or other methods of treatment will never be needed for it, is—despite the jibes of cynics—a surgical ideal. It is an ideal that the next twenty or thirty years should see near to realization. This realization will be brought about by the system of "following down", the results being checked by "following up" and by the study of vital statistics. Cancer is not the only problem, but just one of many, the solutions to which will be approached in this way.

At the moment, however, post-operative endeavours are attracting more attention. The orthopædic surgeons began the drive for the establishment of rehabilitation centres, so that their patients might be cared for from the time of sustaining a fracture or other injury up to the day on which they returned to work. The same concept of complete after-care is being approached in every other department of surgery. It is being generally realized that the surgeon's responsibility begins to end only when his patient is restored to his previous occupation as fit as, if not fitter than, when he left it.

Increasing, too, and again bound to increase further in the future, is the knowledge of the importance and the difficulty of finally assessing the results of operation. Astley Paston Cooper followed up his patients by getting the "sack-'em-up men" to secure their bodies, months or years after operation. The surgeons engaged in dealing with cases of cancer brought the modern "follow-up" system into being. Time and again they found that patients operated on apparently successfully died of a recurrence of the cancerous condition a few years after operation. Gradually there evolved a system of re-examining these patients at intervals of six and twelve months after operation. Surgeons began to talk about three-year "cures", meaning that the patient had been seen at fairly regular intervals up to three years after operation and had remained apparently well. Where the growth reappeared within these three years the system worked well and ensured that the recurrence would be diagnosed and treated at a reasonably early stage. The extension of this system to a period of five years followed the recognition that a proportion of patients had recurrences in the fourth and fifth years after operation. Now it is generally accepted that many of these patients should be seen regularly for so long as they will continue to attend the hospital or clinic or consulting-room. But it is also accepted that this careful study of the late results of cancer treatment is of no lasting value. Progress in prevention, which is the vital thing, will come from a study of what happened to the patient long before operation, and not after it—a truism which applies to every condition demanding surgical treatment. Prevention is brought about only very slowly, however, and meanwhile it is important that the patient should be treated by the operation which gives the best and most lasting results. How to determine which of many procedures may be regarded as best for the patient is the urgent and immediate problem. It is a problem that will not exist once preventive methods have been fully established so far as any particular condition is concerned, but the knowledge that his grandchild will never suffer from the condition about which he himself is complaining so bitterly gives the patient of today little comfort. He wants the best treatment, and must have it. In deciding whether to operate or not to operate, and if the former, the best operation to be performed, the old Astley

Paston Cooper principle—if not the old Astley Paston Cooper technique—has been invoked. It cannot be said with certainty of any patient, with say tuberculosis, that he is cured of his condition until the pathologists write finis to his medical history in the post-mortem room. In the long run the same applies to every other surgical condition. Only the pathologist can say with finality that this, that, or the other surgical procedure was completely successful.

The pathologist's decision cannot be given till after the patient's death. When the condition to be treated is one occurring in relatively young people, some tentative conclusion must be reached at an earlier stage of the proceedings. Even in these comparatively enlightened days such conclusions are too often arrived at by pure guesswork. A surgeon devises some new operation, tries it out in perhaps twenty patients, and rushes into print. Twenty cases have been dealt with, and all seem to be doing well. This operation is therefore a Good Thing. Now all this means nothing, and the chances that the operation is not only not a Good Thing but actually a Bad Thing are exactly even. Many of the younger surgeons, brought up in the research laboratories, are refusing to fall into this error, but they are still too few. Years hence this state of affairs will no longer exist. No new procedure will be brought forward except after a carefully controlled and statistically impeccable clinical experiment. To achieve these things in working with human material is difficult but not impossible. It means applying the new procedure to only every other case of the condition being treated. The even numbers receive orthodox treatment, the odd numbers the new treatment. At the end of the experiment the two groups are reviewed. All the patients in both groups are of much the same age, of the same race and sex, drawn from the same class of the population, nursed under the same circumstances, and so on. In effect, all possible variables in the experiment are eliminated by making them equal in the two groups. The only difference will lie in the fact that one group has been treated by the new procedure and the other by the old and accepted method. At the end of such an experiment, perhaps six months, twelve months, or even longer, after the operations, it should be possible to say that in the group dealt with the new procedure is better than, as good as, or less successful than, the old. If the first conclusion is reached, then more extended clinical experiments can be undertaken till it is possible to state that "This new procedure is better than the old methods and should be generally adopted". At that point and at that point only the surgeon should lay down his knife and take up his pen. The shape these new procedures will take will be determined by co-operation between physicians, surgeons, and innumerable other workers, and will be changed step by step with the changes in human material.

For many centuries surgeons were just accessory methods of treatment in the hands of the physicians. Slowly they won an equal status, and more slowly still the contemptuous "Mister" became a title compelling as much respect as "Doctor". At this phase—and the phase has not yet passed so far as some senior surgeons are concerned—the not unnatural reaction of the long subservient was a mild arrogance. The cycle is almost complete now. The younger physicians have much to offer the surgeon. Contemporary surgeons have as much to offer the physician. The most important recent surgical advances have been made by teams of workers. A physician and a surgeon form the spearhead of the attack. Radiologists, electro-cardiographers, anæsthetists, neurologists, psychiatrists, and a bewildering variety of other specialists assist them. And behind all this serried array stand the exponents of the basic medical sciences—pathologists, bacteriologists, anatomists, and physiologists. From them comes the thought which the physicians and surgeons translate into action.

We cannot boast today men like the sturdy individualists who contributed so much to the surgery of the past. There are a few names which will be conjured with in the future, but they are those of representatives of a vanishing race. The many advances yet to be made will come from different teams, or groups, or schools. Already the hall-marks of good medical and surgical articles are changing. The papers which merit attention because they bear the name of a single famous individual are becoming fewer every year. Instead, every other article in the medical press has as many authors as an all-star film has credit titles, and their names are of less significance than the legend "From This Clinic" or "From That Institute".

It is in this way that future advances will be brought about, by close co-operation and unflagging teamwork. What the immediate effects of such co-operation will be is fairly clear. For the last fifty years there has been a constant interchange between surgeons and physicians of patients and conditions. There used to be a surgery of diabetes. Untreated diabetics developed gangrene and needed their limbs amputated. The discovery of insulin has allowed diabetics the world over to live long enough to die of anything other than gangrene—or diabetes. Diabetic gangrene is now a surgical rarity. Streptococcal infections used to be surgical problems. Now they are being dealt with by sulphanilamide preparations, and it is likely that further chemical compounds will be found capable of dealing with other bacteria giving rise to surgical conditions.

On the other hand, the surgeons have taken from the physicians many cases of disease of the heart or lungs, many patients with obscure abdominal conditions, and many more with tumours of the brain. This interchange will continue, and though in the near future there will be a steady advance in the surgery of the heart and lungs, in the surgery of the brain and spinal cord, and in the surgery of the endocrine glands and the autonomic nervous system, patients will no longer be shifted bodily from the hands of the physician to the care of the surgeon. Instead they will probably be dealt with by a surgeon and a physician in co-operation, and the changes will be brought about only in the policy to be pursued in treatment. In some groups of cases where the emphasis today is on surgery, physicians may play an increasingly greater part, till a stage is reached at which surgery will be called for only occasionally. In the same way some cases in which medical and drug treatment hold pride of place today may be treated largely by surgeons, with physicians in attendance.

There has been a phase recently in which some of our most successful surgeons attributed their success to the fact that they were physicians practising surgery. But the enormous advances brought about in the last twenty years have made the physician practising surgery a legendary figure, symbol of a now-unattainable ideal. The ideal itself has become a little worn. Surgery and medicine would need to be very limited for one man, no matter how brilliant, to lead both fields. Specialism may not be a desirable thing, but it has become more and more necessary with the passing years, and it is an undoubted fact that the co-operation of specialists in innumerable overlapping departments has effected changes in the structure of medicine and surgery greater and more lasting than any previously known. By this same technique of co-operative specialism greater changes still will be brought about in the future.

[*407*]

Medicine and surgery depend for their very existence on improving the service they can give to the individual patient. The changing needs of the individual determine the changes which must be brought about in medical and surgical, as well as in all other, sciences. The surgery of the future, just as was the surgery of the past, will be directed to the saving of lives and limbs and the promotion of human happiness. The dangers which threaten man, and necessarily the surgery which is designed to meet them, are modified day by day with the progress of civilization. Today's environmental changes determine what the morrow will demand from surgery. This being so, it is possible to hazard a guess as to the part surgery will have to play in the future.

It seems that there will always be a surgery of war. This will contribute as much to progress as war itself.

There will always be the surgery of accidents, reflecting in every particular man's mode of life and means of transport. Already a pathology of motoring has sprung up and bumper fractures and dashboard dislocations have become orthopædic entities. The bumper fracture line is just below the knee at present. Changes in chassis design will probably bring it progressively nearer and nearer the ankle. The dashboard dislocation is a dislocation of the hip sustained in head-on collisions by the man who will sit next to the driver. His knee strikes the dashboard, the force of the impact is transmitted along his femur, and the head of that bone slips untidily but not unnaturally from its socket in the hip-joint. Accidents on the roads will probably increase for the next few years, then diminish as we take to the air and present the orthopædist with a new set of problems.

Just as concerned as the orthopædist in the accidents of the present and the future is the plastic surgeon. Unbreakable windscreens have altered the type and not the quantity of his work. Plastic surgery reflects, too, the changing dictates of fashion. Some surgeons in the English-speaking countries— though there is still some doubt as to what title they merit— devote much time and labour to the reduction of breasts and bellies to fashionable proportions. In France women are still expected to look like women, and it is not the over-developed but the under-developed who approach the plastic surgeon, demanding that their breasts be built up by means of paraffin injections, or grafts of fat or rubber.

The fate of several other departments of surgery hinges not upon feminine fashions, the toll of the road, or the growth of air-mindedness, but on a factor even more incalculable—the food we eat. The food with which we so often insult our alimentary canals has itself been subjected to a series of insults before it reaches our tables. We eat refined sugar in increasing quantities, and we put cereals through so many different processes that we might as well eat the morning newspaper for all the good the average plateful does us. Rarely do we consume any foodstuff as and when it was intended to be eaten. The mass production of foodstuffs has created a market for vitamin concentrates and a host of alimentary cripples. The incidence of appendicitis is increasing, as is that of peptic ulcer. In addition, new conditions of the alimentary tract are being recognized, notable among them being Crohn's disease or regional ileitis, a localized inflammation of the small intestine, which was first described in 1932. Crohn's disease and other alimentary disturbances as yet ill-defined seem to be Nature's revenge for the snooks we have cocked at her in processing out of all recognition the foods she had balanced so well. Not only the abdominal surgeons are concerned in dealing with the late effects of a civilized dietary. Obstetricians and gynæcologists are directly involved, and less directly such specialists as the ophthalmologists, otorhinolaryngologists, and urologists. How much further they will all need to be invoked is doubtful. It may not be for long. Already sufficient knowledge of dietetics has been gained for authorities the world over to be in general agreement as to just what we should eat. The education of the general public has begun, and is proceeding, albeit spasmodically and sometimes a little uncertainly. It will continue, and its effects may finally be seen three or four generations hence. By that time alimentary conditions may be so mild and so few that they will need little or no surgery. All of which means that surgeons generally will be able to concentrate their attention on two other groups of problems.

The first arises from the pace and the pressure at which we live. The best-known and most typical effects of high-pressure living present themselves in the form of duodenal ulcers and high blood-pressure. Ten years ago it was agreed that duodenal ulcer was a surgical condition, high blood-pressure a medical problem. Nowadays the consensus of opinion is that duodenal ulcer is a medical condition, and high blood-pressure a medical condition with some surgical aspects. Ten years hence there is no doubt that duodenal ulceration will have no meaning for the surgeon except when the ulcer perforates, or when it causes a complete block of the upper alimentary canal—a mechanical difficulty that only mechanical reconstruction will correct. Duodenal ulcer is associated with worry, overwork, and the excessive smoking that almost always accompanies them. Operation is simply an unnecessarily drastic method of restricting the patient's activities long enough for the ulcer to heal. As soon as he gets back to the work and worry an ulcer starts developing again.

High blood-pressure is also a disease of civilization. It used to be a condition affecting the aged, now it affects more and more commonly men and women around the age of thirty. It is brought about because civilization has stifled all our normal responses to certain stimuli. When prehistoric man was frightened, or annoyed, or lustful, his blood-pressure rose and he jumped into flight, fight, or fornication, thereby allowing the rise in blood-pressure to fulfil the purpose for which it was intended. Nowadays we are far more often annoyed, frightened, worried, or stimulated, and we cannot bring our suddenly raised blood-pressure down to a normal level by some violent activity. The nearest we ever get to aggressive action is putting the telephone receiver down with a bang. The result is that time and time again we suffer an emotional rise of blood-pressure and never reduce it as it should be reduced—by kicking the other fellow to death, or racing the hussy to a standstill. Blood-vessels are so often contracted that they stay that way, and the rest follows with horrible inevitability. Constant headaches, inability to concentrate, and failing vision are among the first consequences—and our response to them is further annoyance, further worry, and further rises of blood-pressure. The surgical attack upon this latter-day problem has only just begun. Different procedures have been elaborated by Heuer, Crile, Adson, Max Peet, and others, but all have the same end in view—the removal of parts of the autonomic nervous system which are in some measure responsible for conveying to the blood-vessels the recurrent constricting impulses. Already there have been recorded a few spectacular successes, many less dramatic improvements, and as many failures, some explicable on various grounds, others as yet unexplained. This physiological surgery may or may not be on the right lines, but it is probably fair to say that the surgery of the future will have much to contribute to the correction of an emotional reflex that civilization only superficially suppresses.

The second group of problems has barely been faced as yet. These problems are appearing because, despite his over-civilization, man's span of life is steadily increasing. This is due to the unpublicized efforts of workers in preventive medicine and public health. Hornell Hart seriously suggests that the average duration of human life by the end of this century will be a century, and that babies born after A.D. 2000 may even live to be two hundred. The mere suggestion makes the present-day fumbling attempts at operations of rejuvenation and operations for the prolongation of life seem rather silly. Hornell Hart may be wrong, but he is much more likely to be right, and if he is right, our great-grandchildren may be applying their scalpels to problems the very nature of which is unknown to us. Their cosmetic, plastic, and orthopædic surgery will be greatly advanced, but probably still necessary. Machines may be made foolproof, but never man. They will know nothing, however, of many of the conditions the surgeons of today have to deal with.

Tuberculosis we know as a disappearing disease, while cancer is one of our major unsolved problems. Our great-grandchildren will never have heard of the first, and the second they will find preventible; and they will be amused to learn that their immediate seniors were delighted at merely finding it curable. The surgery of old age will provide most exercise for their scalpels, but they may also be tampering with the surgery of the unborn—removing a gene here and implanting another there. The surgery of the brain and spinal cord, of nerves and blood-vessels, and of the endocrine glands and the autonomic nervous system they will probably have mastered. They will be able then to hold the fort till their brothers emerge from the laboratories with the news that they can drop scalpels—for surgery will never again be needed.

One day this will happen. Surgery is still that science which deals with the failures of medicine or preventive medicine. One day complete success will be recorded by the workers in these two great fields, and at that moment the surgeon must needs say *"Vale!"*

FINIS.

[*411*]

BIBLIOGRAPHY

Listed here are only those books most often consulted. To the authors of all of them I am indebted in greater or less degree. My acknowledgements are also due, but can only be given in general terms, to the authors of innumerable articles and essays which have appeared in many different journals.

ABRAHAM, J. A. *Lettsom: His Life, Times, Friends and Descendants.* William Heinemann, Ltd. London, 1933.

ALLBUTT, Sir T. Clifford. *The Historical Relations of Medicine and Surgery.* Macmillan and Co., Ltd. London, 1905.

ALLBUTT, Sir T. Clifford. *Greek Medicine in Rome.* Macmillan and Co., Ltd. London, 1921.

ASHHURST, John. *International Encyclopædia of Surgery.* Macmillan and Co., Ltd. London, 1886.

BASHFORD, H. H. *The Harley Street Calendar.* Constable and Co., Ltd. London, 1929.

BHISHAGRATNA, K. K. L. *The Sushruta Samhitá.* Calcutta, 1907.

BROCK, Arthur J. *Greek Medicine.* J. M. Dent and Sons. London, 1929.

BROWN, Alfred. *Old Masterpieces in Surgery.* Privately printed. Omaha, Nebraska. 1928.

BROWNE, E. G. *Arabian Medicine.* Cambridge University Press. 1921.

BRYAN, Cyril P. *The Papyrus Ebers.* Geoffrey Bles. London, 1930.

CAMPBELL, D. *Arabian Medicine.* Kegan Paul, Trench, Trubner and Co., Ltd. London, 1926.

COCKAYNE, Oswald. *Leechdoms, Wort-Cunning, and Starcraft.* Longman, Green, Longman, Roberts, and Green. London, 1864.

COOPER, Bransby Blake. *The Life of Sir Astley Cooper, Bart.* John W. Parker. London, 1843.

DANA, C. L. *The Peaks of Medical History.* Paul B. Hoeber. New York, 1926.

DAWSON, W. R. *A Leech-book of the Fifteenth Century.* Macmillan and Co., Ltd. London, 1934.

DAWSON, W. R. *The Beginnings—Egypt and Assyria.* Clio Medica Series. Paul B. Hoeber. New York, 1930.

DEELMAN, H. T. *Surgery a Hundred Years Ago.* Geoffrey Bles. London, 1925.

ELGOOD, Cyril. *Medicine in Persia.* Clio Medica Series. Paul B. Hoeber. New York, 1934.

FREIND, J. *History of Physick.* Fourth Edition. M. Cooper. London, 1750.

FUJIKAWA, Y. *Japanese Medicine.* Clio Medica Series. Paul B. Hoeber. New York, 1934.

GARRISON, F. H. *History of Medicine.* Fourth Edition. W. B. Saunders and Co. Philadelphia, 1929.

GASQUET, F. A. *The Great Pestilence.* Simpkin, Marshall, Hamilton, Kent and Co., Ltd. London, 1893.

GODLEE, Sir Rickman John. *Lord Lister.* Clarendon Press. Oxford, 1924.

GORDON, H. Laing. *Sir James Young Simpson and Chloroform.* T. Fisher Unwin. London, 1897.

HAGGARD, H. W. *Devils, Drugs, and Doctors.* William Heinemann, Ltd. London, 1929.

HALE-WHITE, Sir William. *Great Doctors of the Nineteenth Century.* Edward Arnold and Co. London, 1935.

HARINGTON, Sir John. *The School of Salernum.* Paul B. Hoeber. New York, 1920.

HARTLEY, Sir Percival Horton-Smith, and ALDRIDGE, H. R. *Johannes de Mirfield.* Cambridge University Press. 1936.

HUNTER, R. H. *A Short History of Anatomy.* John Bale, Sons, and Danielsson. London, 1931.

HURRY, J. B. *Imhotep.* Oxford University Press. 1928.

JEE, Bhagvet Sinh. *A Short History of Aryan Medical Science.* Macmillan and Co. London, 1896.

LITTLE, E. M. *History of the British Medical Association.* Harrison and Sons, Ltd. London, 1932.

LIVINGSTONE, R. W. *The Legacy of Greece.* Clarendon Press. Oxford, 1921.

LLOYD, Wyndham E. B. *A Hundred Years of Medicine.* Duckworth. London, 1936.

MCKENZIE, Dan. *The Infancy of Medicine.* Macmillan and Co. London, 1927.

MALLOCH, Archibald. *William Harvey.* Paul B. Hoeber. New York, 1929.

MAYO FOUNDATION. *Lectures on the History of Medicine.* W. B. Saunders and Co. Philadelphia, 1933.

MILES, Alex. *The Edinburgh School of Surgery Before Lister.* A. and C. Black, Ltd. London, 1918.

MORSE, William R. *Chinese Medicine.* Clio Medica Series. Paul B. Hoeber. New York, 1934.

OSLER, Sir William. *The Evolution of Modern Medicine.* Yale University Press. New Haven, 1923.

PARKER, G. *Early History of Surgery in Great Britain.* A. and C. Black, Ltd. London, 1920.

PARRY, T. Wilson. *Collected Papers* (1914–30).

PEACHEY, George C. *A Memoir of William and John Hunter.* William Brendon and Son, Ltd. Plymouth, 1924.

POWER, Sir D'Arcy. *A Short History of Surgery.* John Bale, Sons, and Danielsson. London, 1933.

POWER, Sir D'Arcy. *British Masters of Medicine.* Medical Press and Circular. London, 1936.

POWER, Sir D'Arcy. *Selected Writings.* Clarendon Press. Oxford, 1931.

REMONDINO, P. C. *History of Circumcision.* F. A. Davis Co. Philadelphia, 1891.

RUFFER, M. A. *Studies in the Palæopathology of Egypt.* University of Chicago Press. Illinois, 1921.

SHARP, Samuel. *A Critical Enquiry into the Present State of Surgery.* J. and R. Tonson and S. Draper. London, 1750.

SIGERIST, H. E. *Great Doctors: A Biographical History of Medicine.* G. Allen and Unwin, Ltd. London, 1933.

SINCLAIR, W. J. *Semmelweis: His Life and His Doctrine.* Manchester University Press. 1909.

SINGER, Charles. *From Magic to Science.* Ernest Benn, Ltd. London, 1928.

SINGER, Charles. *Greek Biology and Greek Medicine.* Clarendon Press. Oxford, 1922.

SORSBY, Arnold. *A Short History of Ophthalmology.* John Bale, Sons, and Danielsson, Ltd. London, 1933.

SOUTH, J. F. *Craft of Surgery.* Cassell and Co., Ltd. London, 1886.

STUBBS, S. G. B., and BLIGH, E. W. *Sixty Centuries of Health and Physick.* Sampson Low, Marston and Co., Ltd. London, 1931.

SUDHOFF, Karl. *Essays in the History of Medicine.* Medical Life Press. New York, 1920.

THOMPSON, C. J. S. *Quacks of Old London.* Brentano's Ltd. London, 1928.

TURNER, C. H. *The Inhumanists.* Alexander Ouseley, Ltd. London, 1932.

VALLERY-RADOT, R. *Life of Pasteur.* Constable and Co., Ltd. London, 1911.

WALL, Cecil. *The History of the Surgeons' Company.* Hutchinson. London, 1937.

WATSON, F. *Life of Sir Robert Jones.* Hodder and Stoughton, Ltd. London, 1934.

WISE, T. A. *Commentary on the Hindu System of Medicine.* Messrs. Thacker and Co. Calcutta, 1845.

WONG, K. Chimin, and LIEN-TEH, Wu. *History of Chinese Medicine.* Tientsin Press, Ltd. China, 1932.

YOUNG, Sidney. *Annals of the Barber-Surgeons.* Blades, East, and Blades. London, 1890.

INDEX OF NAMES

INDEX OF SUBJECTS

INDEX OF SUBJECTS